CONTENTS

3

PREFACE

When this work first appeared in 1974 it was entitled the *International Directory of Current Research in the History of Cartography and in Carto-Bibliography*. Several previous prefaces have introduced changes or announced new initiatives. Most of you who are reading this preface will probably be relieved to learn that there is no such intention this time. The colloquial title, the shorthand 'D', has merely moved to the next number, 'D9', indicating that this is the ninth edition of the original directory.

The changes introduced in the last edition, D8, met with general approval, and there has been no reason to alter them. The *vade mecum*, the 'What's What in the History of Cartography', has been updated but keeps broadly to the same formula. The directory of current research in the subject, the 'Who's Who' section, remains the work's main purpose. You can see at a glance who else is working in your own country, or you can find out – by using the indexes – with whom you could profitably collaborate or consult over a specialist query.

While it is the quality of the 'Who's Who' we would wish readers to dwell on, we are delighted at the continued increase in its size. What started off quarter of a century ago under the joint editorship of Eila Campbell and Peter Clark as a listing of some 200 researchers from 25 countries, now encompasses 630 individuals from 45 countries. For the statistically minded, the progressive increase in researchers has been as follows:

D1	(1974)	206	D4	(1983)	298	D7	(1992)	365
D2	(1976)	254	D5	(1985)	354	D8	(1995)	508
D3	(1981)	256	D6	(1989)	353	D9	(1998)	630

Does this reflect an expansion in the number of those active in our subject, a wider definition of 'the history of cartography', or greater success at identifying and persuading relevant individuals to contribute? No doubt, all these reasons form part of the answer. The original editors acknowledged in their D3 preface (1981) that 'there must be at least four times as many scholars pursuing research and publishing in this field' as they have been able to list. One of the D8 reviewers, Douglas Sims, concluded that 'for the first time the number of major researchers omitted is small enough that D8 can claim to be a fair overall directory of scholars'. We – Imago Mundi Ltd, the editor, and the publisher – would like to think he is right. The steady stream of people of whose work on early maps we hear of only by accident, however, or who, in their turn, stumble on *Who's Who...* equally by chance, cautions us against any complacency.

We are also very much aware of the disappointingly high number of italicized entries, indicating that we have failed to elicit an update this time for an individual who submitted an entry for D8. Recent publications by these researchers can often be found instead in the annual bibliography included in *Imago Mundi: The International Journal for the History of Cartography*.

The overall issue is communication. Whatever else may stay the same, the speed and ease of international communication is changing radically and irrevocably. D8's introduction of e-mail addresses made it the first Internet edition, although this was relevant only to a minority of those listed, and then mainly in the English-speaking world. The present edition, D9, documents the welcome spread of electronic mail that has now become a truly global network. We can safely predict that by the time of the next edition the great majority of researchers will be reachable by that route.

Although no more than three years have intervened since the last edition, D9 clearly signals the next major impact, that of the World Wide Web. The present trickle of Web publications will no doubt become a steady stream in future editions. We should not disguise the many frustrations that accompany Web use, but it does offer undreamed of possibilities for sharing (or hiding) information. Much of the updating to the 'What's What' section for this edition has involved the addition of URLs (Web addresses). Some of these may change over the life of this edition, and numerous new web pages will certainly be launched. However, one site offers itself as a single, dynamic gateway to this potentially confusing electronic babel: the Map History homepage, which is found at < http://www.ihrinfo.ac.uk/maps/ > (see p.17). Researchers based in other disciplines – and a gratifyingly large number are listed within the following pages – are urged to follow this simple route to obtain current and comprehensive information about the initiatives, activities and resources that make up the history of cartography.

One question will certainly be raised. If *Who's Who in the History of Cartography* is so tied up with the World Wide Web, why is the entire text not made available on the Internet? The answer is that, in time, it may well be. Two factors need to be understood though. In the first place, each edition is the result of a laborious effort, by volunteers, to coax entries from a growing body of researchers, many of whom apparently suffer from inappropriate modesty. All original entries are edited and given shape through the indexes. Such a painstaking and time-consuming operation cannot be contemplated at less than three-yearly intervals. A Web version of D9 would thus be no more up to date than the printed format.

The second consideration is one of economics. Each enlarged edition depends on sufficient sales to defray its costs. Were D9 to be accessed via the Web, especially by those who in the past would have been purchasers, there would, quite simply, be no D10. It is possible – and there are some indications in that direction – that Web access might actually *increase* sales, by alerting people to the existence of a work hitherto unsuspected and, crucially, to the far greater convenience of an easily manageable volume on a nearby shelf rather than the cumbersome and often frustrating processes of the Web. We hold an open mind on this point and will seek to balance our aim of greater accessibility with the need to guarantee continuation of a work many researchers have for long found indispensable.

D9 sees itself as part of a nexus, embracing individuals, institutions, publications, activities and events. The history of cartography's relatively intimate scale – our international conferences are attended by around 200 people – has enabled the subject to achieve an unusual degree of organization. It also has a reputation for carrying on discussions with a surprising lack of rancour! We hope that some of those we are welcoming into 'Who's Who' for the first time (and, in all, you number 168) will become better acquainted with us and our subject over the next years.

It may be helpful to repeat the intentionally tolerant definition of our subject, set out in D8 as follows: 'Research should concern (even if indirectly) some aspect of the history of non-current maps, that it should be original, and that it should be destined for publication. Empirical studies (such as detailed biography or cartobibliography) and theoretical debate (on the application of aspects of mainstream thinking to the history of maps, for instance) are equally welcomed'.

As in past years, we acknowledge with thanks the assistance of the *Imago Mundi* National Representatives (listed inside that journal's front cover) for helping to ensure that their country's contribution to the subject is properly recognized. Others – and it would be invidious to name names – responded with helpful leads via the Internet MapHist list.

Finally, we have the sad duty to record the deaths of the following who had been listed in D8: Aoki Chieko (Japan); Cao Wan-Ru (China); Joshua Hane (USA); Derek Howse (UK); Josef Hursky (Czech Republic); William L D Ravenhill (UK); Gordon Scurfield (Australia); Dušan Trávníček (Czech Republic); Peter George Vasey (UK); Erik Wihtol (Finland).

Tony Campbell
Chairman, *Imago Mundi* Ltd
September 1998

PART I

WHAT'S WHAT IN THE HISTORY OF CARTOGRAPHY

1. LITERATURE

How do you find your way into a literature that is characteristically international in publication, multi-lingual, and widely interdisciplinary? The following references have been selected for their authority and general accessibility. The listings do not claim to be inclusive. Standard 'first steps' such as general encyclopaedias, for instance, have been omitted. Nor have we been able to include publications of less than international circulation, which may mean some nationally useful publications, or publications in languages other than English, French and German, are missing.

1.1 General

The essential work of reference for the subject must be the *History of Cartography,* a multi-volumed series of which two of the projected six volumes have been published. It is both a work of reference (comprehensive in coverage and rich in bibliographies, illustrations and other reader aids) and of scholarly interpretation (authoritative, factually up-to-date, revisionist and espousing deliberately broad terms of reference).

John Brian Harley and David Woodward (eds), *The History of Cartography* (Chicago and London: University of Chicago Press, 1987-):

> Volume 1 (1987): *Cartography in Prehistoric, Ancient, and Medieval Europe and the Mediterranean.*

> Volume 2, Book 1 (1992): *Cartography in the Traditional Islamic and South Asian Societies.*

> Volume 2, Book 2 (1994): *Cartography in the Traditional East and Southeast Asian Societies.*

> Volume 2, Book 3 (1998): *Cartography in the Traditional African, American, Arctic, Australian, and Pacific Societies.*

> Volume 3 (forthcoming): *Cartography in the European Renaissance.*

The History of Cartography Project, Department of Geography, University of Wisconsin, Madison, WI 53706, issues an occasional newsletter with details of the publication schedule for forthcoming volumes. See < http://feature.geography.wisc.edu/histcart/ >.

Other general works, with those suitable as a general (English-language) introduction to the subject preceded by *:

Leo Bagrow, *History of Cartography,* ed. Raleigh. A. Skelton, revised 2nd ed. (Chicago: Precedent, 1985).

* Peter Barber and Christopher Board, *Tales from the Map Room: Fact and Fiction about Maps and Their Makers* (London: BBC, 1993). [Complements, with much original material, the television series with the same name.]

* Lloyd A. Brown, *The Story of Maps* (New York: Dover Publications, 1979). [Reprint of the original ed., 1949. One of the most accessible and comprehensive accounts, albeit rather dated.]

Tony Campbell, *Early Maps* (New York: Abbeville, 1981).

Tony Campbell, *The Earliest Printed Maps, 1472-1500* (London: British Library; Berkeley: University of California Press, 1987).

* Gerald Roe Crone, *Maps and Their Makers,* 5th ed. (Folkestone: Dawson, 1978).

François de Dainville, *Le langage des géographes: termes, signes, couleurs des cartes anciennes 1500-1800* (Paris: Picard, 1964). [Still a useful illustrated glossary of map terms.]

Wilma George, *Animals and Maps* (London: Secker & Warburg, 1969).

* John Goss, *The Mapmakers Art: A History of Cartography* (London: Studio Editions, 1993). [Very well illustrated.]

Paul D.A. Harvey, *The History of Topographical Maps: Symbols, Pictures and Surveys* (London: Thames & Hudson, 1980). [Well-illustrated, detailed and wide-ranging account, along developmental lines, of map history from the Old and New Worlds. Useful bibliographies.]

Paul D.A. Harvey, *Medieval Maps* (London: The British Library, 1991). [Excellently illustrated overview, by genre, of extant maps from Europe up to the fifteenth century.]

* Alan G. Hodgkiss, *Discovering Antique Maps* (Princes Risborough: Shire Publications, 1996). [A useful, small guide.]

Alan G. Hodgkiss, *Understanding Maps: A Systematic History of Their Use and Development* (Folkestone: Dawson, 1981). [A systematic survey of map development focusing on the 'art and technique' of 'using maps as a visual means of communicating'.]

Institut Cartogràfic de Catalunya, Barcelona — a continuing course of lectures given each year by representatives from a different country. Publication by the Institut follows soon afterwards. The course schedule to date has been: 1. 'Introducció general a la història de la cartografia' (1990); 2. 'La cartografia de la Península Ibèrica i la seva extensió al continent Americà' (1991); 3. 'La cartografia italiana' (1992); 4. 'La cartografia de los Paises Bajos' (1993); 5. 'La cartografia francesa' (1994); 6. 'La cartografia dels països de parla alemanya — Alemanya, Austria, Suïssa' (1995); 7. 'English cartography: an introduction to its history' (1996); 8. 'La cartographie des pays slavs' (1997); 9. 'La cartografía iberoamericana' (1998); forthcoming: Catalan Cartography (1999); Approaches and challenges in the worldwide history of cartography (2000).

George Kish, *La Carte: Images des Civilisations* (Paris: Seuil, 1980). [Illustrated selection of maps from prehistoric times to the twentieth century.]

Ingrid Kretschmer, Johannes Dörflinger, and Franz Wawrik (eds), *Lexikon zur Geschichte der Kartographie*, 2 vols. (Vienna: Deuticke, 1986). [Encyclopaedic presentation with an emphasis on geographical areas, map schools and individual mapmakers, with bibliographies — an important reference work and useful starting point.]

Ivan Kupčík, *Alte Landkarten: von der Antike bis zum Ende des 19. Jahrhunderts*, 2nd ed. (Hanau a. M: Dausien, 1984). Also French ed: *Cartes géographiques anciennes: évolution de la représentation cartographique du monde: de l'antiquité à la fin du XIXe siècle*, 2nd ed. (Paris: Gründ, 1984).

Edward Lynam, *The Mapmaker's Art* (London: Batchworth, 1953). [Not yet entirely superseded.]

* Francis J. Manasek, *Collecting Old Maps* (Norwich, VT: Terra Nova Press, 1998). [Including much useful and unexpected information, e.g. about the physical characteristics of paper, engraving, etc.]

Michel Mollat du Jourdin and Monique de la Roncière, *Sea Charts of the Early Explorers: 13th to 17th Century* (New York: Thames & Hudson, 1984). [Well-illustrated.]

* Carl Moreland and David Bannister, *Antique Maps,* 3rd ed. [London: Phaidon, 1993.]

Adolf Erik Nordenskiöld, *Facsimile-Atlas to the Early History of Cartography* (New York: Dover Publications, 1973). [Reprint of the original ed., 1889.]

Adolf Erik Nordenskiöld, *Periplus: An Essay on the Early History of Charts and Sailing-Directions* (New York: B. Franklin, 1967). [Reprint of the original ed., 1897.]

* Jonathan Potter, *Collecting Antique Maps: An Introduction to the History of Cartography* (London: Studio Editions, 1992). [Reprint of *The Country Life Book of Antique Maps* (Country Life Books, 1988).]

Günter Schilder, *Monumenta Cartographica Neerlandica*, 5 vols. (Alphen aan den Rijn: Canaletto, 1986-1996). [A truly monumental, and continuing, series of facsimiles of early Dutch maps, with exhaustive bibliographical commentary. For details, see < http://www.swaen.com/monumenta.html >].

Rodney W. Shirley, *The Mapping of the World: Early Printed World Maps, 1472-1700,* 3rd ed. (London: New Holland, 1993). [With Corrigenda and Addenda to the original ed., 1984. Remarkably comprehensive, well-illustrated catalogue of all known printed maps of the world, including separately printed maps, wall-maps and maps in books.]

* Raleigh A. Skelton, *Decorative Printed Maps of the 15th to 18th Centuries* (London: Spring Books, 1952). [A well illustrated, useful introduction.]

Raleigh A. Skelton, *Explorers' Maps* (London: Routledge & Kegan Paul, 1958).

Norman J.W. Thrower, *Maps and Civilization: Cartography in Culture and Society* (Chicago and London: University of Chicago Press, 1996). [Based on the author's 1972 book *Maps & Man.*]

* Ronald V. Tooley, Charles Bricker, and Gerald R. Crone, *Landmarks of Mapmaking: An Illustrated Survey of Maps and Mapmakers* (Oxford: Phaidon, 1976).

Helen M. Wallis and Arthur H. Robinson (eds), *Cartographical Innovations: An International Handbook of Mapping Terms to 1900* (Tring: Map Collector Publications in association with the International Cartographic Association, 1987). [Each of the 191 entries provides a definition, details of innovation and diffusion, and bibliography.]

Peter Whitfield, *The Charting of the Oceans: Ten Centuries of Maritime Maps* (London: British Library, 1996).

* Peter Whitfield, *The Image of the World: 20 Centuries of World Maps* (London: British Library, 1994).

Peter Whitfield, *The Mapping of the Heavens* (London: British Library, 1995).

* John Noble Wilford, *The Mapmakers: The Story of the Great Pioneers in Cartography – from Antiquity to the Space Age* (New York: Knopf; London: Junction, 1981).

John A. Wolter and Ronald E. Grim (eds), *Images of the World: The Atlas through History* (New York: McGraw-Hill, 1997).

David Woodward (ed.), *Art and Cartography. Six Historical Essays* (The Kenneth Nebenzahl Jr. Lectures in the History of Cartography at The Newberry Library; Chicago, University of Chicago Press, 1987). [Contains a number of important essays on this rarely-treated aspect.]

David Woodward (ed.), *Five Centuries of Map-Printing* (The Kenneth Nebenzahl Jr. Lectures in the History of Cartography at The Newberry Library; Chicago, University of Chicago Press, 1975). [Essential for the understanding of map production processes as a significant determinant of map content.]

1.2 **Area Studies**

Most of the literature on the history of cartography is defined by geographical region. No single, up-to-date bibliography can be cited for this material as a whole. To include here the best cartobibliography or map study for every region and sub-region of the world would require a volume by itself. The user is referred instead to the catalogues of major map collections (see Section 8.2), which are usually arranged geographically. The best single source is still:

Christopher R. Perkins and Robert B. Parry (eds), *Information Sources in Cartography* (London: Bowker-Saur, 1990), 89-114 (where the entries are arranged according to a geographical hierarchy).

1.3 **Bibliographies (general)**

The following are specialized bibliographies in the history of cartography. They include both monographs and periodical articles. Some are cumulative bibliographies, frozen by the act of publication; others include periodic listings of current literature on the subject.

Biblioteca cartographica (Bad Godesberg, 1958-1972), afterward *Bibliographia cartographica* (Munich, 1974-). [Issued annually, with separate area, author and subject sections.]

Alan G. Hodgkiss and Andrew F. Tatham, *Keyguide to Information Sources in Cartography* (London: Mansell, 1986). ['Information sources on the history of cartography', 81-127.]

Imago Mundi. The International Journal for the History of Cartography (formerly subtitled, '*The Journal of the Society for the History of Cartography*') (Berlin &c, now London, 1935-). [Contains an authoritative annual bibliography with a nominal index and also, since Vol. 46 (1994), geographical and subject indexes.]

Library of Congress, *The Bibliography of Cartography*, 5 vols. (Boston: Hall, 1973). *First Supplement*, 2 vols. (1980). [Reproductions of catalogue cards for material received in Library of Congress up to 1977, with repeated entries under area, author and subject. It contains some 120,000 entries, dating from the early 19th century onwards and is particularly valuable for its systematic listing of journal articles.]

Christopher R. Perkins, and Robert B. Parry (eds), *Information Sources in Cartography* (London: Bowker-Saur, 1990). [This is the most thorough and current general guide. It contains bibliographical listings on the history of cartography, with connecting notes, as follows:

> General sources, 75-88
>
> Area studies in the history of cartography [arranged in a geographical hierarchy, including Extra-Terrestrial and Oceans], 89-114
>
> Map types, design and production, 115-125 [under the following headings – map types: atlases, aviation cartography, exploration, facsimiles, fantasy and curiosities, fire insurance plans, geological maps, globes, nautical charts, panoramas and views, roads, thematic mapping, towns, travel, wall maps; production processes: geodesy and surveying, design, production.]

The Portolan (the journal of the Washington Map Society – see Section 2). Issued three times a year, this includes a list of recent publications, by Eric W. Wolf.

[For recent publications see also Part 2 of this work and its indexes.]

1.4 Bibliographies (regional)

BULGARIA: Bojan Beševliev, 'Kurzer Überblick über die Untersuchungen alter Landkarten von Bulgarien', *Actes du XIe Congrès international des sciences onomastiques* (Sofia: Académie Bulgare des Sciences. Centre de linguistique et littérature, 1974), Vol. 1, 117-124.

CANADA: (see below under United States – Conzen).

EASTERN EUROPE: (see below under Germany – Jäger).

GERMANY: Eckhard Jäger, *Bibliographie zur Kartengeschichte von Deutschland und Osteuropa* (Lüneburg: Nordostdeutsches Kulturwerk, 1978).

Lothar Zögner and Evelyn Schulte, *Bibliographie zur Geschichte der deutschen Kartographie* (Bibliotheca cartographica; supplement 2; Munich &c, 1984).

IRELAND: Paul Ferguson, *Irish Map History: A Select Bibliography of Secondary Works, 1850-1983, on the History of Cartography in Ireland* (Dublin, 1983).

ITALY: Osvaldo Baldacci, 'Storia della cartografia', in *Un sessantennio di ricerca geografica in Italia* (Memorie della Società Geografica Italiana, 26; Rome: Società Geografica Italiana, 1964). [278 bibliographical entries.]

E. Manzi, 'La storia della cartografia', *La ricerca geografica in Italia – 1960-1980* (Varese: Ask Edizioni, 1980). [138 bibliographical entries; found in the proceedings of a conference organized by Associazione dei Geografi Italiani, ed. C. Corna Pellegrini and C. Brusa.]

JAPAN: I. Hasegawa, *Chizu Kankei Bunken Mokuroku: Meiji, Taishō, Shōwa* (Tokyo: Chizukyōkai, 1971).

Kazutaka Unno, 'Cartography in Japan', in John Brian Harley and David Woodward (eds), *The History of Cartography, Vol. 2, Book 2* (Chicago: University of Chicago Press, 1994), especially 350-351.

THE NETHERLANDS: Peter van der Krogt, Marc Hameleers and Paul van den Brink, *Bibliografie van de Geschiedenis van de Kartografie van de Nederlanden* (Utrecht: HES, 1993).

NEW ZEALAND: Phillip L. Barton, 'A bibliography of material relating to the surveying and mapping of New Zealand', Special Libraries Association, Geography & Map Division, *Bulletin*, 109 (1977), 24-33.

Brian Marshall, *Map Making and Map Keeping in New Zealand: A Review and Bibliography* (Bibliographical Bulletin 18; Auckland University, [1992]).

POLAND: *Bibliografia polskiej historii geografii i kartografii*. [Published every five years; the first, by Wiesława Wernerowa, issued in 1978, covered 1970-1975.]

T. Gwardak, *Polskie piśmiennictwo kartograficzne 1659-1939* (Warsaw and Wrocław: Zakład Narodowy im. Ossolińskich, 1977).

Bolesław Olszewicz, *Dorobek polskiej historii geografii i kartografii w latach 1945-1969* (Warsaw: Instytut Geografii Polskiej Akademii Nauk, 1971).

SCOTLAND: John N. Moore, *The Historical Cartography of Scotland: A Guide to the Literature of Scottish Maps and Mapping prior to the Ordnance Survey,* 2nd rev. ed. (Aberdeen: University of Aberdeen, Department of Geography, 1991). [O'Dell Memorial Monograph No. 24.]

SWITZERLAND: Franchino Giudicetti, *Eine Ergänzung der Bibliographie der Gesamtkarten der Schweiz von Mercator bis 1802* (Murten: Cartographica Helvetica, 1996).

Hans-Peter Höhener, 'Zur Geschichte der Kartendokumentation in der Schweiz', in Joachim Neumann (ed.) *Karten hüten und bewahren. Festgabe für Lothar Zögner* (Gotha: Justus Perthes, 1995), 57-66.

UNITED KINGDOM: Geoffrey Armitage, 'County cartobibliographies of England and Wales: a select list', *The Map Collector*, 52 (1990), 16-24. 'Addendum', *The Map Collector,* 73 (1995), 20-23.

UNITED STATES: Michael P. Conzen et al., *A Scholar's Guide to Geographical Writing on the American and Canadian Past* (Chicago and London: University of Chicago Press, 1993).

Ronald E. Grim, *Historical Geography of the United States: A Guide to Information Sources* (Detroit: Gale Research, 1982). [One of the three main sections is 'Cartographic sources'.]

Clara E. LeGear, *United States Atlases: A Checklist of National, State, County, City and Regional Atlases in the Library of Congress,* 2 vols. (Washington, D.C.: Library of Congress, 1950-1953).

See also the *Bibliography of Cartography*, which is strong on North American sources, under 'Library of Congress' in Section 1.3.

1.5 Biographical Dictionaries

It is always worth consulting general biographical dictionaries, both universal and national. The following are the major specialist sources.

Sarah Bendall, *Dictionary of Land Surveyors and Local Cartographers of Great Britain and Ireland 1530-1850*, 2 vols. (London: British Library, 1997). [A much extended revision of the 1st ed. by P. Eden, 1979.]

Wilhelm Bonacker, *Kartenmacher aller Länder und Zeiten* (Stuttgart: Hiersemann, 1966). [Comprising bio-bibliographical references on the most important people in the subject.]

Robert W. Karrow, Jr, *Mapmakers of the Sixteenth Century and Their Maps: Biobibliographies of the Cartographers of Abraham Ortelius, 1570* (Winnetka, Illinois: for The Newberry Library by Speculum Orbis Press, 1993). [An extraordinarily comprehensive approach, simultaneously biographical, carto-bibliographical, bibliographical and historiographical. Esssential for almost any aspect of research on the sixteenth century.]

Monique Pelletier (ed.), *How to Identify a Mapmaker / Comment identifier un cartographe: guide bibliographique internationale* (Tring: Map Collector Publications; Paris: Comité français de cartographie, 1996, for the International Cartographic Association, 1996). [Includes national bibliographies of biographical dictionaries and other relevant works.]

Ronald V. Tooley, *Tooley's Dictionary of Mapmakers* (Tring: Map Collector Publications, 1979). *Supplement* (1985). [Provides summary information on a large number of people, but without specific bibliographical references. A revised edition is forthcoming.]

Sarah Tyacke, *London Map-Sellers 1660-1720* (Tring: Map Collector Publications, 1978).

Vladimiro Valerio, *Società, uomini e istituzioni cartografiche nel mezzogiorno d'Italia* (Florence: Istituto Geografico Militare, 1993). [Includes biographies of about 200 people involved with the cartography of southern Italy.]

[For globemakers see Section 8.3.]

1.6 Cartobibliographies

GENERAL: Montserrat Galera Monegal, 'Les obres de referència i la investigació. El cas concret de la historia de la cartografia', in *Introducció general a la història de la cartografia* (Barcelona: Institut Cartogràfic de Catalunya, 1990), 25-53.

Map Collectors' Series (London, 1963-1975). [A series of 110 monographs, most of which comprise detailed cartobibliographies. An index by Barbara B. McCorkle was published in Special Libraries Association, Geography & Map Division, *Bulletin*, 161 (1990), 2-12, or see the cover of the last number for the titles of 21-110, and earlier covers for the first twenty numbers.]

The following (except the British Isles group) are defined by place of publication, and not by map subject. For a comment on cartobibliographies of specific areas, see Section 1.2. For regional map collections see Section 8.1.

AUSTRIAN: Ingrid Kretschmer and Johannes Dörflinger (eds), *Atlantes Austriaci: Kommentierter Katalog der österreichischen Atlanten von 1561 bis 1994,* 3 vols. (Vienna: Böhlau, 1995).

BRITISH ISLES: Thomas Chubb, *The Printed Maps in the Atlases of Great Britain and Ireland: A Bibliography, 1579-1870* (Folkestone and London: Dawson, 1977). [Reprint of 1927 edition; for the period before 1789 use Hodson and Skelton below.]

Donald Hodson, *County Atlases of the British Isles Published after 1703. Vol. 1 Atlases Published 1704 to 1742 and Their Subsequent Editions. Vol. 2 . . . 1743 to 1763 . . . Vol. 3 . . . 1764 to 1789* (Tewin: Tewin Press, 1984-1989; London: British Library, 1997). [The series is a continuation of R.A. Skelton's work, see next title.]

Raleigh A. Skelton, *County Atlases of the British Isles 1579-1850: A Bibliography. 1579-1703* (London: Carta Press, 1970; reprinted 1978). [For the period after 1703 see D. Hodson, above.]

DUTCH AND BELGIAN: Cornelis Koeman, *Atlantes Neerlandici,* 6 vols. (Amsterdam: Theatrum Orbis Terrarum, 1967-1985). (Vol. 6 by C. Koeman and H.J.A. Homan, published Alphen aan den Rijn by Canaletto).

Peter van der Krogt, *Bibliography of Terrestrial, Maritime and Celestial Atlases and Pilot Books, Published in The Netherlands from 1570 up to the 20th Century.* Vol.1 [of a projected 10-vol. work] *The Folio Atlases by Gerard Mercator, Jodocus Hondius, Henricus Hondius, Johannes Janssonius and Their Successors* ('t Goy-Houten: HES Publishers, 1997). [A completely revised, illustrated edition of Koeman above.] For progress on this work, see < http://kartoserver.frw.ruu.nl/HTML/STAFF/krogt/atlantes.htm >.

FRENCH: Mireille Pastoureau, *Les atlas français XVIe-XVIIe siècles: répertoire bibliographique et étude* (Paris: Bibliothèque Nationale, 1984). [Full collations of French atlases, with valuable biographical introductions. The work is being continued by Catherine Hofmann.]

GERMAN: Peter H. Meurer, *Atlantes Colonienses* (Bad Neustadt a.d. Saale: Pfaehler, 1988). [Full collations of atlases published in Cologne.]

UNITED STATES: Philip D. Burden. *The Mapping of North America: A List of Printed Maps 1511-1670* (Rickmansworth: Raleigh Publications, 1996). [The modest title conceals an invaluable work, well illustrated.]

William P. Cumming, *The Southeast in Early Maps,* 3rd ed., revised and enlarged by Louis De Vorsey (Chapel Hill: University of North Carolina Press, 1998).

Robert W. Karrow, *Checklist of Printed Maps of the Middle West to 1900,* 14 vols. in 12 (Boston: G.K. Hall, 1981-1983).

Carl I. Wheat, *Mapping the Transmississippi West, 1540-1861*, 5 vols. in 6 (San Francisco, 1957-1963; reprinted [1995]).

James Clement Wheat and Christian F. Brun, *Maps and Charts Published in America before 1800: A Bibliography*, rev. ed. (London: Holland Press, 1978).

1.7. Theory and Interpretation

A relatively new but rapidly expanding aspect of the history of cartography, bringing to bear on map history major conceptual developments in, especially, literary criticism and textual analysis.

John H. Andrews, 'Map and language: a metaphor extended', *Cartographica* 27, 1 (1990), 1-19.

John H. Andrews, 'Meaning, knowledge and power in the map philosophy of J. B. Harley', *Trinity Papers in Geography* 6 (Dublin: Department of Geography, Trinity College Dublin, 1994).

John H. Andrews, 'What was a map? The lexicographers reply', *Cartographica* 33, 4 (1996, [i.e. 1997]), 1-11. [See, for the 321 source definitions from 1649 to 1996, < http://www.usm.maine.edu/~maps/essays/andrews.htm >.]

Barbara Belyea, 'Images of power: Derrida/Foucault/Harley', *Cartographica*, 29, 2 (1992), 1-9.

Michael J. Blakemore and J. Brian Harley, 'Concepts in the history of cartography: a review and perspective', *Cartographica*, 17, 4, Monograph 26 (1980).

Jeremy Crampton, 'Harley's critical cartography: in search of a language of rhetoric', *Working Paper 26* (Portsmouth, Department of Geography, University of Portsmouth, 1993).

Edward H. Dahl, Matthew H. Edney, Christian Jacob and Catherine Delano Smith, 'Theoretical aspects of cartography', *Imago Mundi* 48 (1996), 185-205.

John Brian Harley, 'Can there be a cartographic ethics?' *Cartographic Perspectives*, 10 (1991), 9-16.

John Brian Harley, 'Cartography, ethics and social theory', *Cartographica*, 27, 1 (1990), 1-23.

John Brian Harley, 'Deconstructing the map'. *Cartographica*, 26, 2 (1989), 1-20. Altered reprint in T.J. Barnes and J.S. Duncan (eds), *Writing Worlds: Discourse, Text and Metaphor* (London, 1992), 231-47.

John Brian Harley, 'The evaluation of early maps: towards a methodology', *Imago Mundi*, 22 (1968), 62-74.

John Brian Harley, 'Silences and secrecy: the hidden agenda of cartography in early modern Europe', *Imago Mundi* 40 (1988), 57-76.

Christian Jacob, *L'Empire des cartes. Approches théorique de la cartographie à travers l'histoire* (Paris: Albin Michel, 1992). [An English edition is forthcoming from the University of Chicago Press.]

Alan M. MacEachren, *How Maps Work: Representation, Visualization, Design* (New York: Guilford Press, 1995).

Mark Monmonier, *How to Lie with Maps*, 2nd ed. (Chicago and London: University of Chicago Press, 1996).

Arthur H. Robinson and Barbara B. Petchenik, *The Nature of Maps* (Chicago and London: University of Chicago Press, 1976).

Raleigh A. Skelton, *Looking at an Early Map* (Lawrence: University of Kansas Libraries, 1965). [The pioneering essay of its day.]

David Turnbull, 'Cartography and science in early modern Europe: mapping the construction of knowledge spaces', *Imago Mundi*, 48 (1996), 5-24.

David Turnbull, *Maps Are Territories: Science Is an Atlas. A Portfolio of Exhibits* (Chicago: University of Chicago Press, 1993).

Denis Wood, *The Power of Maps* (New York: Guilford Press, 1992).

David Woodward, 'The study of the history of cartography: a suggested framework', *American Cartographer*, 1 (1974), 101-15.

David Woodward, 'The form of maps: an introductory framework', *AB Bookman's Yearbook*, 1 (1976), 11-20.

1.8. Historiography

John Brian Harley, 'The map and the development of the history of cartography', in J.B. Harley and D. Woodward (eds), *The History of Cartography* (Chicago and London: University of Chicago Press, 1987), Vol. 1, 1-42.

Raleigh A. Skelton, *Maps: A Historical Survey of Their Study and Collecting: Illustrated Edition* (Chicago and London: University of Chicago Press, 1972).

2. JOURNALS

The following are exclusively or largely concerned with the history of cartography. Several other journals occasionally contain articles on the subject. For information about tracing earlier periodical articles see Section 1.3.

Caert-Thresoor: tijdschrift voor de historische kartografie in Nederland [latterly] . . . *tijdschrift voor de geschiedenis van der kartografie in Nederland* (Alphen aan den Rijn, 1982-). Quarterly. Largely concerned with mapping of The Netherlands. An index was issued to the first ten volumes (1982-1991). < http://kartoserver.frw.ruu.nl/HTML/STAFF/krogt/ct.htm >.

Cartographica Helvetica: Fachzeitschrift für Kartengeschichte (Murten, 1990-). Published for the Arbeitsgruppe für Kartengeschichte der Schweizerischen Gesellschaft für Kartographie (see Section 9.2). Since the cessation of *Speculum Orbis*, this has been extended to cover the cartography of the German-speaking world and more general subjects. Index to Nos 1-15 (1997).
< http://www.stub.unibe.ch/dach/ch/ch/carhe-en.html >.

Cartographica Hungarica: Térképtörténeti Magazin (Novafeltria, Italy, 1992-1994; Budapest, 1996-). Previously irregular, now annual.

Cartomania, the Newsletter of the Association of Map Memorabilia Collectors (1986-). Notionally four times, usually twice, a year (see Section 9.1).

Carto-Philatelist (1955-). Quarterly. The journal of the Carto-Philatelists (see Section 9.1), including some articles on early maps.

Z dziejów kartografii (1979-). Annual, published by the Wrocław branch of the Institute of the History of Science, Education and Technology of the Polish Academy of Sciences, containing papers from the preceding conference on the history of Polish cartography (see Section 5.2).

Der Globusfreund: Wissenschaftliche Zeitschrift für Globen- und Instrumentenkunde. Journal for the Study of Globes and Related Instruments (Vienna, 1952-). Annual (though numbers are often combined); the journal of the Internationale Coronelli-Gesellschaft für Globen- und Instrumentenkunde (see Sections 8.3 and 9.1). No.40/41 (1992) included indexes on issues 1-40/41 and *Information* 1-18 (pp.147-199).

Imago Mundi: The International Journal for the History of Cartography (formerly subtitled, *The Journal of the International Society for the History of Cartography*) (Berlin, etc, now London, 1935-). Annual. Index to 1-50 in preparation. < http://www.ihrinfo.ac.uk/maps/imago.html >.

IMCoS Journal (formerly *Newsletter*) (London, 1980-). Quarterly. The journal of the International Map Collectors' Society (see Section 9.1). Index (for the period 1980-1994), 1995.

The Map Collector (Tring, Herts, 1977-1996). Quarterly. Indexes to Issues 1-20, 21-30, 31-40, 41-50, 51-60. Ended with Issue 74 (1996).

Mapline: A Newsletter Published by the Hermon Dunlap Smith Center for the History of Cartography at the Newberry Library (Chicago, 1976-). Originally quarterly, now three times a year. Index to Nos 1-44 (1987) issued as its *Special Number Six*. < http://www.newberry.org/smith/publications.htm#mapline >.

Mercator's World: The Magazine of Maps, Atlases, Globes, and Charts (Eugene, Oregon, 1996-). Bi-monthly. < http://www.mercatormag.com >.

Meridian: A Journal of the Map and Geography Round Table of the American Library Association (1989-). Twice yearly.

The Portolan (Rockville, Maryland, 1984-). Three times a year. The journal of the Washington Map Society (see Section 9.2). Includes a bibliography of recent publications, by Eric W. Wolf. The Fall 1992 issue contains an 'Index to feature articles'. For an index covering 1-40 (1998) see < http://www.cyberia.com/pages/jdocktor/portolan.htm#Top >.

Sheetlines (1981-). Three times a year. The journal of the Charles Close Society for the Study of Ordnance Survey maps (see also Section 9.2). Index to Nos 1-45 (1996).

Speculum Orbis: Zeitschrift für alte Kartographie und Vedutenkunde (Bad Neustadt a.d. Saale, 1985-1993). Twice yearly; not indexed. Concerned with German cartography. Ceased publication; its coverage passed to *Cartographica Helvetica*.

Terrae Incognitae (1969-). Annual. The journal of the Society for the History of Discoveries (see Section 9.1). Bibliography of recent literature in discovery history by Fred Musto (Barbara McCorkle compiled the bibliographies from Vol.11, 1979 to Vol.27, 1995). Indexes to vols. 1-28 (1969-1996) by Eric W. Wolf in Vol. 29.

3. NEWS

For personal news about those working in the field, notices of forthcoming conferences, lectures, society meetings, exhibitions etc, and reports on past events, see in particular (in Section 2) *Cartographica Helvetica* (for the German-speaking world), *Imago Mundi*, the *IMCoS Journal, Mapline, Mercator's World, The Portolan* and (in Section 9.1) the ISCEM Newsletter. The 'Chronicle' section in the annual *Imago Mundi* provides the subject's formal record under six headings: personal news, conferences and meetings, institutional and general news, exhibitions, notable acquisitions, and unusual items that have come up for sale. See < http://www.ihrinfo.ac.uk/maps/imago.html > under Conferences; Exhibitions; and News.

The information from two webpages containing current news is subsequently transferred to an archive page. Trace the links from the current page. See, for exhibitions < http://www.cyberia.com/pages/jdocktor/exhibit.htm > and for events < http://www.cyberia.com/pages/jdocktor/index.htm >.

4. INTERNET LISTS AND THE WORLD WIDE WEB

The 'Internet' is a general term denoting numerous intertwined computer networks. MapHist and the other Internet lists (see 4.1) form part of it. The most rapidly growing area of the Internet is the World Wide Web (WWW or 'the Web', see 4.2), a discovery and retrieval tool which allows users remote access to high resolution images, among them the digitized forms of early maps as well as audio and video clips. Users can also access a growing body of individual library catalogues and booksellers' inventories and, by using search engines, seek out bibliographical references or topical information.

4.1 Internet Lists

The MapHist list:

MapHist is the daily forum for the history of cartography. It was established in 1994 to notify the results of current research; evaluate methods and tools of analysis; announce important acquisitions and news; publicise position vacancies; draw attention to new publications; investigate library holdings; and circulate information between conferences and the appearance of relevant journals. In practice, most messages contain information or a contribution to the sometimes lively debates.

Each message posted to it is broadcast to all subscribers. Contributions sent to the list are automatically archived and can be retrieved by subject or date of posting. Indexed hard copies were produced by Peter van der Krogt for 1994, 1995 and 1996. A fully searchable CD-ROM has been issued containing the discussions of the first four years. See the MapHist homepage < http://kartoserver.frw.ruu.nl/HTML/STAFF/krogt/maphist.htm > for instructions on retrieving archived messages and on obtaining a list of subscribers with their e-mail addresses. The site also includes pages for illustrations and large files.

To subscribe to MapHist assuming your name is John Smith:

      [send to] listserv@harvarda.harvard.edu

      [type nothing under 'subject']

      [type, in the body of the message] subscribe maphist   John Smith

      [once joined, address to send message] maphist@harvarda.harvard.edu

To leave the list, send this message to: listserv@harvarda.harvard.edu:/ SIGNOFF MAPHIST

For enquiries via e-mail: cobb@fas.harvard.edu. Or write to David A. Cobb, Harvard Map Collection, Harvard College Library, Cambridge, MA 02138, USA.

Other Lists:

Other lists, are as follows, with their subscribing instructions (again using John Smith as an example):
NB: You need first to 'subscribe' (free of charge) to a list before receiving details of the different address used for sending messages to that list.

General: Maps-L.   [send to] listserv@uga.cc.uga.edu
          [type nothing under 'subject']
          [type, in the body of the message] subscribe maps-l John Smith

Canada: Carta.   [send to] mailserv@sask.usask.ca
          [type nothing under 'subject']
          [type, in the body of the message, NB without including your name] SUBSCRIBE CARTA

United Kingdom: Lis-maps [send to] mailbase@mailbase.ac.uk
          [type nothing under 'subject']
          [type, in the body of the message] join lis-maps John Smith

History of Discoveries: Discovery. [send to] majordomo@win.tue.nl
          [type nothing under 'subject']
          [type in the body of the message, NB without including your name] subscribe discovery

Road maps: Roadmaps-L. [send to] majordomo@teleport.com
          [type nothing under 'subject']
          [type in the body of the message, NB without including your name] SUBSCRIBE ROADMAPS-L

For the Maptrade list, see Section 10.1.

4.2 The World Wide Web

The 'Web' comprises literally millions of sites or homepages. It is growing very rapidly. Some people enjoy the process of exploration, enlisting the help of a search engine's indexes, or just following from one link to another. Others – especially those with a specific quest – find the hunt time-wasting and frustrating. The history of cartography is lucky to have a number of volunteers who are, collectively, providing some order out of this chaos.

During the expected three-year life of this edition of *Who's Who in the History of Cartography* many unpredicted developments will occur. What should not change is the central role played by the subject's 'gateway' site, set up on 'History', the server of the Institute of Historical Research, University of London in 1997 < http://www.ihrinfo.ac.uk/maps/ >. Directly, or indirectly via links to other sites, the Map History/History of Cartography homepage offers easy and regularly updated access to all aspects of the subject, both electronic and traditional. The headings, which reflect those in this 'What's What' section are: Conferences, meetings and talks; Exhibitions; Fellowships, prizes and awards; Globes – history; Guide to the subject; Internet resources; Journals; Lecture series; Literature; Map collections; Map-interest societies; Marketplace; News; Related subjects.

You should also bookmark the invaluable list of cartographic links kept at Oddens's Bookmarks < http://kartoserver.geog.uu.nl/html/staff/oddens/oddens.htm >. The following historical sub-sections (as at summer 1998) may be reached individually via the Map History/History of Cartography homepage described above (select 'Internet Resources'): Cartographic Curiosities; Literature: History of Cartography; Maps and Atlases – Old: Universe; [ditto]: Countries; Map Collections – General; Map Collections – Catalogues; Sellers of Cartographic Material: Antiquarian.

5. REGULAR CONFERENCES AND LECTURE SERIES

In addition to the many special conferences and seminars that include material relevant to the history of cartography, the following are the established meetings specifically on the subject. For further details of the sponsoring organizations see Section 9. For a regularly updated calendar of meetings and talks see < http://www.cyberia.com/pages/jdocktor/ >.

5.1 International Conferences

German-speaking countries. Arbeitsgruppe D-A-CH: biennial Kartographiehistorisches Colloquium (in even years). The talks are published by *Cartographica Helvetica*. Forthcoming meetings: Bonn, 14-16 September 2000; Nürnberg, 2002.

International Cartographic Association. Biennial (in odd years). Includes meetings of the Standing Commission on the History of Cartography. Forthcoming meeting: Ottawa, 14-21 August 1999.

International Conference on the History of Cartography. Biennial (in odd years), held under the auspices of *Imago Mundi*, which publishes a number of the papers. A day, usually beforehand, is devoted to the meeting of the International Society for the Curators of Early Maps (ISCEM), see Section 9.1. Forthcoming meetings: Athens, 11-16 July 1999; Madrid (2001); Portland, Maine, and Cambridge, Massachusetts (2003). Updated details are posted to the History of Cartography homepage: < http://www.ihrinfo.ac.uk/maps/ >.

International Map Collectors' Society. Holds an annual international symposium. Papers are published in the *IMCoS Journal* (see Section 2). Forthcoming meetings: Istanbul, October 1999; Reykjavik, September 2000. A travel grant of £300 is open to members under 32. < http://www.harvey27.demon.co.uk/imcos/ >.

International Reunion for the History of Nautical Science and Hydrography. Held irregularly, usually in Portugal or Brazil (see Lisbon, Section 6).

Internationale Coronelli-Gesellschaft für Globen- und Instrumentenkunde. Meets every few years in Europe to hear papers on globe history. These are published in *Der Globusfreund* (see Section 2).

Society for the History of Discoveries (SHD). Meets annually, usually in the United States. Papers are often included in *Terrae Incognitae* (see Section 2). Forthcoming meeting: Flagstaff, Arizona (November 1999). Index to 'Papers and panels presented at annual meetings, 1962-94' by Eric W. Wolf, distributed with the 1994 Annual Report.

5.2 National Conferences

Canada: Three organizations put on conferences in early summer which include historical sessions: the Association of Canadian Map Libraries and Archives (the papers are usually published in the *ACMLA Bulletin*); Association québecoise de cartographie; and the Canadian Cartographic Association (the papers are usually published in *Cartographica*).

Czech Republic: An annual national symposium is held in the National Technical Museum, Prague, on the history of geodesy and cartography in the Czech Republic. The papers are published (some years afterwards) by the museum in *Rozpravy Národního technického musea*.

Poland: A conference on the history of Polish cartography is held at different venues every one or two years. The papers are published in *Z dziejów kartografii*.

United Kingdom: The International Map Collectors' Society (IMCoS), based in England, holds regular meetings in the United Kingdom. See Section 5.1 for the annual meetings outside the British Isles. < http://www.harvey27.demon.co.uk/imcos/ >.

5.3 Public Lecture Series

Courses of lectures on the history of cartography are given in a number of universities around the world (usually in geography departments). These are not generally open to the public. For an earlier review of these see: Richard I. Ruggles, 'The teaching of the history of cartography', *A Report to the Standing Commission on the History of Cartography* (Budapest: International Cartographic Association, 1989).

Other lectures are on an individual or irregular basis, often hosted by map societies. For a calendar including talks see < http://www.cyberia.com/pages/jdocktor/index.htm >. What follow are regular series of lectures, open to the public.

Chicago: Kenneth Nebenzahl, Jr., Lectures in the History of Cartography given on a different, specific theme at the Hermon Dunlap Smith Center, Newberry Library, every two or three years (1964-). The lectures are subsequently published by the University of Chicago Press. Forthcoming series: 'Narratives and Maps: Historical Studies in the Relationship between Maps and Stories', 21-23 October 1999. Contact: The Director, Hermon Dunlap Smith Center, The Newberry Library, 60 West Walton Street, Chicago, IL 60610-3380, USA. < http://www.newberry.org/smith/publications.htm#kenneth >.

London: Historical Geographical Information Systems training courses (1996-), held each summer. Contact: Ian Gregory, Department of Geography, Queen Mary & Westfield College, London E1 4NS, UK. E-mail: I.N.Gregory@qmw.ac.uk.

London: 'Maps and Society', eight winter lectures given at the Warburg Institute, University of London (1991-). Contact: Tony Campbell, Map Library, British Library, 96 Euston Road, London NW1 2DB, UK. Details are posted on the History of Cartography homepage: < http://www.ihrinfo.ac.uk/maps/lecture.html >.

Milwaukee: 'Maps and America', annual lecture series at the American Geographical Society Collection, University of Wisconsin-Milwaukee (1990-), sponsored by Arthur and Janet Holzheimer. The lectures are published in the AGS Collection Special Publications series. Contact: Chris Baruth, AGS Collection, P.O. Box 399, Milwaukee, WI 53211-0399, USA. E-mail: cmb@uwm.edu.

Oxford: 'Oxford Seminars in Cartography' (1993-). Held three times a year at the Bodleian Library. Contact: Nick Millea, Map Room, Bodleian Library, Oxford, OX1 3BG, UK. E-mail: nam@bodley.ox.ac.uk.

Paris: Bibliothèque Nationale, Département des Cartes et Plans (with Comité Français de Cartographie), annual reunion on the history of cartography. The lectures are published in the *Bulletin* of the Comité Français de Cartographie.

Paris: École Pratique des Hautes Études, Section des Sciences historiques et philologiques, bi-monthly seminars by Catherine Bressolier-Bousquet.

6. RESEARCH CENTRES

All major research libraries act as research centres (see Section 8). The following have more specific functions in the history of cartography.

Arlington, Texas: Center for Greater Southwestern Studies and the History of Cartography, Department of History, University of Texas at Arlington. Director: David Buisseret, Jenkins and Virginia Garrett Professor.

Chicago: Hermon Dunlap Smith Center for the History of Cartography, Newberry Library. It runs fellowships (see Section 7.1) and issues *Mapline*. Address: The Newberry Library, 60 West Walton Street, Chicago, IL 60610-3380, USA. < http://www.newberry.org/smith/index.htm >.

Lisbon: Centro de Estudos de Historia e Cartografia Antiga. Founded in 1958, this is part of the Institute of Tropical Scientific Research and sponsors the Reunions for the History of Nautical Science and Hydrography. Address: Rua Jau 54, 1300 Lisbon, Portugal.

Madison: University of Wisconsin-Madison, History of Cartography Project. Director: Prof. David Woodward, Department of Geography, University of Wisconsin, Madison, WI 53706-1491, USA. < http://feature.geography.wisc.edu/histcart/ >.

Portland, Maine: Osher Map Library and Smith Center for Cartographic Education at the University of Southern Maine. It issues the *Norumbega News*. Contact: Yolanda Theunissen, Curator, Osher Map Library, University of Southern Maine, P.O. Box 9301, 314 Forest Avenue, Portland, ME 04104-9301, USA. < http://www.usm.maine.edu/~maps/exit.html >.

Rome: Centro Italiano per gli Studi Storico-geografici (1992) comprises four sections, one of which is Storia della cartografia. Contact: Prof. Luciano Lago, c/o La Sezione di Scienze Geografiche e Cartografiche, Dipartimento di Studi Storici dal Medioevo all'Età Contemporanea, III Università degli studi di Roma, Piazza della Repubblica 10, I-00185 Rome, Italy.

Utrecht: Faculty of Geographical Sciences, University of Utrecht. Director: Prof. Günter Schilder, P.O. Box 80115, NL-3508 TC Utrecht, Netherlands. The Institute directs various working groups of the Explokart Research Team in the preparation of cartobibliographies of Dutch maps. It is also closely linked with the Stichting Historische Cartografie van de Nederlanden (SHCN). This was founded in 1997, with the intention of offering support to researchers working on the history of Dutch cartography. It fundraises by organizing the European Map Fair. Contact: SHCN, Secretariaat, Witrijtseweg 16, 5571 XJ Bergeijk, Netherlands. E-mail: kinds@ping.be. See also Section 10.2.

7. RESEARCH FELLOWSHIPS, PRIZES AND GRANTS

Research topics in the history of cartography come within the scope of a number of general fellowships in both the sciences and the humanities. Listed below are awards specifically concerned with the history of cartography. In each case the applicant would need to demonstrate the relevance of the particular collection to their research.

7.1 Research Fellowships

Alexander O. Vietor Fellowship, Yale University Library, New Haven, to support travel and living expenses for research in cartography and related fields. One month fellowships. Contact: The Director, Beinecke Rare Book and Manuscript Library, Box 1603A, Yale Station, New Haven, CT 06520-1603, USA. < http://www.library.yale.edu/beinecke/brblhome.htm >.

Helen Wallis Fellowship, British Library. An annual fellowship, giving preference to proposals that relate particularly to the collections of the

British Library, that seek to explore the interdependence of cartographic and other sources in historical investigation, and that have an international dimension. Fellowship of 6 to 12 months. Contact: Map Librarian, British Library, 96 Euston Road, London NW1 2DB, UK. E-mail: tony.campbell@bl.uk.

J.B. Harley Research Fellowships in the History of Cartography, to promote use of the cartographic material available in London (particularly at the British Library, National Maritime Museum, Public Record Office and Royal Geographical Society). Fellowships of 2 to 4 weeks. Closing date: 1 November. Hon. Sec.: Tony Campbell, Map Library, British Library, 96 Euston Road, London NW1 2DB, UK. E-mail: tony.campbell@bl.uk.

Jeannette D. Black Memorial Fellowship, John Carter Brown Library, Providence, Rhode Island. Fellowships usually of 2 to 4 months. Closing date: mid-January. Contact: The Director, John Carter Brown Library, Box 1894, Providence, RI 02912, USA.

Newberry Library, Hermon Dunlap Smith Center, Chicago. Fellowships of 1, 3 or 6 months. Contact: Office of Research and Education, The Newberry Library, 60 West Walton Street, Chicago, IL 60610-3380. < http://www.newberry.org/smith/index.htm >.

7.2 **Prizes and Grants**

Caert-Thresoor Award. An annual award to promote the study of the history of cartography of the Netherlands, open to researchers in the Netherlands or Flanders who are not professionally involved in the subject and who have published their articles in *Caert-Thresoor* (see Section 2).

IMCoS-Helen Wallis Award [formerly IMCoS-R.V. Tooley Award]. Given annually by the International Map Collectors' Society to the individual (or organization) who 'has been responsible for cartographic contribution of great merit and wide interest to map collectors worldwide'. Contact: Jenny Harvey, 27 Landford Road, Putney, London SW15 1AQ, UK. E-mail: jeh@harvey27.demon.co.uk.

International Map Collectors' Society offers a travel grant of up to £300 to enable members under the age of 32 to attend symposia abroad. Contact: Jenny Harvey, 27 Landford Road, Putney, London SW15 1AQ, UK. E-mail: jeh@harvey27.demon.co.uk. < http://www.harvey27.demon.co.uk/imcos/ >.

Internationale Coronelli-Gesellschaft für Globen- und Instrumentenkunde, 'Fiorini-Haardt Prize', to further research into globes, particularly among young people. Contact address: Dominikanerbastei 21/28, A-1010 Wien, Austria.

The Nebenzahl Prize for Dissertations in the History of Cartography. Awarded every two years to the author of a recently completed dissertation. This prize is the successor to the now discontinued 'Nebenzahl Prize for Books in the History of Cartography'. Contact: The Director, Hermon Dunlap Smith Center, Newberry Library, 60 West Walton Street, Chicago, IL 60610-3380. E-mail: akermanj@newberry.org.

Sir George Fordham Award for Cartobibliography, made triennially by the Royal Geographical Society (with the Institute of British Geographers) for distinguished contributions to the field of cartobibliography. Nominations should be sent (with the nominee's outline curriculum vitae) by 31 July 1999 to The Keeper, Royal Geographical Society, 1 Kensington Gore, London SW7 2AR, UK.

Society for the History of Discoveries annual prize essay contest, open to anyone without a doctorate. Essays may be on any aspect of discoveries, including cartography. Closing date: 1 May. Contact: Prof. Carol Urness, James Ford Bell Library, University of Minnesota, 309 19th Avenue South, Minneapolis, MN 55455, USA. E-mail: c-urne@tc.umn.edu.

Walter W. Ristow Essay Prize, issued annually by the Washington Map Society to foster achievement in cartographic history and librarianship. Open to full or part-time students of at least upper-level undergraduate status of accredited institutions of higher learning worldwide. Closing date: 1 June. Contact: Ed Redmond, Secretary, Washington Map Society, c/o Library of Congress, Geography and Map Division, Washington, DC 20540-4650, USA. E-mail: ered@loc.gov.

8. MAP COLLECTIONS

For Web sites containing catalogues of map collections or selected images of scanned maps see
< http://kartoserver.frw.ruu.nl/html/staff/oddens/oddens.htm > under 'Maps and Atlases' and 'Map Collections'.

8.1 Directories

GENERAL: Lorraine Dubreuil (ed.), *World Directory of Map Collections*, 3rd ed. (Munich and London: Saur, 1993). [IFLA Publications 63.] [The fourth edition, edited by Olivier Loiseaux, Bibliothèque nationale de France, is expected in 1999.]

AUSTRALIA: Maura O'Connor, *Map Collections in Australia: A Directory*, 4th ed. (Canberra: National Library of Australia, 1991).

AUSTRIA: Franz Wawrik, 'Kartographische Sammlungen in Österreich', in Jürgen Dodt and Werner Herzog (eds), *Kartographisches Taschenbuch 1992/93* (Bonn: Kirschbaum, 1992), 110-121.

CANADA: Tim Ross (ed.), *Directory of Canadian Map Collections*, 6th ed. (Ottawa: Association of Canadian Map Libraries and Archives, 1992). [A new edition is in preparation.]

CZECH REPUBLIC: Ivan Kupčík, 'Collections of old maps, atlases and globes in Bohemia', *Imago et mensura mundi (Atti del IX Congresso Internazionale di Storia della Cartografia, Pisa-Firenze-Roma 1981)* (Florence: Istituto della Enciclopedia Italiana, 1985), 377-384.

DENMARK: Marie Louise Brandt et al., *Danske Kortsamlinger: en Guide* (Copenhagen: Dansk Kartografisk Selskab og det Kongelige Bibliotek, 1989).

FRANCE: Anne-Marie Briend and Denis Gabay, *Répertoire des cartothèques de France,* 2nd ed. (Paris: Laboratoire Intergéo, 1991). Extract from *Intergéo Bulletin*, 100 (1990).

Monique Pelletier, 'Les collections de cartes. Leur passé et leur avenir', *Introducció general a la història de la cartografia* (Barcelona: Institut Cartogràfic de Catalunya, 1990), 55-88.

GERMANY: Bibliotheksverband der Deutschen Demokratischen Republik, *Jahrbuch der Bibliotheken, Archiven und Informationseinrichtungen der Deutschen Demokratischen Republik, Jahrgang 11, 1978/79* (Leipzig: Bibliographisches Institut, 1981).

Wolfgang Scharfe, 'Map collections and map librarianship in Germany', in *La cartografia dels països de parla alemanya – Alemanya, Austria i Suïssa* (Barcelona: Institut Cartogràfic de Catalunya, 1997), 107-118.

Lothar Zögner, Egon Klemp and Gudrun Maurer, *Verzeichnis der Kartensammlungen in Deutschland*, 2nd ed. (Wiesbaden: Otto Harrassowitz, 1998).

ITALY: Leonardo Rombai, 'Le cartoteche in Italia. Il patrimonio cartografico italiano: ceni sulla sua consistenza e conservazione' in *La cartografia italiana* (Barcelona: Institut Cartogràfic de Catalunya, 1993), 205-229.

JAPAN: Kazutaka Unno, 'Cartography in Japan', in John Brian Harley and David Woodward (eds), *The History of Cartography, Vol. 2, Book 2* (Chicago and London: University of Chicago Press, 1994), especially 351-352.

THE NETHERLANDS: Paul van den Brink, *Almanak verzamelingen topografisch beeldmateriaal: een overzicht van kaartverzamelingen en topografisch-historische atlassen in Nederland* (The Hague: Koninklijke Bibliotheek, 1995).

Cornelis Koeman, *Collections of Maps and Atlases in the Netherlands: Their History and Present State* (Leiden: Brill, 1961).

Annemieke van Slobbe, *Gids voor kaartenverzamelingen in Nederland* (Amersfoort: Nederlands Vereniging voor Kartografie; Alphen aan den Rijn: Canaletto, 1980).

NEW ZEALAND: *Directory of New Zealand Map Collections* (Auckland: New Zealand Map Society, 1989).

NORWAY: Rolf Fladby, *Gamle norske kart: samkatalog over utrykte kart fra de siste 300 år*, 18 vols. (Oslo, Bergen and Tromsö: Universitetsforlaget for Norsk Lokalhistorisk Institutt, 1979-1985).

POLAND: Daniela Kosacka, *Zbiory kartograficzne w Polskiej Rzeczypospolitej Ludowej. Informator* (Warsaw: Naczelna Dyrekcja Archiwow Państwowych, 1972).

Marian T. W. Lodyński et al., *Centralny katalog zbiorów kartograficznych w Polsce,* 6 vols. (Warsaw: Polska Akademia Nauk, Instytut Geografii, 1961-).

SINGAPORE: Nicholas Martland, *Guide to Map Collections in Singapore: With a Bibliographical Essay on Official Publications Relating to Cartography in Singapore and Malaysia* (Singapore: References Division, National Library, 1987).

SPAIN: Montserrat Galera Monegal, 'Les cartotèques a la Península Ibèrica', in *La cartografía de la Península Ibèrica i la seva extensió al continent Americà* (Barcelona: Institut Cartogràfic de Catalunya, 1991), 17-152.

SWITZERLAND: Hans-Uli Feldmann, 'Map publishers, map collections and documentation, electronic information and map archives in Switzerland', in *La cartografia dels països de parla alemanya — Alemanya, Austria i Suïssa* (Barcelona: Institut Cartogràfic de Catalunya, 1997), 235-242.

Karten in Schweizer Bibliotheken und Archiven (Zurich: ETH-Bibliothek, 1992). [Also in French and Italian.]

UNITED KINGDOM: Joan Chibnall, *A Directory of UK Map Collections*, 3rd ed. (British Cartographic Society, Map Curators' Group Publication No. 4, 1995).

Catherine Delano Smith, 'Map collections and libraries in England and their place in the history of cartography', in *La cartografia anglesa: English Cartography* (Barcelona: Institut Cartogràfic de Catalunya, 1997), 253-269.

Helen Wallis, assisted by Anita McConnell (ed.), *Historians' Guide to Early British Maps: A Guide to the Location of Pre-1900 Maps of the British Isles Preserved in the United Kingdom and Ireland* (London: Royal Historical Society, 1994).

UNITED STATES: David K. Carrington and Richard W. Stephenson, *Map Collections in the United States and Canada: A Directory*, 4th ed. (New York: Special Libraries Association, 1985). [Includes some smaller collections not in Cobb.]

David A. Cobb, *Guide to U.S. Map Resources*, 2nd ed. (Chicago: American Library Association, 1990).

8.2 Catalogues of Major Collections

BIBLIOTHÈQUE NATIONALE DE FRANCE: the steadily growing BN-Opaline/Cartes et Plans is available at < http://www.bnf.fr >.

BRITISH LIBRARY: *The British Library Map Catalogue on CD-ROM* (Reading: Primary Source Media, 1998). [The CD provides enhanced access to four catalogues: the 15-volume catalogue of printed maps (1967), its ten-year supplement (1978), the post-1974 automated file, and the catalogue of manuscript maps (1844-1861).] < http://www.bl.uk/collections/maps >.

'Indexes to material of cartographic interest in the Department of Manuscripts and to manuscript cartographic items elsewhere in the British Library' (typescript, 1992). [Database listings, available in the British Library, arranged in five sequences: geographical (hierarchical), manuscript number, personal names, chronological, and thematic. Brief extracts can be provided on request.]

HELSINKI UNIVERSITY LIBRARY: Ann-Mari Mickwitz, Leena Miekkavaara and Tuula Rantanen, *The A. E. Nordenskiöld Collection in the Helsinki University Library*, 5 vols. in 6. (Helsinki, 1979-1995). [Nordenskiöld, a 19th-century explorer, amassed a significant collection for the early history of cartography in general. The maps are individually listed and indexed by title. The two parts of vol. 5 contain indexes by Cecilia af Forselles-Riska: chronological, nominal, and two geographical indexes arranged, respectively, alphabetically and hierarchically.]

LIBRARY OF CONGRESS: Philip L. Phillips and Clara E. LeGear, *A List of Geographical Atlases*, 9 vols. (Washington, D.C., 1909-1992). [A

very extensive atlas collection; the early volumes itemize the maps of America only, the later ones give comprehensive listings.}
< http://lcweb.loc.gov/rr/geogmap/ >.

NATIONAL ARCHIVES OF CANADA: *Catalogue of the National Map Collection,* 16 vols. (Boston: Hall, 1976).

NATIONAL MARITIME MUSEUM: *Catalogue of the Library. Volume 3: Atlases & Cartography,* 2 vols. (London: HMSO, 1971). [Concentrating on sea charts, which are individually listed and indexed.]

PUBLIC RECORD OFFICE: *Maps and Plans in the Public Record Office,* 4 vols. (London, 1967-1998). [The volumes cover, respectively, British Isles; America and the West Indies; Africa; Europe.}

ROYAL GEOGRAPHICAL SOCIETY: *Catalogue of {the} Map Room, 1881* (London: Murray, 1882).

8.3 Globe History

Older globes are both scientific instruments and geographical or astronomical statements. They may be studied, inventoried, sold and collected in the context of either the history of science or the history of cartography/astronomy. For the Internationale Coronelli-Gesellschaft, the only society devoted to the study of historical globes, see Section 9.1. Its periodical *Der Globusfreund* (see Section 2) has included numerous national and regional inventories of surviving globes. For globes sold at auction see the occasional 'Information' issued by the Internationale Coronelli-Gesellschaft.

Peter E. Allmeyer-Beck, *Modelle der Welt: Erd- und Himmelsgloben* (Vienna: Bibliophile Edition, 1997).

Wilhelm Bonacker, *Das Schriftthum zur Globenkunde* (Leiden: Brill, 1960); with supplements in *Der Globusfreund* 10 (1961), 29-34 and 11 (1962), 151-57.

Wilhelm Bonacker, 'Globenmacher aller Zeiten', *Der Globusfreund*, 5 (1956), 17-28; 6 (1957), 41-45; 12 (1963), 55-60.

Elly Dekker and Peter van der Krogt, *Globes from the Western World* (London: Zwemmer, 1993).

Peter van der Krogt, *Globi Neerlandici: The Production of Globes in the Low Countries* (Utrecht: HES, 1993).

Thomas Lamb and Jeremy Collins. *The World in Your Hands* (London: Christie's, 1994). [Catalogue of an exhibition of the Rudolf Schmidt collection.}

Edward Luther Stevenson, *Terrestrial and Celestial Globes: Their History and Construction Including a Consideration of Their Value as Aids in the Study of Geography and Astronomy*, 2 vols. (New Haven: Yale University Press for the Hispanic Society of America, 1921). [Reprinted New York: Johnson Reprint Corp., 1971.}

8.4 Map Curatorship

Most of the manuals and cataloguing rules devised for map librarians are concerned with current materials. However, many also have relevance to historical materials. All who curate early maps, whether as librarians or archivists, are urged to join ISCEM (see Section 9.1) if only to receive the Newsletter.

Christopher R. Perkins and Robert B. Parry (eds), *Information Sources in Cartography* (London: Bowker-Saur, 1990). ['Part 4 Map Librarianship', 235-308, provides bibliographical listings, interspersed with commentary, under the general headings: map library management, map selection and acquisition, cataloguing and classification, automated search and retrieval, preservation and storage, exploiting cartographic resources.]

The Map and Geography Round Table of the American Library Association (MAGERT) has launched a series of electronic publications on map librarianship, see < http://www.sunysb.edu/libmap/elecpubs.htm >.

9 MAP ORGANIZATIONS AND SOCIETIES

For updated information see the Map Societies homepage < http://www.csuohio.edu/CUT/MapSoc/Index.htm >.
The following listing is of non-professional societies that are concerned with the history of cartography and open to anyone. It does not include professional groupings of cartographers, geographers, map curators, surveyors etc. For a good listing of those, see Christopher R. Perkins and Robert B. Parry (eds), *Information Sources in Cartography* (London: Bowker-Saur, 1990), 473-481. For details of the journals, awards and grants referred to, see Sections 2 and 7.2.

9.1 International

Association of Map Memorabilia Collectors. [Produces *Cartomania*.] Contact: Siegfried Feller, 8 Amherst Road, Pelham, MA 01002, USA.

Brussels International Map Collectors' Circle (BIMCC) [Founded in 1998 with the intention of organizing talks and visits.] Contact: Wulf Bodenstein, 71 Avenue des Camélias, B-1150 Brussels, Belgium. E-mail: veronique.v.d.kerckhof@fine-arts-museum.be.

Carto-Philatelists. [Founded in 1955; produces the *Carto-Philatelist*.] Contact: Miklos Pinther, 206 Grayson Place, Teaneck, NJ 07666, USA.

International Map Collectors' Society. [Founded in 1980, based in England, with regular regional meetings, a United Kingdom symposium every alternate year, and an international symposium annually. Publishes the *IMCoS Journal*, makes the annual IMCoS-Helen Wallis Award, and offers a Travel Grant.] Contact: Jenny Harvey, 27 Landford Road, Putney, London SW15 1AQ, UK. E-mail: jeh@harvey27.demon.co.uk. < http://www.harvey27.demon.co.uk/imcos/ >.

International Society for the Curators of Early Maps (ISCEM). [Founded in 1987, meets in alternate years at the International Conference on the History of Cartography. Produces an occasional Newsletter, with reports, notices of exhibitions, news of members and their institutions etc.] Contact: R.W. Karrow, The Newberry Library, 60 W. Walton Street, Chicago, IL 60610-3380, U.S.A. E-mail: karrowr@newberry.org.

Internationale Coronelli-Gesellschaft für Globen- und Instrumentenkunde. [Founded in 1952, this is the only society concerned with the history of globes. It holds regular conferences, publishes *Der Globusfreund*, and offers the Fiorini-Haardt Prize.] Address: Dominikanerbastei 21/28, A-1010 Wien, Austria.

Society for the History of Discoveries. [Founded in 1960, meets annually, usually in the United States, publishes the annual *Terrae Incognitae*, issues a newsletter, and offers an annual essay prize.] Secretary-Treasurer: Russell Magnaghi, History Department, North Michigan University, 1401 Presque Isle Avenue, Marquette, MI 49855-5352, U.S.A. E-mail: rmagnagh@nmu.edu.

9.2 Regional

AUSTRALIA: Australian Map Circle (formed 1973). [Issues *The Globe* and a newsletter. Some states have their own branches.] Contact: c/o Department of Geography, University of Melbourne, Parkville, VIC, 3052. < http://www.lib.unimelb.edu.au/collections/maps/amc.htm >.

AUSTRIA: Österreichische Geographische Gesellschaft, Kartographische Kommission, Karl-Schweighofer-Gasse 3, A-1070, Wien, Austria. E-mail: johannes.doerflinger@univie.ac.at.

CANADA: British Columbia, Map Society of (formed 1975). Contact address: P.O. Box 37109, 2930 Lonsdale Avenue, North Vancouver, B.C. V7N 4M4.

FINLAND: Chartarum Amici [Helsinki] (formed 1964). Contact: Leena Miekkavaara, Pyörrekuja 12, 04300 Tuusula, Finland.

GERMANY: Arbeitsgemeinschaft der Historischen Kommissionen der Länder und Landesgeschichtlicher Institut (formed 1896). Publishes the proceedings of annual meetings (1970-). Contact: Dr W. Irgang, Herder-Institut, Gisonenweg 5, D-35037 Marburg.

Deutsche Gesellschaft für Kartographie. Arbeitskreis Geschichte der Kartographie (formed 1954). Contact: Prof. Dr. W. Scharfe, Weimarische Str. 4, D-10715 Berlin.

Freundeskreis für Cartographica in der Stiftung Preußischer Kulturbesitz (formed 1986). Publishes a *Mitteilungsblatt*. Contact address: c/o Kartenabteilung, Staatsbibliothek zu Berlin, Unter den Linden 8, D-10102, Berlin.

GREECE: Society for Hellenic Cartography (formed 1988). Contact: Themis Strongilos, 6 Patriarchou Ioachim Street, GR-106 74 Athens. E-mail: strong@otenet.gr

ISRAEL: Israel Map Collectors' Society (formed 1985). Issues *Journal*. Contact: Eva Wajntraub, 4 Brenner Street, IL 92103 Jerusalem.

JAPAN: Nihon Kotizu Gakkai (formed 1995, in succession to Nihon Chizu Shiryō Kyōkai. The bi-monthly *Kochizu kenkyū Nyūsu* replaces the monthly newsletter *Gekkan Kochizu Kenkyū*. < http://www.asahi-net.or.jp/~wa7y-inue/amse.htm >.

THE NETHERLANDS: Nederlandse Vereniging voor Kartografie. Werkgroep voor de Geschiedenis van de Kartografie (formed 1974). Issues *Caert-thresoor*. Contact: Drs Marc Hameleers, Municipal Archives, P.O. Box 51140, 1007 EC Amsterdam. < http://nvkserver.frw.ruu.nl/HTML/NVK/werkgroepen/Geschiedenis/Geschiedenis.html >.

NEW ZEALAND: New Zealand Map Society (formed 1977; current name 1987). Issues *New Zealand Map Society Journal*, and newsletter *Datum*. Contact: Phil Barton, P.O. Box 10-179, Wellington.

SWEDEN: Kartografiska sällskapet, historiska sektionen. Contact: Göran Bäärnhielm, Kungl. Biblioteket, P.O. Box 5039, 102 41 Stockholm. < http://www.geomatics.kth.se/~ks/index.html >.

SWITZERLAND: Arbeitsgruppe für Kartengeschichte der Schweizerischen Gesellschaft für Kartographie (1977). Issues *Cartographica Helvetica*. Contact. Prof. Arthur Dürst, Promenadengasse 12, CH-8001 Zürich. E-mail: arthur@duerst.ch. < http://www.geod.ethz.ch/karto/sgk/kartogesch.html >.

UNITED KINGDOM: Charles Close Society [for the Study of Ordnance Survey Maps] (formed 1980). Issues *Sheetlines*. Membership Sec.: Roger Hellyer, 60 Albany Road, Stratford-on-Avon, Warwickshire, CV37 6PQ. < http://ourworld.compuserve.com/homepages/pstubbs/ccshome.htm >.

UNITED STATES: Boston Map Society (formed 1994). Produces a newsletter. Contact: David A. Cobb, Harvard Map Collection, Harvard College Library, Cambridge, MA 02138. < http://icg.harvard.edu/~maps/hpbms.htm >.

California, Map Society of (formed 1978). Produces a newsletter. Contact: Bill Warren, 1109 Linda Glen Drive, Pasadena, CA 91105. < http://www.raremaps.com/cms/ >.

Chicago Map Society (formed 1976). Contact: c/o The Newberry Library, 60 West Walton Street, Chicago, IL 60610-3380. < http://www.newberry.org/smith/chicago.htm >.

Delaware Valley, Map Society of (formed 1983). Contact address: c/o Free Library of Philadelphia, 1901 Vine Street, Philadelphia, PA 19103.

Mercator Society of The New York Public Library (formed 1986 to support the Map Division of the New York Public Library). Produces a newsletter. Contact: Alice Hudson, Chief, Map Division, NYPL, The Research Libraries, 5th Avenue & 42nd Street, New York, NY 10018-2788.

Michigan Map Society (formed 1977). Contact: Brian L. Dunnigan, P.O. Box 1201, Ann Arbor, MI 48106.

New York Map Society (formed 1978). Produces a newsletter, *Rhumblines*. Contact: Alice Hudson, Chief, Map Division, NYPL, The Research Libraries, 5th Avenue & 42nd Street, New York, NY 10018-2788.

Northeast Map Society. Produces the NEMO newsletter. Contact address: c/o Eric Riback, 2506 Hillwood Place, Charlottesville, VA 22901.

Northern Ohio Map Society (formed 1994). Contact: Maureen Farrell, Map Department, Cleveland Public Library, 801 Superior Avenue, Cleveland, OH 44111. < http://www.csuohio.edu/CUT/Clevmaps.htm#NOMS >.

Osher Library Associates (formed 1990 to support the Osher Map Library and Smith Center for Cartographic Education). Contact: Yolanda Theunissen, Curator, Osher Map Library, University of Southern Maine, P.O. Box 9301, Portland, ME 04104.

Philip Lee Phillips Society (formed 1995 to support the Library of Congress). Produces a newsletter. Contact address: c/o Geography and Map Division, Library of Congress, Washington, D.C. 20540. < http://lcweb.loc.gov/rr/geogmap/phillips.html >.

Road Map Collectors of America (formed 1994). Produces a newsletter. Contact: Dave Schul, 2214 Princeton Blvd, Lawrence, KS 66049. < http://www.roadmaps.org >.

Rocky Mountain Map Society (formed 1991). Contact: Wes Brown, 1736 Hudson St., Denver, CO 80220.

Texas Map Society (formed 1996). c/o Special Collections Division, UTA Libraries, Box 19497, Arlington, Texas 76019-0497. < http://www.acu.edu/~armstrongl/geography/txmapsoc.htm >.

Washington Map Society (formed 1979). Issues *The Portolan* three times a year. Contact: Ed Redmond, c/o Geography and Map Division, Library of Congress, Washington D.C. 20540-4650. < http://www.cyberia.com/pages/jdocktor/washmap.htm >.

Wisconsin, Map Society of (formed 1996). Contact: Sharon Hill, American Geographical Society Collection, P.O. Box 399, Milwaukee, WI 53201.

10. THE MARKETPLACE

For information on the growing list of websites see < http://kartoserver.frw.ruu.nl/HTML/STAFF/oddens/sellers.htm#Antiq >.

10.1 Map Dealers

Sheppard's International Directory of Print and Map Sellers, 3rd ed. (Farnham, Surrey: Richard Joseph, 1995). [Lists 1500 dealers in 48 countries.]

The Maptrade Internet list carries notices about dealers' catalogues and maps for sale. To join:

> [send to] majordomo@raremaps.com
>
> [type nothing under 'subject']
>
> [type, in the body of the message:] subscribe maptrade

10.2 Map Fairs

Most antiquarian book fairs include at least a few map dealers. There are also some regional map fairs – a local dealer will provide details. The three annual events listed below are the only regular fairs with an international dimension.

Annual International Miami Map Fair (1994-). Held in Miami each February. Contact: Map Fair Coordinator, Historical Museum of Southern Florida, 101 West Flagler Street, Miami, FL 33130, USA. E-mail: mapfair@historical-museum.org.

European Map Fair, organized by the Stichting Historische Cartografie van de Nederlanden (SHCN). Founded in 1997; first annual fair in Breda, November 1998. Contact: SHCN, Secretariaat, Witrijtseweg 16, 5571 XJ Bergeijk, Netherlands. E-mail: kinds@ping.be. See also Section 6, Utrecht.

International Map Collectors' Society (1981-). Held in central London each June. Contact: Roger Brown, 160 Croxdale Road, Borehamwood, Herts, WD6 4QB, UK.

10.3 Map Sales and Prices

American Book Prices Current ([Washington, D.C.:] Bancroft-Parkman). [Annual listing of material coming through the world's major auction houses, with indexes at irregular intervals. Cartographic entries grouped under 'atlas' and 'maps and charts'.]

Antique Map Price Record and Handbook (Amherst, MA: Kimmel Publications, 1994-). [Biennial listing of maps passing through selected dealers. Formerly David C. Jolly, *Antique Maps, Sea Charts, City Views, Celestial Charts and Battle Plans: Price Guide and Collectors' Handbook* (Brookline, MA: Jolly, 1983-1992).]

Book Auction Records (Folkestone: Dawson). [Annual listing of material coming through the world's major auction houses, with indexes at irregular intervals. Cartographic entries grouped under 'atlases' and a separate section 'printed maps, charts and plans'.]

Imago Mundi. The International Journal for the History of Cartography (see Section 2). [The annual 'Chronicle' lists (without giving prices) rare and important items that have come up for sale, via auctions or dealers. There are also lists of notable acquisitions, arranged by institution.]

Mercator's World (see Section 2). [Includes 'Auction Block' by Ian McKay.]

*　　*　　*

Postscript: We have done our best to ensure all details are correct at the time of going to press. Please notify inaccuracies or omissions *immediately* to the Chairman of *Imago Mundi* (c/o Map Library, British Library, 96 Euston Road, London NW1 2DB, UK), for incorporation into the 10th edition. If more convenient, notify by e-mail to: tony.campbell@bl.uk.

PART II

11. WHO'S WHO IN THE HISTORY OF CARTOGRAPHY

ABEYDEERA, Ananda (Dr)
119, boulevard de la Boissière
93100 MONTREUIL
France

South and South-east Asia
with special emphasis on
Taprobane

'Taprobane, Ceylan ou Sumatra? Une confusion féconde', *Archipel*
47 (1994): 87-123.

Caerte van Oostlant of the Dutch Chartographer Cornelis Anthoniszoon,
1543 (Wolfenbüttel: Herzog August Bibliothek, 1995 (facsimile).

The Chart of West Indies and Central America – Attributed to Gerolamo
Verrazano pre-1528 (Wolfenbüttel: Herzog August Bibliothek,
1995 (facsimile).

'Encore Taprobane. A propos du témoignage tardif de Thomaso
Porcacchi (1576)', *Archipel* 49 (1995): 125-136.

'Facsimiles of the charts attributed to Reinel, Ribeiro/Chaves,
Verrazano and a painted map by Cornelis Anthoniszoon from the
Herzog August Bibliothek Wolfenbüttel', *Wolfenbütteler Bibliotheks-*
Informationen, 20:1-2 (1995): 18-25.

The First Original Portuguese Chart of the Indian Ocean Attributed to
Jorge or Pedro Reinel circa 1510 (Wolfenbüttel: Herzog August
Bibliothek, 1995 (facsimile).

Landkarten, Herzog August Bibliothek, Wolfenbüttel, 1995 (set of
10 postcard maps).

The Wolfenbüttel Spanish Chart of the Far East Attributed to Diogo
Ribeiro, circa 1532 (Wolfenbüttel: Herzog August Bibliothek, 1995
(facsimile).

The Wolfenbüttel Spanish Chart of the New World Attributed to Diogo
Ribeiro, circa 1532 (Wolfenbüttel: Herzog August Bibliothek, 1995
(facsimile).

'Une contribution portugaise à la cartographie des Grandes
Découvertes: la découverte portugaise de Ceylan: problèmes de
transition de la représentation ptolémène de Taprobane à Ceilão',
Studia 54-55 (1996): 211-235.

'The factual description of a sea route to India and Ceylon by a
Greek master mariner from Roman Egypt', *Deutsches*
Schiffahrtsarchiv 19 (1996): 127-216.

d'ABOVILLE, Christian
5 Av Horace Vernet
78110 LE VESINET
France
Tel: (33) 1 39 76 12 57

Maps and engravings of
Dauphiné of France in the
17th and 18th centuries
(mostly the area of
Briançon)

ADAMS, Brian W.
Flat 3
30 Munster Road
LONDON SW6 4EW
UK
Tel: (44) 0171 731 2416

Ordnance Survey projec-
tions and co-ordinate systems before the national
grid

'Hounslow Heath, Hampton and Heathrow – Roy re-visited and
re-measured', *Sheetlines* 50 (1997): 46-47.

'The contruction of Ordnance Survey maps', in *Ordnance Survey*
Small-Scale Maps Indexes: 1800-1998 (Kerry: David Archer, 1998).

AKERMAN, James R. (Dr)
Director
Hermon Dunlap Smith Center
    for the History of Cartography
The Newberry Library
60 Walton Street
CHICAGO, Illinois 60610-3380
USA
Tel: (1) 312 255 3523 (office)
     (1) 773 907 0271 (home)
Fax: (1) 312 255 3513
E-mail: akermanj@newberry.org

American and British road
and tourism maps (late
19th-early 20th centuries);
history of educational cartography; history of atlases;
social history of cartography

'Blazing a well-worn path: cartographic commercialism, highway
promotion, and automobile tourism in the United States, ca.1880-
1930', in Robert Rundstrom (ed), *Introducing Cultural and Social*
Cartography, *Cartographica* 30:1 (1993): 10-20.

'Atlas, la genèse d'un titre', in Marcel Watelet (ed), *Gerardi*
Mercatoris Atlas Europae. Facsimilé des cartes de Gérard Mercator con-
tenues dans l'Atlas de l'Europe, vers 1570-1572 (Anvers, Fonds

Mercator, 1994), 14-29. [English edition: *The Mercator Atlas of Europe* (Pleasant Hill, Oregon: Walking Tree Press, 1997).]

'From books with maps to books as maps: the editor in the creation of the atlas idea', in Joan Winearls (ed), *Editing Early and Historical Atlases* (Toronto: University of Toronto Press, 1995), 3-48.

'The structuring of political territory in early printed atlases', *Imago Mundi* 47 (1995): 138-154.

(with Gerald Danzer), *Paper Trails: Geographic Literacy via American Highway Maps* (Chicago: The Newberry Library, 1996).

ÅKERSTRÖM-HOUGEN, Gunilla (Prof)
Art History Department
University of Gothenburg
Box 200
S-40530 GOTHENBURG
Sweden
Tel: (46) 031 773 2793 (office)   (46) 031 185 187 (home)
Fax: (46) 031 773 2780 (office)   (46) 031 185 187 (home)

Old maps of Rome

'Urbis Romae Prospectus 1593: Antonio Tempestas karta över Rom', in I. Bergström et al (eds), *Det skapande jaget: konsthistoriska texter tillägnadeMaj-Brit Wadell* (Göteborg: Konstvetenskapliga institutionen, Göteborgs universitet, 1995), 159-172.

ALA'I, Cyrus (Dr)
1 Golders Park Close
LONDON NW11 7QR
UK
Tel & fax: (44) 0181 209 0785

Persia, Persian Gulf, Caspian Sea; Islamic cartography and cartographers

'Persia or Iran? What do the maps say?' *The Map Collector* 70 (1995): 12-17.

'The rise and fall of cartography in the pre-modern Islamic societies' *Iranshenasi* 8:1 (1996): 92-105 (in Persian with English abstract, 24-25).

'A new home for an old map (Hereford map)', *Mercator's World* 2:3 (1997): 62-63.

'The map of Mamun', *Mercator's World* 3:1 (1998): 52-57.

ALKHOVEN, Patricia (Dr)
Koninklijke Bibliotheek
Library Research Department
PO Box 90407
2509 LK THE HAGUE
Netherlands
Tel: (31) 70 314 0441 (office)
      (31) 71 531 4563 (home)
Fax: (31) 70 314 0427
E-mail: patricia.alkhoven@konbib.nl

History of architecture, architectural drawings, urban development; history of the city, town plans/views; representation methods of cities; three-dimensional visualization/representation techniques, CA(A)D

The Changing Image of the City: A Study of the Transformation of the Townscape Using Computer-Aided Architectural Design and Visualization Techniques. A Case Study: Heusden (Alphen a/d Rijn: Canaletto, 1995).

'Van draadmodel tot Virtual Reality. Computer visualisaties van historische architectuur en stedebouw', *Cahier Vereniging voor Geschiedenis en Informatica* 8 (1995).

ALANEN, Timo
Kurintie 23
FIN-31530 PYÖLI
Finland
Tel: (358) 24 748 4654
Fax: (358) 24 748 4605

Place names on old maps

ALLEN, David Yehling (Dr)
Melville Library, Map Collection
State University of New York
   Stony Brook
STONY BROOK, NY 11794-3331
USA
Tel: (1) 516 632 1159
Fax: (1) 516 632 7106
E-mail: dyallen@ccmail.sunysb.edu

East coast of North America, particularly 17th, 18th, early 19th centuries

'Long Island triangulated: nineteenth-century maps and charts of the U.S. Coast Survey', *Long Island Historical Journal* 6 (Spring, 1994): 191-207.

'The digital imaging of maps and aerial photographs: an overview', *Meridian* 12 (1997): 5-13.

Long Island Maps and Their Makers (Mattituck, NY: Amereon House, 1997).

ALSOP, James D. (Dr)
Department of History
McMaster University
HAMILTON, Ontario L85 4L9
Canada
Tel: (1) 905 525 9140
E-mail: alsopj@mcmaster.ca

Cartographical knowledge
and overseas expansion
within England's maritime
community, c. 1550-1625

'William Towerson's rutter for the Margate-Emden navigation, 1564', *Mariner's Mirror* **82** (1996): 154-159.

AMARAL, Joaquim Ferreira do
Rua Dr Gabriel de Freitas 7 r/c
2750 CASCAIS
Portugal
Tel: (351) 01 483 6375
E-mail: famaral@mail.telepac.pt

Pedro Reinel

Pedro Reinel me Fez: À volta de um mapa dos Descobrimentos (Lisbon: Quetzal, 1995).

ANDREWS, John Harwood (Dr)
32 Restway Wall
Garden City Way
CHEPSTOW NP6 5EF
UK
Tel: (44) 01291 623166

Ireland; Mercator's maps of
England and Wales, 1595

'Irish placenames and the Ordnance Survey: commentary', *Cartographica* (Calgary), **31**:1 (Autumn 1994): 60-61.

'What was a map? The lexicographers reply', *Cartographica* (Calgary), **33**:4 (Winter 1996): 1-11.

'Paper landscapes: mapping Ireland's physical geography', in John Wilson Foster and Helena C.G. Chesney (eds), *Nature in Ireland: A Scientific and Cultural History* (Dublin: The Lilliput Press, 1997), 199-218.

Shapes of Ireland – Maps and Their Makers 1564-1839 (Dublin: Geography Publications, 1997).

ARMITAGE, Geoffrey
Map Library
British Library
Euston Road
LONDON NW1 2DB
England
Tel: (44) 0171 412 7701 (office)
Fax: (44) 0171 412 7780
E-mail: geoff.armitage@bl.uk

Eclipse mapping; 18th-
century double-hemisphere
world maps, cartobibliographies; archaeology on pre-
OS maps

(44) 0181 641 0146 (home)

'County cartobibliographies of England and Wales: addendum', *The Map Collector* **73** (1995): 20-23.

The Shadow of the Moon: British Solar Eclipse Mapping in the Eighteenth Century (Tring, Herts.: Map Collector Publications, 1997).

ARNAU, Vicente Guillermo
Arenales 947 4"C
BUENOS AIRES
Argentina
Tel: (54) 1 393 3220 / 393 7091

Falkland Islands (Malvinas)
on Spanish maps of the
16th century

ARUNACHALAM, B. (Prof)
305, New Moonlight Apartments
Mahakali Caves Road
Andheri (East)
MUMBAI 400 093
India
Tel: (91) 022 835 2998

Indigenous traditions of
Indian cartography; Indian
and European cartography
of Indian Ocean

(with P. Gogate), 'Area maps in Maratha cartography: a study in native maps of Western India', *Imago Mundi*, **50** (1998): 126-140.

ASHWORTH, William B. (Prof)
Department of History
University of Missouri-Kansas City
KANSAS CITY, MO 64110
USA
Tel: (1) 816 926 8719 (office)
Fax: (1) 816 926 8790
E-mail: ashwortb@lhl.lib.mo.us

Celestial cartography (star
maps), 1450-1650; lunar
cartography, 1600-1980

(1) 913 262 3823 (home)

Out of This World: The Golden Age of the Celestial Atlas (A virtual exhibition catalogue for the Web; Kansas City: Linda Hall

Library, 1995). [URL is:
www.lhl.lib.mo.us/pubserv/hos/stars/welcome.htm]

ASTENGO, Corradino (Prof)
Istituto di Geografia
Facoltà di Lettere e Filosofia
Università di Genova
Via Bensa 1
16124 GENOVA
Italy

Mediterranean portolan
charts and atlases; captions
in medieval mappaemundi

Tel: (39) 010 209 9607 (office)   (39) 019 811451 (home)
Fax: (39) 010 246 1520 (office)   (39) 019 811451 (home)

'La produzione cartografica di Francesco Ghisolfi', *Annali di Ricerca
e Studi di Geografia* **49** (1993): 1-16.

'La cartografia nautica manoscritta a Livorno nei secoli XVI e
XVII', *Annali di Ricerca e Studi di Geografia* **50** (1994): 1-15.

'La fabbricazione di carte ed atlanti nautici', *Studi e Ricerche di
Geografia* **17**:2 (1994): 153-172.

'L'asse del Mediterraneo nella cartografia nautica dei secoli XVI e
XVII', *Studei e Ricerche di Geografia* **18**:2 (1995): 213-237.

*Elenco preliminare di carte ed atlanti nautici manoscritti eseguiti nell'area
mediterranea nel periodo 1500-1700 e conservati presso enti pubblici*
(Genova: Istituto di Geografia, 1996).

'Der genuesische Kartograph Vesconte Maggiolo und sein Werk',
Cartographica Helvetica **13** (1996): 9-17.

ATKINSON, David A. (Dr)
Lecturer in Human Geography
University of Hull
HULL HU6 7RX
UK

Geopolitical mapping in
fascist Italy and interwar
Europe; use of geographical
knowledges (including cartography) in European
imperialisms, especially the
Italian case

'Geopolitics, cartography, and geographical knowledge: envisaging
Africa from fascist Italy', in Morag Bell, Robin Butlin and Michael
Heffernan (eds), *Geography and Imperialism, 1820-1940*
(Manchester: Manchester University Press, 1995), 290-332.

'The politics of geography and the Italian occupation of Libya'.
Lybian Studies **27** (1996): 71-84.

AUJAC, Germaine J.J. (Prof)
6 Boulevard Joffre
92340 BOURG-LA REINE
France

Greek maps: Ptolemy and
the Italian renaissance;
Paduan Greek maps (1200)

Tel: (33) 01 46 65 71 44
    or (33) 05 63 32 17 40

'L'Eulie, l'île des merveilles', in *Strabone e la Grecio* (Perugia, 1994),
211-236.

'Le peintre florentin Piero del Massaio et la *Cosmographia* de
Ptolémée', *Geographia antiqua*, **3-4** (1994-1995): 187-210.

La redécouverte de Ptolémée et de la geographie grecque au XVe
siècle', in Danielle Lecoq and Antoine Chambard (eds), *Terre à
découvrir, terres à parcourir, éléments pour une histoire de la découverte de
la Terre et de la géographie* (Paris: Publications de l'Université Paris
7–Denis Diderot, 1996), 54-73.

'La sphère grècque', *Bulletin du Comité Français de Cartographie* **148**
(1996): 7-18.

AURINGER WOOD,
  Alberta Gjertine
Maps, Data and Media Librarian
Queen Elizabeth II Library
Memorial University of Newfoundland
ST. JOHN'S, NF A1B 3Y1
Canada

Cartobibliography of
Newfoundland

Tel: (1) 709 737 8892 (office)   (1) 709 753 3895 (home)
Fax: (1) 709 737 2153
E-mail: awood@morgan.ucs.mun.ca

(with James C. Coombs), *Index to the Library of Congress 'G' Schedule:
A Map and Atlas Classification Aid* (MAGERT Circular no. 2;
Chicago: American Library Association, Map and Geography
Round Table, 1996).

BÄÄRNHIELM, Göran (Dr)
Map Curator
Royal Library
P.O. Box 5039
S-10241 STOCKHOLM
Sweden
Tel: (46) 8 463 4180 (office)   (46) 8 643 7741 (home)
Fax: (46) 8 463 4004
E-mail: goran.baarnhielm@kb.se

Digitizing library collections; ancient and medieval maps; portolan charts

BABICZ, Józef (Prof)
Institute of the History of Science
Nowy Swiat 72
OO-330 WARSAW
Poland
Tel: (48) 022 65 72 858 (office)   (48) 022 828 88 51 (home)
Fax: (48) 022 266 137

Cartography in the 19th century; military and topographical maps

'Die Kugelgestalt der Erde als Grundlage des Modells der Kartenzeichung von Gerhard Mercator bei der Redaktion der Ptolemäischen Geographie', *Der Globusfreund* 43/44 (1995): 55-58.

'Nowe Materiały kartograficzne i opisowe do dziejów powstanis Mapy kwatermistrzostwa w kontekśois źródeł i literatury' [New graphic and text materials to military map 1843], *Studia z Dziejów Kartografii* 7 (Warsaw 1995): 141-179.

'Der christliche Universalismus der Frührenaissance im Werk von Nicolaus Cusanus und sein Einfluß auf die Entwicklung der Geographie, *Arbeiten aus dem Institut der Geographie der Karl-Franzens Universität Graz; Beiträge zur Geographie der Steiermark* 35 (1997): 1-9.

(with Alexei V. Postnikov), 'Statistical atlas of the Polish Kingdom (1840) as the thematic atlas, the monument of cartography, and the source on the history of science', *Proceedings, 18th ICA/ACI Cartographic Conference*, Stockholm, 23-27 June 1997, Vol. 4 (Gävle, 1997), 2187-2194.

BAIGENT, Elizabeth (Dr)
St Hugh's College
OXFORD OX2 6LE
UK
Tel: (44) 01865 267012
Fax: (44) 01865 267035
E-mail: ebaigent@oup.co.uk

Cadastral maps of Europe; biographical memoirs of British surveyors, geographers and cartographers for the new Dictionary of National Biography

BALDWIN, Robert Charles
    Duncan
St Just Cottage
Brightling Road
ROBERTSBRIDGE, E. Sussex
UK
Tel: (44) 0171 821 7157 (office)
    (44) 01580 880 512 (home)

15th to 17th century cartography, hydrography, navigation; Wales and Ireland, 1400-1800; colonial cartography; mapping of British highways and railways

Cartography in Thomas Harriot's Circle (Thomas Harriot Seminar, Occasional Papers no 22; Durham: School of Education, University of Durham, 1996).

BANNISTER, David
26 Kings Road
CHELTENHAM GL52 6BG
UK
Tel: (44) 01242 514287
Fax: (44) 01242 513890

On-going research for a fully revised edition of Moreland & Bannister's *Antique Maps*

BARBER, Peter Michael
Map Library
The British Library
Euston Road
LONDON NW1 2DB
UK
Tel: (44) 0171 412 7701
Fax: (44) 0171 412 7780
E-mail: peter.barber@bl.uk

Provenance of maps and collections in the British Library, particularly the King's Topographical Collection; catalogue of `Cotton Augustus' and related maps; medieval world maps; Tudor England; maps and government in Europe; military mapping in Britain to 1791

'Les Iles Britanniques', in Marcel Watelet (ed), *Gerardi Mercatoris: Atlas Europae. Facsimilé des cartes de Gérard Mercator contenues dans l'Atlas de l'Europe, vers 1570-1572* (Antwerp: Fonds Mercator,

1994), 43-78. [English edition: *The Mercator Atlas of Europe* (Pleasant Hill, Oregon: Walking Tree Press, 1997).]

'The Evesham world map: a late medieval English view of God and the world', *Imago Mundi* 47 (1995): 13-33.

'A glimpse of the earliest map-view of London?' *London Topographical Record* 27 (1995): 91-102.

(with Jeremy Black), 'Maps and the complexities of eighteenth-century Europe's territorial divisions: Holstein in 1762', *Archives* 22/93 (April 1995): 79-82.

'A revision of the catalogue of Crace's London plans', *London Topographical Newsletter*, November 1996.

'Maps and monarchs in Europe, 1550-1800', in Robert Oresko, et al (eds), *Royal and Republican Sovereignty in Early Modern Europe. Essays in Memory of Ragnhild Hattton* (Cambridge: Cambridge University Press, 1997), 75-124.

'Mapping Britain from afar', *Mercator's World* 3:4 (1998): 21-27.

BARKHAM, Selma Huxley 7 Chapel Street CHICHESTER, Sussex PO19 1BU UK Tel: (44) 01243 783302	Toponymy of the Gulf of St Lawrence area, the west coast of Newfoundland and the Strait of Belle Isle; Basque contributions to mapping the area
BARRON, Roderick Michael 21 Bayam Road SEVENOAKS, Kent TN13 3XD UK Tel & fax: (44) 01732 742 558 E-mail: barron@centrenet.co.uk	European cartography of Far East and South-east Asia
BARROW, William C. 13537 Cedar Road UNIVERSITY HEIGHTS, Ohio 44118 USA Tel: (1) 216 397 8327 E-mail: w.barrow@popmail.csuohio.edu	Land subdivision maps, real estate history, GIS

BARTHA, Lajos J.M. Hungarian Astronomical Association Magyar Csillagászati Egyesület P O Box 219 H-1461 BUDAPEST Hungary Tel: (36) 1 186 2313	Cartography and surveying in Hungary; old globes; instruments and methods of surveying and astronomy

'A Debreceni kollégium kéziratos glóbuszai: elözetes beszámoló a rézmetzö deákok földgömbjeiröl' [Manuscript globes of the Debrecen Calvinist College: preliminary report of globes engraved by the students], *Geodézia és Kartográfia* 47:4 (1995): 216-222.

'The first educatinal globes in the Hungarian language', *Bericht über das VIII. Symposium der Internationalen Coronelli-Gesellschaft ... Praha* (Vienna: Internationale Coronelli-Gesellschaft, 1995), 237-256.

BARTON, Phillip Lionel P O Box 10-179 WELLINGTON New Zealand Tel: (64) 04 384 5561	Maori cartography and place-names; hydrographical surveying and charting of the New Zealand coastline; surveying and mapping New Zealand

'Surveying and mapping the Tararua mountain system (part one)' *Otaki Historical Society: Historical Journal* 20 (1997): 40-50.

BARUTH, Christopher (Dr)
American Geographical Society
    Collection
University of Wisconsin-Milwaukee
    Library
P O Box 399
MILWAUKEE, WI 53201
USA
Tel: (1) 414 229 6282 (office)
Fax: (1) 414 229 3624
E-mail: cmb@uwm.edu
	19th-century American cartography; United States Lake Survey; map libraries
	
	(1) 414 964 7048 (home)	

BASKES, Roger S.
980 N. Michigan Avenue
Suite 1380
CHICAGO, Illinois 60611
USA
Tel: (1) 312 642 3737 (office)
   (1) 773 871 7666 (home)
Fax: (1) 312 642 0937 (office)
   (1) 773 871 8814 (home)
E-mail: rbaskes@aol.com

List of atlases and collections of maps (and of maps therein) in personal collection and in Newberry Library; books (other than atlases) with maps

'The book-bound world', *Mercator's World* 1:3 (1996): 44-49.

BASSETT, Thomas Joseph
Department of Geography
220 Davenport Hall
University of Illinois
607 S. Mathews
URBANA, IL 61801
USA
Tel: (1) 217 244 3200
Fax: (1) 217 244 1785
E-mail: bassett@uiuc.edu

Indigenous African mapmaking; cartography and empire building in West Africa

'Mapping the terrain of tenure reform: the rural landholdings project of Côte d'Ivoire', in J. Stone (ed), *Maps and Africa* (Aberdeen: Aberdeen University African Studies Group, 1994), 128-146.

'African maps and mapmaking', in H. Selin (ed), *Encyclopedia of the History of Science, Technology, and Medicine in Non-Western Cultures* (Dordrecht: Kluwer 1997), 554-558.

BATTEN, Kit
Auehrhahnweg 7
70499 STUTTGART
Germany
Tel & fax: (49) 711 865524
E-mail: kitthemap@aol.com

County maps of Devon; Liebig trade cards; nontourist postcard maps

'The St Michael's Mount of Devonshire (Borough Island), *IMCoS Journal* 62 (1995): 35-39.

(with Francis Bennett), *The Printed Maps of Devon, County Maps 1575-1837* (Tiverton: Devon Books, 1996).

'Ten-block showing Deutschland' [the Kiel Canal on stamps], *The Map Collector* 74 (1996): 48-49.

'German history through postcards – a personal history of modern Germany', *Mercator's World* 3:2 (1998): 52-57.

'Justus Liebig's trade card maps', *IMCoS Journal* 73 (1998): 19-23.

BEDERMAN, Sanford H.
Georgia State University
University Plaza
ATLANTA, Georgia 30340
USA
Tel: (1) 404 651 1833
Fax: (1) 404 651 3235
E-mail: sbederman@gsu.edu

Late 19th-early 20th century maps of Africa

BEECH, Geraldine
Head
Map and Picture Department
Public Record Office
KEW, Surry TW9 4DU
UK
Tel: (44) 0181 392 5231
Fax: (44) 0181 878 8905

Guide to maps in the PRO; maps as archives; maps and government; international boundaries; maps of Europe in the PRO; tithe maps

BELLEC, François-Paul
   (Rear-Admiral)
Institut Oceanographique
195 rue Saint-Jacques
F75005 PARIS
France
Tel: (33) 01 4757 7910
Fax: (33) 01 4757 7943

Exploration and discoveries in the Pacific and Indian ocean areas; navigation and mapping

'L'astronomie nautique le long des routes de la soie', in *Les routes de la soie, patrimoine commun, identités plurielles* (Paris: UNESCO, 1994).

Le livre de l'aventure maritime (Paris: Philippe Lebaud, 1994).

'L'irritant problème de la longitude', in *Revue des Arts et Métiers* (Paris, Décembre 1995).

'L'image de la Terre', in *Communications et mémoirs* (Paris: Academie de Marine; January-March 1996).

'A Chinese art of navigation across the Muslim waters', in *Quanzhou ISCICMSR–UNESCO Maritime Silk Route Studies* (Fujian

Education Publishing House, 1997).

'Discobrimentos, une révolution mentale ouvre les océans à l'Occident', *Revue Française d'Histoire du Livre* (Bordeaux, 1997).

'Les usagers du blanc des cartes', in *Apologie pour la géographie* (Paris: Société de Géographie, 1997).

'Le sextant', *Cahiers du CNAM* (Reims, January 1998).

BELY, Alexander V.
54a-6 Dolginovski trout
220 053 MINSK
Belarus
Tel & fax: (375) 17 213 7085
E-mail: bely@belsonet.net

Cartography of the Grand Duchy of Lithuania; Russia Alba (Belarus) on Western maps since the 14th century

BELYEA, Barbara (Dr)
Department of English
University of Calgary
CALGARY, Alberta, T2N 1N4
Canada
Tel: (1) 403 220 4656/5470
Fax: (1) 403 289 1123
E-mail: belyea@acs.ucalgary.ca
web: http://www.telusplanet.net/public/belyea

Theory of cartography; North American native maps; North American exploration and cartography, 1700-1850

'Mapping the Marias: the interface of Native and scientific cartographies." *Great Plains Quarterly* 17: 3/4 (Summer/Fall 1997): 165-184.

BENDALL, Sarah (Dr)
Librarian and Archivist
Merton College
OXFORD OX1 4JD
UK
Tel: (44) 01865 276308
Fax: (44) 01865 276361
E-mail: sarah.bendall@merton.oxford.ac.uk

English large-scale local maps and mapmakers, 1530-1850; local maps of Romney Marsh; map-making for Oxford and Cambridge colleges; maps of English forests

'Enquire "when the same platte was made and by whome and to what intent": Tudor maps of Romney Marsh', *Imago Mundi* 47 (1995): 34-48.

'Estate maps of an English county: Cambridgeshire 1600-1836', in David Buisseret (ed) *Rural Images: Estate Maps in the Old and New*

Worlds (Chicago: University of Chicago Press, 1996), 63-90.

Dictionary of Land Surveyors and Local Map-Makers of Great Britain and Ireland 1530-1850 (2nd ed; London: British Library, 1997).

BENNETT, Francis
Menryn
NEWTON FERRERS,
    Devon PL8 1BW
UK
Tel: (44) 01752 872528

Victorian county maps of Devon (with Kit Batten); Devon roads (with carto-bibliography); West Country charts cartobibliography

(with Kit Batten) *The Printed Maps of Devon, County Maps 1575-1837* (Tiverton: Devon Books, 1996).

BENNETT, James Arthur (Dr)
Museum of the History of Science
Broad Street
OXFORD OX1 3AZ
UK
Tel: (44) 01865 277281 (office)   (44) 01865 512959 (home)
Fax: (44) 01865 277288
E-mail: jim.bennett@mhs.ox.ac.uk

Maps of the 16th and 17th centuries in the context of practical geometry

The Measures: A Flemish Image of Mathematics in the Sixteenth Century (Oxford: Museum of the History of Science, 1995).

(with S. Johnston), *The Geometry of War, 1500-1750* (Oxford: Museum of the History of Science, 1996).

'Projection and the ubiquitous virtue of geometry in the Renaissance', in C. Smith and J. Agar (eds), *Making Space for Science: Territorial Themes in the Shaping of Knowledge* (London: Macmillan, 1998), 27-38.

BERESINER, Yasha
43 Templars Crescent
LONDON N3 3QR
UK
Tel: (44) 0171 354 2599 (office)   (44) 0181 349 2207 (home)
Fax: (44) 0181 346 9539
E-mail: yasha@compuserve.com

Cartographical playing cards; British county maps

(with J.R. Block), 'Dealing out maps on playing cards: a four-hundred-year-old idea revived', *Mercator's World* 2:1 (1997): 40-42.

BERGS, Irene-Annette
Badische Landesbibliothek
Erbprinzenstr. 15
76133 KARLSRUHE
Germany
Tel: (49) 0721 175 2249 (office)
Fax: (4() 0721 175 2333
E-mail: bergs@bib-karlsruhe.de

Historical cartography of south-western Germany

(49) 0721 3744 79 (home)

'Alte und moderne Landkarten in der Badischen Landesbibliothek', in *40 Jahre Ortsverein Karlsruhe der Deutschen Gesellschaft für Kartographie e. V. Red. Helmut Lehmann* (Karlsruhe, 1994), 223-238.

'Schulatlanten des 19. Jahrhunderts in einer Bibliothek heute', in Joachim Naumann (ed), *Karten hüten und bewahren, Festgabe für Lothar Zögner* (Gotha, 1995), 29-31.

(contributions to) *Auf dem Weg zur Großstadt: Karlsruhe in Plänen, Karten und Bildern 1834-1915* (Manfred Koch, ed; Karlsruhe: Ausstellungskatalog, 1997).

BEŠEVLIEV, Bojan
Institute for Balkan Studies
ul. G. Bonćev, bl. 6
BG-1113 SOFIA
Bulgaria
Tel: (359) 02 897365

Lower Danube; maps and plans of Bulgarian settlements; mapping the western coast of the Black Sea; Bulgarian lands and the Balkan peninsula

BEVILACQUA, Mario (Dr)
Centro Studi Cultura e Immagine di Roma
c/o Accademia Nazionale dei Lincei
via della Lungara, 10
00165 ROME
Italy
Tel & Fax: (39) 06 689 3758

Urban cartography: Italy in the 18th century, Europe in the Enlightenment

BHATTASALI, Deepak (Dr)
3404 Mansfield Road
FALLS CHURCH, Virginia 22041
USA
Tel: (1) 703 998 3126

Pre-1800 cartography and maps of India, Pakistan and Bangladesh

BIAŁAS, Zbigniew (Dr)
Department of English
University of Silesia
Zytnia 10
41-205 SOSNOWIEC
Poland
Tel: (48) 32 291 7417 (office)
     (48) 32 660 916 (home)
Fax: (48) 32 291 7417
E-mail: zbialas@us.edu.pl

Culture of map and colonial logocentrism; cartographical scopophilia, the visual metaphor, travel writing; cartographical discourse and philosophy

'From Vasco da Gama's astrolabe to John Barrow's artificial horizon: the Cape Colony and cartographical momentum', in Jürgen Klein and Dirk Vanderbeke (eds), *Anglistentag 1995 Greifswald; Proceedings* (Tübingen: Max Niemeyer Verlag, 1996), 361-368.

Mapping Wild Gardens: The Symbolic Conquest of South Africa (Essen: Verlag Die Blaue Eule, 1997).

BIANCHIN, Alberta
Dipartimento di Urbanistica
Istituto Universitario di Architettura di Venezia
Santa Croce 1957
30135 VENEZIA
Italy
Tel: (39) 041 257 2220
Fax: (39) 041 524 0434
e-mail: alberta@brezza.iuav.unive.it

Origins of contemporary cartography and evolution of concepts related to new technologies, ie, photogrammetry and remote sensing; cartography and town planning; uses, techniques and content: their interdependence in mapping

BIRCHMEIER, Christian
Blaurochstr. 7
CH-8260 STEIN AM RHEIN
Switzerland
Tel: (41) 052 632 21 00 (office)
     (41) 052 741 34 60 (home)
Fax: (41) 052 632 21 99

Surveying methods and the various linear measures used in 18th-century Switzerland; 18th-century maps and plans of Switzerland, Austria and Germany; biographies of 18th-century surveyors

'Die Feldnesskunst des 18. Jahrhunderts am Beispiel von Stein am Rhein', *Cartographica Helvetica* 15 (1997): 11-21.*Die Region Stein am Rhein im Bild alter Karten und Pläne des 18. Jahrhunderts* (Stein am Rhein 1997).

BLACK, Jeremy Martin (Prof)
7 Baring Crescent
EXETER EX1 1TL
UK
Tel: (44) 01392 254567 (home)
Fax: (44) 01392 264377 (office)

Historical atlases

(with Peter M. Barber), 'Maps and the complexities of eighteenth-century Europe's territorial divisions: Holstein in 1762', *Archives* 22/93 (April 1995): 79-82.

Maps and History (New Haven and London: Yale University Press, 1997).

Maps and Politics (London: Reaktion, 1997; Chicago: University of Chicago Press, 1997).

BLAKE, Erin C.
1370 W. Greenleaf Ave. No. 2-S
CHICAGO, Illinois 60626-2973
USA
Tel: (1) 773 274 5614
E-mail: ecblake@ibm.net

The use of `vue d'optique' of cities in 18th-century Europe

BLANSETT, Lisa A. (Dr)
Department of English
DM 461A
Florida International University
MIAMI, FL 33199
USA
Tel: (1) 305 348 2507
Fax: (1) 305 348 3878
E-mail: blansett@fiu.edu

17th and 18th century British cartography; theory of space (with Matthew Edney); gender issues; intersections of cartography, history, literature

BLISS, Winfried
Geheimes Staatsarchiv Preussischer
    Kulturbesitz
Archivstrasse 12-14
D-14195 BERLIN
Germany
Tel: (49) 030 839 01148 (office)
    (49) 030 693 4983 (home)
Fax: (49) 030 839 01180

Invertory of maps of the former West Pressian province in the Geheimes Staatsarchiv; military cartography: maps and plans of Prussian fortresses and their environs

'Allgemeine Kartensammlung: Provinz Ostpreussen.

Spezialinventar', *Veröffentlichungen aus den Archiven Preußischer Kulturbesitz* 43 (Köln: Böhlau, 1996).

'Die Überlieferung amtlicher Karten in Brandenburg und Preußen', in *Aus der Arbeit des Geheimen Staatsarchivs Preußischer Kulturbesitz, Arbeitsberichte I* (Berlin: Selbstverlag des Geheimen Staatsarchivs, 1996), 239-261.

BLUNCK, Jürgen (Dr)
Staatsbibliothek zu Berlin
10772 BERLIN
Germany
Tel: (49) 030 266 2740 (office)   (49) 030 492 7132 (home)

Maps and globes of the moon and the planets

'Der Rote Planet im Kartenbild', *Mitteilungen. Freundeskreis für Cartographica* 8 (1994): 18-25.

'Die Geschichte der Globen des Mars und seiner Monde', *Der Globusfreund* 43/44 (1995): 257-264.

'Wilhelm Beer, genannt der "Mondmann"', *Sterne und Weltraum* 35:12 (1996): 904-912.

'Beer und Mädler als Mondkartographen: Eine Blick in die Bestände der Staatsbibliothek zu Berlin', *Mitteilungen. Freudeskreis für Cartographica* 11 (1997): 25-33.

'G.C.F. Kunowski: Ein Jurist am Fernrohr', *Sterne und Weltraum* 37:2 (1998): 1224-128.

BOARD, Christopher (Dr)
Department of Geography &
    Economics
London School of Economics
Houghton Street
LONDON WC2A 2AE
UK
Tel: (1) 0171 955 7597 (office)   (1) 0181 771 9503 (home)
Fax: (1) 0171 955 7412 (office)   (1) 0181 771 9503 (home)
E-mail: c.board@lse.ac.uk

Ordnance Survey of Great Britain: air-photo mosaics: policy and products; quarter-inch to one-mile map; three-inch map of London, 1933-1943

'Air photo mosaics: a short-term solution to topographic map revision in Great Britain 1944-51', *Proceedings of the 17th International Cartographic Conference, Barcelona, 3-9 September 1995*, 1:1246-1255.

'The secret map of the county of London, 1926, and its sequels', *London Topographical Record* 27 (1995): 257-280.

'The three-inch map of London and its predecessors of 1926', *Sheetlines* 43 (1995): 48-50.

'The really secret map of London is re-discovered', London Topographical Society *Newsletter* 44 (1997): 3-4.

BONAR LAW, Andrew
Shankill Castle
SHANKILL, County Dublin
Ireland
Tel: (353) 1 282 2139

Cartobibliography of printed maps of Ireland from the earliest times

The Printed Maps of Ireland 1612-1850 (Dublin: The Neptune Gallery, 1997).

BOSSE, David
Historc Deerfield Library
P.O.Box 53
DEERFIELD, Massachusetts 01342
USA
Tel: (1) 413 774 5581
Fax: (1) 413 774 3081
E-mail: dbosse@historic-deerfield.org

Boston map trade in the 18th century; Matthew Clark's 1790 atlas of sea charts

'Maps, charts, and atlases', in Steven E. Woodworth (ed), *The American Civil War* (Westport, CT: Greenwood Press, 1996), 99-110.

'Osgood Carleton, mathematical practitioner of Boston', *Proceedings of the Massachusetts Historical Society* 107 (1996): 141-164.

BOUD, Roy C.
26 North Park Grove
ROUNDAY, Leeds LS8 1JJ
UK
Tel: (44) 0113 266 2039

Early Scottish geological maps, with special reference to the role of the Highland and Agricultural Society; Ordnance Survey of Scotland, 1809-1875

BOUDREAU, Claude (Dr)
Archives nationales du Québec
1210 ave. du Séminaire
SAINTE-FOY, Québec G1S 4C2
Canada
Tel: (1) 418 643 7549 (office)   (1) 418 682 8830 (home)
Fax: (1) 418 646 0868
E-mail: claude.boudreau@mccq.gouv.qc.ca

Survey and cartography of Québec province before 1900

La cartographie au Québec 1760-1840 (Sainte-Foy: Les presses de l'Université Laval, 1994).

(with Serge Courville and Normand Séguin), *Le Territoire (Atlas historique du Québec)* (Sainte-Foy: Les presses de l'Université Laval, 1997).

BOURNE, Molly H. (Dr)
c/o Sarzi
Galleria Landucci 2
46100 MANTUA
Italy

Map mural cycles as palace decoration in Italy; map collecting by Francesco II Gonzaga (1484-1519)

'Towards the study of the Renaissance courts of the Gonzaga' *Quaderni di Palazzo* 3 (n.s. 1996): 80-81.

BRAAD, Roelof
Stadsarchief Heerlen
Postbus 1
6400 AA HEERLEN
Netherlands
Tel: (31) 045 (5) 604 581
Fax: (31) 045 (5) 604 579

History of cartography of the south of Limburg and Heerlen

BRAEKEN, Robert
Achter Clarenburgh 2
3511 JJ UTRECHT
Netherlands
Tel & Fax: (31) 030 32 13 42

Cartography of the Caribbean and South America; 16th-17th century single-sheet newsmaps

BRAKE, Scott
1607 Lincoln Blvd.
SANTA MONICA, California 90404
USA
Tel: (1) 310 314 4899
Fax: (1) 310 314 4894

Distorted American railway maps of the 19th century; is the first California 'island' map really the 1594 Ortelius?

BRAVO, Michael T.
Social Anthropology
Manchester University
Oxford Road
MANCHESTER M13 9PL
UK
Tel: (44) 0161 275 2460
Fax: (44) 0161 275 4023
E-mail: michael.bravo@man.ac.uk

Cartography and art; indigenous (non-Western) traditions of cartography; navigation and maps in the 18th and 19th centuries

'Major James Rennell (1742-1830): antiquarian of ocean currents', *Ocean Challenge: Journal of the Challenger Society* 4 (1993): 41-50.

The Accuracy of Ethnoscience: A Study of Inuit Cartography and Cross-Cultural Commensurability (Manchester Papers in Social Anthropology No 2; Manchester University, 1996).

'Ethnographical encounters', in J.A. Secord et al (eds), *Cultures of Natural History* (Cambridge: Cambridge University Press, 1996), 338-357.

BREMNER, Robert Weyman
40 Kingsway
Aldwick
BOGNOR REGIS PO21 4DL
West Sussex
UK
Tel & fax: (44) 01243 267613

Maps of Sicily; cartography from earliest times to c.1600

BRESSOLIER-BOUSQUET,
   Catherine (Dr)
EPHE-Geomorphologie
U.M.R. PRODIG
191 rue Saint-Jacques
F-75005 PARIS
France
Tel: (33) 01 42 34 56 28 (office)
Fax: (33) 01 42 51 10 44 (home)
E-mail: bousquet@univ-paris1.fr

Representing visual space (16th-17th centuries); projection, levelling, perspective (triumphal entries, theatre, maps), and French aesthetic theory of nature imitation in cartography; garden representation; the language of frontispieces (and illustrations) of some scientific books; palaeogeographic reconstruction of shallow marine environments from antique maps

'Expériences physiocratiques autour du Bassin d'Arcachon (1755-1776)', *Bulletin du Comité français de Cartographie* 148 (1996): 66-78.

'Les géographes et l'image du terrain du XVIe siècle à nos jours', *Science Tribune* (http://www/iway.fr.sc), août 1996, 1-8.

(with Marie-Anne Corvisier de Villèle), 'A la naissance de la cartographie moderne: la commission topographique de 1802', *Actes du colloque Scientifique du 6° festival d'histoire de Montbrison* (28 sept.-4 oct. 1996): 'Evolution et représentation du paysage de 1750 à nos jours' (Ville de Montbrison, 1997), 393-405, xxv-xxvi.

'Charles-Antoine Jombert (1712-1784): un libraire entre sciences et arts', *Bulletin du Bibliophile* 2 (1997): 299-333.

'Histoire et méthodes de la représentation de l'espace (XVIe-XVIIe sciècles). La représentation cartographique et ses rapports avec la perception visuelle de l'espace', *Livret* 11 (Paris, Ecole practique des Hautes Etudes, section des sciences historiques et philologiques, 1997), 183-186.

BRICHZIN, Hans (Dr)
Sächsisches Hauptstaatsarchiv
Archivstrasse 14
D-01097 DRESDEN
Germany
Tel: (49) 0351 52501
Fax: (49) 0351 5671274

Saxony; cartobibliography of holdings in Sächsisches Hauptstaatsarchiv

'Ein Ungarnkarte von Nicolaus Angielus, sowie Grund- und Aufrisse ungarischer Festungen aus dem Jahre 1566 im Sächsischen Hauptstaatarchiv zu Dresden, Teil III (Schluss)', *Cartographica Hungarica* 5 (1996): 8-11.

BRINCKEN, Anna-Dorothee
   von den (Prof Dr)
St.-Apern-Str. 26
D-50667 KÖLN (Innenstadt)
Germany
Tel: (49) 221 470 5255 (office)
Fax: (49) 221 470 5042

Medieval cartography in the West; medieval cartography and historiography

(49) 221 258 1784 (home)

'De Middeleeuwse Cartografie / La cartographie médiévale', in Marcel Watelet (ed), *Gerard Mercator Rupelmundanus / Gérard Mercator, cosmographe; le temps et l'espace* (Antwerp: Fonds Mercator Paribas, 1994), 36-49.

'Mappe del cielo e della terra: l'orientamento nel Basso medioevo', in *Atti del XXXII Convegno storico internazionale, Todi 8-11 ottobre 1995* (Atti dei Convegni del 'Centro Italiano di Studi sul Basso Medioevo–Accadenia Tudertina' e del 'Centro di studi sulla spiritualità medievale', NS 9; Spoleto, 1996), 81-96.

'Kosmographische Betrachtungen bei den Kirchenvätern, auf mittelalterlichen Mönchskarten und bei Gerhard Mercator', in Rienk Vermij (ed), *Mercator und siene Welt* (Duisburg, 1997), 28-57.

'Terrae Incognitae. Zur Umschreibung empirisch noch unerschlossener Räume in lateinischen Quellen des Mittelalters bis in die Entdeckungszeit', in Jan Aertsen and Andreas Speer (eds), *Raum und Raumvorstellungen des Mittelalters* (Miscellanea Mediaevalia 25, c.1997/98), 557-572.

BRODERSEN, Kai (Prof Dr) Ancient Greek and Roman
Alte Geschichte mapping
Universitaet
D-68131 MANNHEIM
Germany
Tel & fax: (49) 621 292 5522
E-mail: kai.brodersen@phil.uni-mannheim.de

Terra Cognita: Studien zur römischen Raumerfassung (Hildesheim, Zurich and New York: George Olms, 1995).

'Ein karolingischer Stadtplan von Rom?' *Cartographica Helvetica* 14 (1996): 35-41.

BROECKE, Marcel P.R. van den (Dr) Abraham Ortelius
Soestdijkseweg 101
3721 AA BILTHOVEN
Netherlands
Tel: (31) 30 220 2396
Fax: (31) 30 220 3326
E-mail: cart.neer@tip.nl

'Ortelius zag continenten al drijven' [Ortelius said all continents drift], *Caert-Thresoor* 14:1 (1995): 9-10.

'Unstable editions of Ortelius' atlas', *The Map Collector* 70 (1995): 2-8.

Ortelius Atlas Maps: An Illustrated Guide ('t Goy: HES Publishers, 1996).

'Abraham Ortelius', *Mercator's World* 2:3 (1997): 18-24.

BROTTON, Jerry (Dr) Terrestrial globes in 16th
Department of English century Europe; maps and
Royal Holloway and Bedford New geography in English
 College Renaissance drama
EGHAM, Surry TW20 0EX
UK
Tel: (44) 01784 443225
Fax: (44) 01784 439196
E-mail: j.brotton@rhbnc.ac.uk

'Mapping the early modern nation: cartography along the English margins', *Paragraph* 19:2 (1996): 139-155.

Trading Territories: Mapping the Early Modern World (London: Reaktion Books, 1997).

BRUN, Christian F. Maps and charts published
University of California, Santa Barbara in America before 1800;
5663 Via Trento early North American car-
GOLETA, California 93117-1802 tography
USA
Tel: (1) 805 967 7041

BRUNNER, Kurt (Prof Dr) Early depiction of glaciers
Universität der Bundeswehr München and sea ice on maps; 16th-
Werner-Heisenberg-Weg 39 century regional maps of
D-85577 NEUBIBERG Central Europe; German
Germany colonial cartography; tech-
 niques for facsimiles

'Zwei Regionalkarten Süddeutschlands von David Seltzlin', in Joachmi Neumann (ed), *Kaarten hüten und bewahren: Festgabe für Lothar Zögner* (Gotha: Justus Perthes, 1995), 33-47.

'Expeditionskartographie auf Spitzbergen', *Mitteilungen der Österreichischen Geographischen Gesellschaft* (Wein), 134 (1996): 247-260.

BUISSERET, David
Department of History
University of Texas at Arlington
ARLINGTON, TX 76019-0529
USA
Tel: (1) 817 272 2898
Fax: (1) 817 272 8252
E-mail: buisser@utarlg.uta.edu

Cartographical work of the *ingénieurs du roi* in France before Vauban; a history of early-modern mapping in Europe; the making of the Chicago landscape

Historic Jamaica from the Air (rev. ed.; Kingston, 1995).

(editor), *Rural Images: Estate Maps in the Old World and the New* (Chicago: University of Chicago Press, 1995).

'Jesuit cartography in Central and South America', in J.A. Gagliano and C.E. Ronan (eds), *Jesuit Encounters in the New World* (Rome: Institutum Historicum S.I., 1997), 113-162.

(editor), *Envisioning the City: Six Studies in Urban Cartography* (Chicago: University of Chicago Press, 1998).

BURDEN, Eugene Henry
Lake House
Kings Ride
ASCOT, Berks SL5 7JW
UK
Tel: (44) 01344 620344

Cartobibliography of Berkshire

'Map for the Bagshot Heath manoeuvres, 1792: is it the first published map based on an Ordnance Survey?, *Sheetlines* 46 (1996): 17-19.

Printed Maps of Berkshire 1574-1900, Part 1: *County Maps* (9th revision); Part 2: *Town Plans* (3rd revision); Part 3: *Environs and District Maps* (1st revision); Part 4: *Middle and Upper Thames Maps* (Ascot: Eugene Burden, 1997).

BURDEN, Philip D.
Elmcote House
The Green, Croxley Green
RICKMANSWORTH,
Herts WD3 3HN
UK
Tel: (44) 01923 772387 or 778097
Fax: (44) 01923 896520
E-mail: philip@caburden.com

Pre-1700 cartography of North America; cartography of the British Isles and English county atlases

'A dozen lost sixteenth-century maps of America found', *The Map Collector* 74 (1996): 30-32.

The Mapping of North America: A List of Printed Maps 1511-1670 (Stamford, Connecticut: Raleigh Publications, 1996).

BURGESS, Robert Anthony
Barn Owl
Dwelly Lane
EDENBRIDGE, Kent TN8 6QE
UK
Tel: (44) 01732 863131
Fax: (44) 01732 865189

Printed maps and town plans of the county of Kent to 1900

BURNETT, D. Graham (Dr)
Mellon Fellow in History
Heyman Center
Columbia University, MC 5700
2960 Broadway
NEW YORK, NY 10027
USA
Tel: (1) 212 854 4631
Fax: (1) 212 854 7289
E-mail: dgb15@columbia.edu

History of science; history of geographical exploration, 19th century; cartography and British imperialism; the Guianas; Sir Walter Ralegh, etc.

BURNETTE, Rand (Prof)
Department of History
MacMurray College
JACKSONVILLE, Florida 62650
USA
Tel: (1) 217 479 7171 (office)
E-mail: rburnett@mac.edu

Biography of Thomas Hutchins (1730-1789)

(1) 217 245 5390 (home)

BURROUGHS, Charles
Director, Center for Medieval and
　　Renaissance Studies
Binghamton University, State
　　Univeristy of New York
BINGHAMTON, NY 13902-6000
USA
Tel: (1) 607 777 2130 (office)
　　[777 2730, secretary]
Tel: (1) 607 687 6155 (home)
Fax: (1) 607 777 4373
E-mail: cburrou@binghamton.edu

Italian early modern visual
culture, architecture,
urbanism (especially Rome
in the 1530s and 1540s);
conceptualization, measurement and representation of,
and physical interventions
in space (or at least places),
in city and country

'Absolutism and the rhetoric of topography: streets in the Rome of
Pope Sixtus V', in Zeynep Celik, Diane Favro, and Richard
Ingersoll (eds), *Streets: Critical Perspectives on Public Space* (Berkeley
and Los Angeles: University of California Press, 1994), 189-202.

'The Last Judgment of Michelangelo: pictorial space, sacred topography, and the social world', *Artibus et Historiae* 32 (1996): 55-89.

BZINKOWSKA, Jadwiga
　　Teresa (Dr)
Department of Cartography
Biblioteka Jagiellońska
Uniwersytet Jagielloński
al. Mickiewicza 22
30-059 KRAKÓW
Poland
Tel: (48) 012 6 336377, ex 382
Fax: (48) 012 6 330903
E-mail: ujbzinko@kinga.cyf-kr.edu.pl

Maps of Poland, 16th to
19th centuries

'Katalog map Polski wydanych w atlasach angielskich w XVII i
XVIII wieku ze zbiorów The Bodleian Library w Oxfordzie' [The
catalogue of the maps of Poland published in the English atlases of
the 17th and 18th centuries from the Bodleian Library], *Biuletyn
Biblioteki Jagiellońskiej* 46 (1996): 119-141.

(with E.F. Schnayder) 'Poland', in Monique Pelletier (ed), *How to
Identify a Mapmaker. An International Bibliographic Guide* (Paris,
International Cartographic Association, 1996), 57-60.

CAIN, Mead Taylor
64 E. 86th St., Apt 7C
NEW YORK, NY 10028
USA
Tel: (1) 212 396 3245
Fax: (1) 212 396 3249
E-mail: mcain@pipeline.com

Maps of the Society for the
Diffusion of Useful
Knowledge; map publish-
ing in 19th-century
England

CAMINO, Mercedes Maroto
School of European Languages and
　　Literatures
University of Auckland
Private Bag 92019
AUCKLAND
New Zealand
Tel: (64) 9 373 7599 ex7126
Fax: (64) 9 308 2358
E-mail: m.camino@auckland.ac.nz

Early modern literatures,
literary criticism, history of
cartography, colonialism,
film and media studies,
women's studies

The Stage Am I: Raping Lucrece in Early Modern England (Salzburg
University Studies 120; Salzburg & New York: The Edwin Mellen
Press, 1995).

'"That map which deep impression bears": the politics of conquest
in Lucrece', in Robin Eaden, Madge Mitton and Heather Kerr
(eds), *Shakespeare: World Views* (Newark: University of Delaware
Press; London: Associated University Presses, 1996), 124-145.

'"Methinks I see an evil lurk unespied": visualizing conquest in
Spenser's A View of the Present State of Ireland', *Spenser Studies* 12
(1997): 169-194.

CAMPBELL, Tony
Map Librarian
Map Library
British Library
Euston Road
LONDON NW1 2DB
UK
Tel: (44) 0171 412 7525 (office)　　(44) 0171 359 6477 (home)
Fax: (44) 0171 412 7780
E-mail: tony.campbell@bl.uk

Early portolan charts; maps
in the British Library;
internet resources for the
history of cartography

'Egerton MS: a remarkable display of cartographical invention',
Imago Mundi 48 (1996): 93-102.

'R.H. Major and the British Museum', in R.C. Bridges and P.E.H. Hair (eds), *Compassing the Vaste Globe of the Earth: Studies in the History of the Hakluyt Society 1846-1996* (Second Series No. 183; London: Hakluyt Society, 1996), 81-140.

CARDINAL, Louis
Chief, Cartography and Architecture
National Archives of Canada
395 Wellington Street
OTTAWA, Ontario K1A 0N3
Canada
Tel: (1) 613 996 7619
Fax: (1) 613 995 6226
E-mail: lcardinal@archives.ca

Early and current Canadian map series and their bibliographical control

CARROLL, Raymond Albert
38 Town Drove
Quadring
SPALDING, Lincs PE11 4PU
UK
Tel: (44) 01775 820542

Cartobibliography of Dorset, 1775-1800; Andrew Armstrong

'Andrew Armstrong and the first survey of Lincolnshire at one inch to a mile', in Christopher Sturman (ed), *Lincolnshire People and Places: Essays in Memory of Terence R. Leach* (Lincoln: The Society for Lincolnshire History and Archaeology, 1996), 91-96.

Printed Maps of Lincolnshire, 1576-1900: A Cartobibliography with an Appendix on Road-Books, 1675-1900 (Lincoln Record Society, vol. 84; Woodbridge, Suffolk: Boydell Press, 1996).

CARVALHO DIAS, José António
Praca d. Afonso V, 55 – HAB. 8
P-4150 PORTO
Portugal
Tel: (351) 2 618 0595

Printed maps related to Portuguese expansion in Africa and Asia; maps by, or based on, Portuguese cartographers; maps of Portugal

CASE, Nathaniel
Hedberg Maps, Inc
43 N Main St
WHITE RIVER JCT, Vermont
    05001
USA
Tel: (1) 802 296 7889 (office)
    (1) 802 785 4776 (home)
Fax: (1) 802 295 1640
E-mail: hedberg@vermontel.com

20th-century map design; use of colour; American commercial maps and tourist maps; economics of cartography and map production

CASTI MORESCHI, Emanuela
Università degli Studi di Bergamo
Dipartimento di Linguistica e
    Letterature Comparate
Piazza Vecchia, 8
24129 BERGAMO
Italy
Tel: (39) 035 277409
Fax: (39) 035 235136

Cartography and territorial policy in the Venetian Republic (15th-18th century); cartographical language and the territorial process; Africa in maps and in symbolic representations during the colonial period

(with Giorgio Mangani), *Una geografia dell'Altrove: l'Atlante d'Africa di Arcangelo Ghisleri*, 1997. [Exhibition catalogue.]

CATTANEO, Angelo
Department of History
Istituto Universitario Europeo
Via dei Roccetini 9
50016 SAN DOMENICO DI
    FIESOLE
Italy
Fax: (39) 55 468 5298
E-mail: cattaneo@datacomm.iue.it

Application of new multimedia technologies to ancient cartography; relationship of Renaissance cosmography and cartography

CAVELTI, Alfons
Tulpenweg 56
CH-3098 KÖNIZ
Tel: (41) 031 971 3240
Switzerland

Exhibitions of cartography; cartography of the 19th century; three-dimensional reliefs

CAVELTI HAMMER, Madlena
Untermattstr. 16
CH-6048 HORW
Switzerland
Tel: (41) 041 368 9450 (office)
     (41) 041 340 3144 (home)
Fax: (41) 041 368 9412 (office)
     (41) 041 340 3144 (home)
E-mail: mcavelti@ksluzern.ch

Exhibitions of cartography;
cartography of the 19th
century; three-dimensional
reliefs; co-editor
Cartographica Helvetica

Die Alpen auf Reliefkarten (Bern 1996). [Exhibition catalogue.]

'Das Linthwerk (1807-1822)', *Cartographica Helvetica* 14 (1996): 11-19.

(with Hans-Uli Feldmann and Markus Oehrli), *Fabre, Licht und Schatten. Die Entwicklung der Reliefkartographie seit 1660* (Murten, Cartographica Helvetica, 1997). [Exhibition catalogue.]

Freiburg à la carte. Begleiflexte zur ausstellung (Luzern, 1997). [Exhibition catalogue.]

CEREZO MARTÍNEZ,
     Ricardo (Capt)
Urbanizción 'Las Huertas' Bl 40 –3°A
Majadahonda
28220 MADRID
Spain
Tel: (34) 91 638 5721

Cartology and cartography
of the 16th century

'La carta de Juan de la Cosa', *Revista de Historia Naval* (Madrid: Istituto de Historia y Cultura Naval), 39 (1992): 31-48; **42** (1993): 21-44; **44** (1994): 21-37.

La Cartografia náutica española en los siglos XIV, XV y XVII (Madrid: Consejo Superior de Investigaciones Científicas, 1994).

'El meridiano y el antimeridiano de Tordesillas en la Geografia, la Náutica y la Cartografia', *Revista de Indias* (Madrid: Consejo Superior de Investigaciones Científicas), **65** (1994).

CHANG, Stephen Tseng-Hsin
Department of History
University of Reading
READING
UK
Tel: (44) 0171 706-2810
E-mail: sc21@soas.ac.uk
     s.t.chang@reading.ac.uk

Historical cartography in
the Age of Discoveries;
Portugaliae Monumenta
Cartographica; ancient
Chinese maps in the
gazetteers of the Ming and
Qing dynasties

'Portuguese maritime discoveries along the south-east coast of China in the first half of the sixteenth century: a cartographic view, 1513-1550', *Portolan* 41 (1998): 7-19.

CHANTRENNE, Claire
Scientific Associate
Section des Cartes et Plans
Bibliothèque Royale de Belgique
Boulevard de l'Empereur 4
1000 BRUXELLES
Belgium
Tel: (32) 2 519 57 40
E-mail: savants.belges@kbr.be

19th century cartography;
subject headings in cartography

CHAPUIS, Olivier (Dr)
1 rue Rousseau
92240 MALAKOFF
France
Tel: (33) 01 46 55 98 41

Navigation and hydrogra-
phy (nautical surveying),
from 1600

CHARALAMBOUS, Demetrio
     Antonio
Venezuela 1841
1096 BUENOS AIRES
Argentina
Tel: (54) 1 383 9329 (office)   (54) 1 952 0700 (home)

Atlantic islands on portolan
charts 1300-1500

'The enigma of the isle of gold', *Revista de Historia de América* **118** (1994): 33-49.

Descubrimiento en el Mar de Papel: el mapa americano del Rey Salomón (Buenos Aires, 1995).

'Los grandes ríos incógnitos de América', *Todo es Historia* **338** (1995): 62-68.

IMAGO MUNDI

The International Journal for the History of Cartography

IMAGO MUNDI is the only international scholarly journal solely concerned with the study of early maps in all its aspects. The illustrated articles, in English with trilingual abstracts, deal with all facets of the history and interpretation of maps and mapmaking in any part of the world, at any period.

The original IMAGO MUNDI was Columbus' favourite text. Let its descendant, founded by Leo Bagrow in 1935, be your window into the subject, whether you approach it as an historian of cartography or are interested in how maps fit into the historical aspects of art, ideas, literature or the sciences.

Contents

Current issues comprise approximately 250 pages (30 x 21 cm), with illustrations. Each annual volume includes:

- Articles (about ten per issue)
- Book reviews, and notices of books received
- Bibliography (with indexes of authors, places and subjects)
- Chronicle (personal and institutional news, conferences, exhibitions, map sales and acquisitions)
- Reports, notices and obituaries

All articles are refereed. IMAGO MUNDI is published each summer.

Subscribing to IMAGO MUNDI

The cost of the annual volumes to personal subscribers is as follows:
- Volumes 43 (1991) onwards   £30 (US$60)
- Volumes 27-42   £25 (US$50) *(Prices are inclusive of surface postage)*

Some of the first 26 volumes remain in print. For details please write to the Honorary Treasurer at the address below.

To order send £30 (US$60) to the Secretary/Treasurer, IMAGO MUNDI, c/o The Map Library, The British Library, 96 Euston Road, St Pancras, London NW1 2DB.

For more details of IMAGO MUNDI see: http://www.ihrinfo.ac.uk/maps/imago/html

'Evidence of a pre-columbian map of America', *Terrae Incognitae* **28** (1996): 1-11.

CHEKIN, Leonid S. (Dr)
Institute of the History of Sciences
   and Technology
1/5 Staropanskiy per.
MOSCOW 10312
Russia
Tel: (7) 095 137 7812 (home)
Fax: (7) 095 925 9911 (office)
E-mail: lchekin@history.ihst.ru.

Medieval cartography and geographical ideas, mainly Slavic, Greek, Latin and Scandinavian; beginnings of Russian cartography

'New developments in the history of Russian cartography', *The Portolan* 41 (May 1998), 20-26.

'Die "Warägischen Grenzpfählen" und andere Rätsel einer Regensburgischen Karte der Mitte des 12. Jahrhunderts', in H. Beyer-Thoma (ed), *Bayern und Osteuropa* (Munich: Fink, 1998).

CHEN Jian
Librarian, Map Section
National Library of China
Baishiqiao Road 39
BEIJING 100081
China
Tel: (86) 10 6841 5566,
       ext. 5054 (office)
   (86) 10 6256 3957 (home)
Fax: (86) 10 6256 3957 (home)
E-mail: cnluoyu@public.east.cn.net

Maps in late Qing Dynasty 1840-1911; architectural maps of ancient China (Ming and Qing dynasties); descriptive catalogue of the pre-1949 Chinese maps in the National Library

'The exhibition of tour maps of China held in Beijing', *Cartography* no 3 (1995): 45 [in Chinese].

'On the map of the Grand Channel', *Cartographic Survey of Shanxi* no 2 (1995): 23. [in Chinese]

'On the map of the Hedong Salt Pool in Shanxi', *Cartographic Survey of Shanxi* no 2 (1995): 27 [in Chinese].

'On the map of the panorama of Wutai Mountain' *Cartographic Survey of Shanxi* no 4 (1995): 25 [in Chinese].

'On the map of the Yellow River', *Cartographic Survey of Shanxi* no 1 (1995): 47 [in Chinese].

'The introduction to the Department of Map Collection in the National Library of Hungary', *Cartography* no 3 (1996): 60-61 [in Chinese].

'On the map of Fujian', *Cartographic Survey of Shanxi* no 3 (1996): 43 [in Chinese].

'On the map of Shanxi', *Cartography* no 4 (1996): 59 [in Chinese].
Catalogue of Major Ancient Maps in China (Beijing: National Library of China Publishing House, 1997).

CLARKE, Richard Samuel
   Jessop (Prof)
78 King's Road
BELFAST BT5 6JN
Northern Ireland
Tel: (44) 01232 797155

Charts of waters around Ireland c.1550-c.1800 (including harbours)

COBB, David
Harvard Map Collection
Harvard College Library
Harvard University
CAMBRIDGE, Massachusetts 02138
USA
Tel: (1) 617 495 2417
Fax: (1) 617 496 0440
E-mail: cobb@fas.harvard.edu

WEB-based GIS applications for libraries; the mapping of Boston; the manuscript maps in the Harvard College Libraries

COLLIER, Peter (Dr)
Department of Geography
University of Portsmouth
PORTSMOUTH PO1 3HE
UK
Tel: (44) 01705 842473 (office)
   (44) 01705 839652 (home)
Fax: (44) 01705 842512 (office)
E-mail: collierp@geog.port.ac.uk
   givat97@aol.co

Mapping, empire and development of academic geography: relationships between empire, military mapping, intelligence and development of geography, late 19th and early 20th centuries; the development of topographical mapping; mapping in the Middle East

'Military surveys and intelligence gathering in the 19th and 20th centuries: mapping the Ottoman Empire', *Proceedings*, British Cartographic Societies 34th Annual Symposium, Leicester, 1997.

CONLEY, Tom Clark (Prof)
Department of Romance Languages
201 Boylston Hall
Harvard University
CAMBRIDGE, Massachusetts 02130
USA
Tel: (1) 617 496 6090 (office)
Fax: (1) 617 496 4682 (office)
E-mail: tconley@fas.harvard.edu

Cartography and literature in early modern Europe; cartography and rhetoric; cartography and cultural theory

(1) 617 643 7087 (home)
(1) 617 643 7087 (home)

The Self-Made Map: Cartographic Writing in Early Modern France (Minneapolis: University of Minnesota Press, 1996).

CONTI, Simonetta (Dr)
Via S Saba 7
00153 ROME
Italy
Tel: (39) 06 4991 3916 (office)
    (39) 06 574 3960 (home)
Fax: (39) 06 4331 3874

Nautical cartography, 16th and 17th centuries (Oliva); nautical Mercatorian cartography in Italy (Dudley); medieval nautical cartography (13th century)

'Una particolarità delle carte nautiche "Oliva"', in *Atti del Convegno Esplorazioni geografiche e immagine del mondo nei secoli XV e XVI* (Messina: Grafo, 1994), 83-101.

'L'immagine dell'America centrale r caribica nelle geocarte nautiche del secoli XVI e XVII', *Rendiconti Morali della Academia Nazionale dei Lincei* (Roma) an **392** (ser 9, vol 6, fasc 4, 1995): 733-755.

CONZEN, Michael P. (Prof)
Committee on Geographical Studies
University of Chicago
5828 S. University Avenue
CHICAGO, Illinois 60637-1583
USA
Tel: (1) 773 702 8308 (office)
Fax: (1) 773 702 5140
E-mail: m-conzen@uchicago.edu

Commercial cartography in 19th century America; American county atlases as cultural symbols; city map trades

(1) 773 285 2181 (home)

'The all-American county atlas: styles of commercial landowner-ship mapping and American culture', in John A. Wolter and Ronald E. Grim (eds), *Images of the World: The Atlas through History* (Washington, D.C.: Library of Congress, 1997), 331-365.

COOK, Andrew S. (Dr)
Map Archivist
India Office Records
The British Library
96 Euston Road
LONDON NW1 2DB
Tel: (44) 0171 412 7828
Fax: (44) 0171 412 7858
E-mail: andrew.cook@bl.uk
and
Dalrymple Research Institute for
    the Study of the History of
    Lowland Scots Hydrography
66 Compton Road
Winchmore Hill,
LONDON N21 3NS
UK
Tel: (44) 0181 360 7564
E-mail: ascook@dalrymple.u-net.com

Survey of India Topographical Map Series 1825-1950; surveying and mapping in India 1750-1950; map collections of the East India Company and India Office; charts, sailing directions and other publications of Alexander Dalrymple and James Horsburgh; Admiralty charts, Bibliography of Admiralty Sailing Directions

'Alexander Dalrymple: research, writing and publication of the *Account*', introductory essay in Alexander Dalrymple, *An Account of the Discoveries Made in the South Pacific Ocean previous to 1764* (London, 1767; facsimile, Sydney: Hordern House, 1996).

'An exchange of letters between two hydrographers: Alexander Dalrymple and Jean-Baptiste d'Après de Mannevillette', in Philippe Handrère (ed), *Les Flottes des Compagnies des Indes 1600-1857* (Vincennes: Service historique de la Marine, 1996).

COOK, Karen Severud (Dr)
Department of Geography
Lindley Hall
University of Kansas
LAWRENCE, Kansas 66045
USA
Tel: (1) 785 864 5540
Fax: (1) 785 331 0648
E-mail: kscook@eagle.cc.ukans.edu

Geological cartography; mid-20th century American thematic cartography

'From false starts to firm beginnings: early colour printing of geo-logical maps', *Imago Mundi* 47 (1995): 155-172.

'Der geologische Atlas und seine Entwicklung', in Hans Wolff (ed), *400 Jahre Mercator, 400 Jahre Atlas* (Weissenhorn, 1995).

'Benjamin Franklin and the snake that would not die', in Karen S. Cook (ed), *Images and Icons of the New World: Essays on American Cartography* (= *British Library Journal* 22:1, 1996): 88-111.

COSGROVE, Denis (Prof)
Department of Geography
Royal Holloway and Bedford New
    College,
EGHAM, Surrey TW20 0EX
UK
Tel: (44) 01784 443647
Fax: (44) 01784 472836
E-mail: d.cosgrove@rhbnc.ac.uk

Global and whole earth representations (European culture); Renaissance cosmography

(with Simon Rycroft), 'Mapping the modern nation: Dudley Stamp and the Land Utilisation Survey', *History Workshop Journal* 40 (Autumn 1995): 91-105.

CRAMPTON, Jeremy (Dr)
Department of Geography
George Mason University
FAIRFAX, Virginia 22030
USA
Tel: (1) 703 993 1217
Fax: (1) 703 993 1216
E-mail: jcrampto@gmu.edu

Maps and GIS on the world wide web; virtual geographies; deconstructing maps; politics of projections and maps; James Gall's (1808-1895) projection

'Cartography's defining moment: the Peters projection controversy 1974-1990', *Cartographica* 31 (1994): 16-32.

'Cartography resources on the world wide web', *Cartographic Perspectives* 22 (1995): 3-11.

'The ethics of GIS and privacy', *Cartography and GIS* 22:1 (1995): 84-89.

'Bordering on Bosnia', *The GeoJournal*, 39 (1996): 353-361.

CRIBB, Robert Bridson (Prof)
Nordic Institute of Asian Studies
Leifsgade 33
2300 COPENHAGEN-S
Denmark
Tel: (45) 31 54 88 44
Fax: (45) 32 96 25 30
E-mail: cribb@nias.ku.dk

History of mapping in Southeast Asia, especially Indonesia

CSAPLOVICS, Elmar (Prof Dr)
Department of Earth Sciences
University of Dresden
Mommsenstrasse 13
D-01062 DRESDEN
Germany
Tel: (49) 351 463 3680 (office)
    (49) 351 830 2608 (home)
Fax: (49) 351 463 7266
E-mail: csaplovi@rcs.urz.tu-dresden.de

Time series of historical maps for regional landscape analysis; early cartography of the African sahel; cartography and history of gardens

CUESTA DOMINGO,
    Mariano (Prof Dr)
Catedratico
Historia Descubrimientos Geograficos
    y Geografia de America
Facultad de Geografia e Historia
Universidad Complutense
28040 MADRID
Spain
Tel: (34) 91 394 5793 (office)
    (34) 91 574 8822 (home)
Fax: (34) 91 394 5796 (office)
    (34) 91 574 8822 (home)
E-mail: mcuestad@eucmax.sim.ucm.es

Cosmographical and nautical works in the 16th century (Fernandes de Encisco, Alonso de Chaves, Alonso de Santa Cruz, Martín Cortés, Diego Garcia de Palacio, Pedro Medina, etc); cartographical, nautical and toponymic work on the oceans, the Americas and the Philippines

(with Jesus Varela Marcos), *Portulano de Valladolid: estudío del atlas* (Valladolid: Ayuntamiento, 1996).

DAHL, Bjørn Westerbeek
Willemoesgade 61, 4th
2100 KØBENHAVN
Denmark
Tel: (45) 33 66 23 67 (office)   (45) 35 42 61 92 (home)

Danish military mapmaking 1600-1700

'Carl Heinrich von der Osten og Pufendorfvaerkets plancher af Nyborg', *Militärhistorisk tidskrift* (1994): 7-21.

'Omkring et par tidlige kort over Tranquebar', *Magasin fra Det Kongelige Bibliotek* 10:2 (1995): 23-33.

'Det aeldste kort over Helsingør fra 1658', *Forening & Museum. Medlemsblad for Helsingør Museumsforening* no 1 (1996): 4-8.

'I svenskernes kølvand. Et par kort over Kronborg fra omkring

1660', *Forening & Museum. Medlemsblad for Helsingør Museumsforening* no 2 (1996): 3-6.

'A. Th. Techts grundrids af Helsingør fra 1858-59', *Helsingør Kommunes Museer 1996* (1997): 48-57.

'Daniel Paullis og Johan Huusmans stik fra Skånske Krig 1675-1679', *Magasin fra Det Kongelige Bibliotek* 12:2 (1997): 46-54.

'Det topografiske Danmarkskort', *Bol og by* 1997 no 1: 36-59.

'En havenplan af Fredriksborg Slotshave fra 1680'ernes begyndelse i Københavns Stadsarkiv' *Fabs* no 1 (1997): 48-57.

DAHL, Edward H.
1292 Montée Paiement
GATINEAU, Québec J8R 3K5
Canada
Tel: (1) 819 561 4029
E-mail: edahl@iosphere.net

Cartography of Canada, 1500-1850

(with Greg Hill and Mary E. Murphy) 'The day it rained all night in the cartographic vault: lessons in disaster preparedness and recovery at the National Archives of Canada', *ACMLA Bulletin* 94 (Fall 1995): 1-10.

DAMMERER, Franz Peter (Mag)
Hoher Rain 24
A-3324 EURATSFELD
Austria

Life and achievements of Austrian cartographers

Leben und Werk der österreichischen Kartographen Josef Chavanne und Franz Ritter von Le Monnier (Hamburg: Verlag Dr. Kovac, 1995).

DANFORTH, Susan
John Carter Brown Library
Box 1894
PROVIDENCE, Rhode Island 02912
USA
Tel: (1) 401 863 2725
Fax: (1) 401 863 3477
E-mail: susan_danforth@brown.edu

North and South American maps and mapmakers to 1800

DANZER, Gerald A. (Prof)
Department of History (m/c 19)
University of Illinois at Chicago
930 University Hall
601 S. Morgan Street
CHICAGO, IL 60607-7109
USA
Tel: (1) 312 996 5471 (office)
Fax: (1) 312 996 6377
E-mail: gdanzer@uic.edu

Using old maps in the teaching of history; urban maps and views; Chicago and Illinois maps

(1) 630 773 1493 (home)

Clio Views the City: A Historical Perspective on Chicago's Cityscape (Chicago, American Historical Association, 1995).

'Maps, methods, and motifs: cartographic resources for teaching history', *Perspectives* (American Historical Association Newsletter), 33:9 (December, 1995): 1, 3-5.

Chicago's Black Metropolis: Understanding History through a Historic Place (Teaching with Historic Places series, no. 53; Washington: National Park Service and National Trust for Historic Preservation, 1996).

(with James Akerman), *Paper Trails: Geographic Literacy via American Highway Maps* (Chicago: The Newberry Library, 1996).

(with Mark Newman, ed), *Community Portraits: County Atlases as Resources for Teaching U.S. History* (Chicago: University of Illinois at Chicago, 1997).

DARRAGH, Thomas Alwynne (Dr)
Museum of Victoria
PO Box 666E
MELBOURNE, Victoria 3001
Australia
Tel: (61) 03 9669 9889
Fax: (61) 03 9663 3669
E-mail: tdarragh@mov.vic.gov.au

History of map publishing in Victoria; production of Victorian geological maps; biographies of Victorian map publishers and compilers; biographies of Thomas Ham and William Owen

DAVID, Andrew C. F.
Oak End
West Monkton
TAUNTON, Somerset TA2 8QZ
UK
Tel: (44) 01823 412547

Voyage of Alexandro Malaspina, 1789-1794

'Is it Hurd's or Dalrymple's Channel atlas?' *The Map Collector* 72 (1995): 20-4.

'The Hydrographic Office Seal', *The Map Collector* 74 (1996): 54.

The Voyage of HMS Herald to Australia and the South-West Pacific under the command of Captain Henry Mangles Denham (Melbourne: At the Miegunyah Press, University of Melbourne Press, 1996).

(with Bernard Smith and Rüdiger Joppien), *The Charts and Coastal Views of Captain Cook's Voyages. Volume Three: The Voyage of the Resolution and Discovery, 1776-1780* (Hakluyt Society Extra Series 46; London, 1997).

'From Cook to Vancouver: The British Contribution to the Cartography of Alaska', in Stephen Haycox, James Barnett and Caedmon Liburd (eds), *Enlightenment and Exploration in the North Pacific 1741-1805* (Seattle: University of Washington Press, 1997), 116-131.

DAVIES, Robert
Department of Pictures & Maps
National Library of Wales
ABERYSTWYTH, Dyfed SY23 3BU
UK
Tel: (44) 01970 623816
Fax: (44) 01970 615709
E-mail: rod@aber.ac.uk

Tithe maps of Wales; estate surveyors in Wales

DAY, John D.
The Kendall Whaling Museum
27 Everitt St.
SHARON, Massachusetts 02067
USA
Tel: (1) 617 873 8126 (office)   (1) 781 440 9484 (home)
Fax: (1) 617 873 1896
E-mail: day@bbn.com

Chinese maps; Jesuits' maps; Matteo Ricci; the Jesuits in China

'The search for the origins of the Chinese manuscripts of Matteo Ricci's maps', *Imago Mundi* 47 (1995): 94-117.

'The Voretzsch/Howell Ricci map: a peculiar puzzle', *The Map Collector* 72 (1995): 38-39.

DEBERGH, Minako
Instituts d'Extrême-Orient Hautes
    Études Japonaises
Collège de France
52 rue du Cardinal-Lemoine
75231 PARIS
France
Tel: (331) 44 27 18 06
Fax: (331) 44 27 18 54

Comparative studies in European and Asiatic cartography; Jesuit Mission in Asia (China, Japan, Korea); influence of Ino Tadataka; Dr P.J. Mourier, a 19th-century French observer

DEKKER, Elly (Dr)
Meidoornlaan 13
3461 ES LINSCHOTEN
Netherlands
Tel & fax: (31) 348 415 406

History of astronomy, geography, cartography, globes and instruments before 1600

'Conspicuous features on sixteenth century celestial globes', *Der Globusfreund* 43/44 (1995): 77-98.

'An unrecorded medieval astrolabe quadrant, c.1300', *Annals of Science* 52 (1995): 1-47.

'Andromède sur les globes célestes des XVI et XVII siècles', in Françoise Siguret et Alain Laframboise (eds), *Andromède ou le héros à l'épreuve de la beauté, Actes du colloque international organisé au musée du Louvre par l'université de Montréal et le Service culturel du musée du Louvre les 3 et 4 février 1995* (Paris, 1996), 403-423.

'The Copernican globe: a delayed conception', *Annals of Science* 53:6 (1996): 541-566.

(with Paul Kunitzsch), 'The stars on the rete of the so-called Carolingian astrolabe', in Josep Casulleras and Julio Samsó (eds), *From Bagdad to Barcelona. Studies in the Islamic Exact Sciences in Honour of Prof. Juan Vernet* (Barcelona, 1996), 655-672.

(with Gerard Turner), 'An unusual Elizabethan silver globe by Charles Whitwell', *Antiquaries Journal* 77 (1997): 393-401.

DELANO SMITH, Catherine (Dr)
285 Nether Street
LONDON N3 1PD
UK
Tel & fax: (440) 0181 346 5112
E-mail: c.delano-smith@qmw.ac.uk

Editor, *Imago Mundi*; prehistoric maps; maps in biblical exegesis; maps in the Middle Ages; maps in early libraries; maps and travel (before 1800); map signs (early printed maps)

'Map ownership in sixteenth century Cambridge: probate inventories and the history of cartography', *Imago Mundi* 47 (1995): 67-93.

'Imago Mundi's logo: the Babylonian map of the world', *Imago Mundi* 48 (1996): 209-211.

'Why theory in the history of cartography?' *Imago Mundi* 48 (1996): 148-203.

(with Roger Kain), *La Cartografia Anglesa. English Cartography* (Barcelona: Institut Cartogràfic de Catalunya, 1997).

'Prehistoric maps and mapmaking in Asia', contribution to *Encyclopaedia of the History of Science, Technology, and Medicine in Non-Western Cultures*, ed. Helen Selin (Dordrecht: Kluwer Academic Publishers, 1997), 558-60.

(with Christopher Board), 'The Prime Minister's globe and map cabinet', *Imago Mundi* 49 (1997): 157-159.

'Maps in books', in Ruth S. Luborsky and Elizabeth M. Ingram (eds), *A Guide to English Illustrated Books, 1536-1603* (Tempe: Arizona Center for Medieval & Renaissance Texts & Studies, 1998), 2:1-4.

(editor), *Fascinerende landschappen van Blaanderen en Wallonië in kaart en beeld* (Davidsfonds, 1995).

'Steekkaart van Atlassen', *Kultuurleven* 62:3 (1995): 60-61.

(with H. Decleir), 'Cartography', in J. Denis, *Geographical Research in Belgium* (Belgian National Committee, IGU, 1996).

(with F. Declercq), 'Efficiëntere klassenindeling en kleurgebruik in choropletenkaarten', *Kartografisach Tijdschrift* 22:4 (1996): 21-29.

(editor), *Atlas van alle landen* (Lannoo Tielt: Gottmer Haarlem; London: Dorling Kindersely, 1997).

(with A van Rompacy), 'The large-scale map of Sagalassos: contents and precision', *Sagalassos* 6 (1997): 263-274.

(with A van Rompacy), 'Analoge versus volautomatische detailkartering', *De Aardrijkskunde* 1 (1997): 54-63.

DeMERS, Michael N. (Dr)
Department of Geography
New Mexico State University
MSC MAP, P.O. Box 30001
LAS CRUCES, NM 88003
USA
Tel: (1) 505 646 1842 (office)
     (1) 505 526 6632 (home)
Fax: (1) 505 646 7430
E-mail: mdemers@nmsu.edu
        mdemers@zianet.com

History of zoological mapping 1777 to 1950; history of zoocartographical methods; relationships between zoological mapping and zoogeographical theory

DEPUYDT, Frans (Prof Dr)
Katholieke Universiteit te Leuven
Kartografie
Redingenstrat 16bis
B 3000 LEUVEN
Belgium
Tel: (32) 016 32 64 30 (office)
Fax: (32) 016 32 64 00
E-mail: depuydt@kuleuven.ac.be
     (32) 016 25 57 16 (home)

Archaeological, thematic and atlas cartography; historical cartography: Belgium and metric analysis

DEPUYDT, Joost Frans Filip
University Library K.U. Leuven
Rare Books & Manuscripts
Mgr. Ladeuzeplein 21
B-3000 LEUVEN
Belgium
Tel: (32) 016 32 46 22 (office)
     (32) 016 25 75 32 (home)
Fax: (32) 016 32 46 91
E-mail: joost.depuydt@bib.kuleuven.ac.be

History of 16th-century cartography in the Netherlands; Abraham Ortelius as a humanist and central figure in the humanist 'Republic of Letters'

DeROGATIS, Amy
Department of Philosophy and Religion
Colgate University
13 Oak Drive
HAMILTON, N.Y.
USA
Tel: (1) 315 845 7818
E-mail: aderogatis@center.colgate.edu

Moral geography: how mappers and missionaries separately and morally organized the American West

DESBRIERE, Michel
17 Allée des Pins
F-08000 CHARLEVILLE-MÉZIÈRES
France
Tel: (33) 24 33 03 15

Spanish Netherlands and northern Champagne; regional cartography of north-eastern France and drawing the border, mid-17th century; military mapping, 16th to 18th century

Champagne septentrionale: cartes et mémoires à la l'usage des militaires, 1544-1659 (Charleville-Mézières: Société des études ardennaises, 1995).

DESTEFANI, Laurio (Dr)
Academia Nacional de la Historia
Balcarce 139
BUENOS AIRES 1064
Argentina
Tel: (54) 1 331 5147
Fax: (54) 1 331 4633

Cartography of Patagonia, Tierra del Fuego, South Atlantic islands, and Antractica, 16th-20th centuries

DE VORSEY, Louis (Prof)
Department of Geography
University of Georgia
ATHENS, GA 30602
USA
Tel: (1) 706 542 2324
Fax: (1) 706 542 2388
E-mail: loudev@aol.com

American Indian mapping; maps as evidence in litigation; ocean current mapping

The Southeast in Early Maps (3rd edition revised and enlarged; University of North Carolina Press, 1998).

DE VRIES, Dirk (Drs)
Leiden University Library
Collection Bodel Nijenhuis
Witte Singel 27
P.O. Box 9501
2300 RA LEIDEN
Netherlands
Tel: (31) 71 527 2855 (office)
Fax: (31) 71 527 2836
E-mail: vries@rulub.leidenuniv.nl

Bodel Nijenhuis and his map collection; manuscript sea charts by Gerard van Keulen (1678-1726); Evert Maaskamp, publisher of maps and prints (1769-1834)

(31) 172 490999 (home)

DEWEZ, Simon James
Director
Gowrie Galleries Pty, Ltd
316 Oxford St.
WOOLLAHRA, New South Wales 2025
Australia
Tel: (61) 2 938 74581 (office)
Fax: (61) 2 938 90640
E-mail: maps@sydney.net

Complete database on mapping of Australia

(61) 2 936 09381 (home)

DOCKTOR, John W.
150 S. Strathcona Drive
YORK, Pennsylvania 17403
USA
Tel: (1) 717 846 8995 (office)
Fax: (1) 717 846 8996
E-mail: jdocktor@cyberia.com

Cartography of Pennsylvania prior to 1776

(1) 717 846 8997 (home)

'Seutter/Lotter map of Pensylvania Nova Jersey et Nova York', *The Portolan* 26 (1993): 12-19.

'Nicholas and William Scull of Pennsylvania", *The Portolan* 33 (1995): 11-17.

'Mapping the borders of Pennsylvania 1681-1921', *The Portolan* 40 (1997): 6-20.

'The source for the Janssonius-Visscher maps of New England', *Mercator's World*, 2:3 (1997): 58-61.

DOLZ, Wolfram (Dipl-Ing)
Staatlicher Mathematisch-
  Physikalischer Salon
Zwinger
D-01067 DRESDEN
Germany
Tel: (49) 0351 4 95 13 64
Fax: (49) 0351 4 96 02 01

Globes, spheres and orreries before 1900; surveying instruments before 1900

'Vermessungsmethoden und Feldmessinstrumente zur Zeit Gerard Mercator', in W. Scharfe (ed), *Gerhard Mercator und seine Zeit. 7. Kartographiehistorisches Colloquium Duisburg 1994* (Duisburg: Braun, 1996), 13-38.

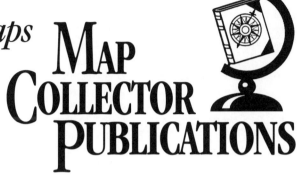

DONKERSLOOT-de-VRIJ,
Marijke (Dr)
Sint Nicolaaslaan 44
3984 JC OKIJK
Netherlands
Tel: (31) 030 656 3566

Cartobibliography of the
Isle of Terschelling; mapmakers in the Netherlands

*Topografische kaarten van Nederland mit de Jode tot en met de igde eeuw.
Een typologische toelichting ten behoeve van het gebruik van onde kaarten
bij landschaps-onderzoch* (Alphen aan der Rijn: Canaletto, 1995).

*Kaarten mit de 16de tot en met de igde eeuw in de collectie van de
Provincie Zuid-Holland* (s'Gravenhage: Provincie Zuid-Holland,
1998).

DÖRFLINGER, Johannes (Prof Dr)
Institut für Geschichte
Universität Wien
Dr Karl Lueger-Ring 1
A-1010 WIEN
Austria
Tel: (43) 1 4277 40801 (office)   (43) 1 887 2638 (home)
Fax: (43) 1 4277 9408
E-mail: johannes.doerflinger@univie.ac.at

Austrian cartography,
18th-early 20th centuries;
German atlases 1930-
1945; historical atlases
(18th-early 20th centuries)

(with H. Hühnel and L. Mucha), *Atlantes Austriaci: Österreichische
Atlanten 1561-1918* (2 vols.; Wien: Böhlau, 1995).

'Geschichtsatlanten vom 16. bis zum Beginn des 20.
Jahrhunderts', in Hans Wolff (ed) , *Vierhundert Jahre Mercator–vier-
hundert Jahre Atlas: Die ganze Welt zwischen zwei Buchdeckeln. Eine
Geschichte der Atlanten* (Weissenhorn: Konrad, 1995): 179-198.

(with G. Schlass and M. Heinz), *Maps, Atlases and Globes in the
Oldest Monastery of Vienna: Exhibition in the Library of the
'Schottenstift'* (Vienna: Schottenstift, 1995).

'Austrian Atlases of the nineteenth and early twentieth centuries',
in John A. Wolter and Ronald E. Grim (eds), *Images of the World:
The Atlas through History* (Washington, DC: Library of Congress,
1997), 233-256.

'Gotha–Justus Perthes–"Museum der Erde"', *Mitteilungen der Österreichischen Geographischen Gesellschaft* **139** (1997): 341-344.

DRÁPELA, Milan V. (Dr)
Department of Geography
Faculty of Science
University T.G. Masaryk
Kotlářská 2
61137 BRNO
Czech Republic
Tel: (420) 5 421 28319 (office)   (420) 5 472 39444 (home)
Fax: (420) 5 421 28300

History of Moravian car-
tography; J.A. Comenius's
map of Moravia, copies and
derivations

(with I. Durec and others), *Tabulae de Collectionibus Archivi
Raygradensis* [Maps from the Collection of the Rajhrad Archives]
(Brno: Tercie Ltd, 1995) {in Czech, English, German}.

DREYER-EIMBCKE,
Oswald (Consul)
Icelandic Consulate
Raboisen 5
D-20095 HAMBURG
Germany
Tel: (49) 040 33 6696 (office)   (49) 04104 2046 (home)
Fax: (49) 040 33 1347 (office)   (49) 04104 2046 (home)

Iceland, Greenland, North
Pole, southern part of
South America, South Pole

'Regensburg und die Welt im Mittelalter: Karte und
Kartographiegeschichte von der Antike bis zur Neuzeit: eine
Einführung', in Martin Angerer and Heinrich Wanderwirz (eds),
Regensburg in Mittelalter (Regensburg: Universitätsverlag
Regensburg, 1995), 13-30.

'Die älteste noch existierende Geographie-Verlag in Deutschland',
*Mitteilungs, Freundekreis für Cartographica in der Stiftung Preussischer
Kulturbesitz* (Berlin), **10** (1996): 14-18.

*Auf den Spuren der Entdecker am südlichsten Ende der Welt: Meilensteine
der Entdeckungs- und Kartographiegeschichte vom 16. bis 20. Jahrhundert
Patagonien, Feuerland, Falklandinseln, Terra australis, Antartika,
Südpol)* (Gotha: Perthes, 1996).

'Conrad Celtis: humanist, poet and cosmographer', *The Map
Collector* **74** (1996): 18-21.

'Germany's oldest existing publishing house', *IMCoS Journal* **65**
(1996): 13-14.

'Island in den Kartenbildern von Mercator', in W. Scharfe (ed),
*Gerhard Mercator und seine Zeit. 7. Kartographiehistorisches Colloquium
Duisburg 1994* (Duisburg: Braun, 1996), 39-48.

'Gedanken über Freunde und Sammler alter Karten', *Mitteilungen, Freundeskreis für Cartographica in der Stiftung Preussischer Kulturbesitz* (Berlin), **11** (1997): 5–15.

'The Pope makes peace with the aid of maps: cartographic aspects of the Beagle Channel dispute', *Mercator's World* **2**:2 (1997), 18–23.

'Two cartographers who made mapping history in Gotha: Heinrich Berghaus and August Petermann', *IMCoS Journal* **70** (1997): 19–21, 23, 25–27.

'Historic map of Poland that bears Stalin's signature' *IMCoS Journal* **73** (1998): 13-17.

'S marks the spot', *Mercator's World* **3**:4 (1998): 59-61.

DRIEVER, Steven Leiby (Prof)
Department of Geosciences
University of Missouri-Kansas City
5100 Rockhill Road
KANSAS CITY, Missouri 64110-
    2499
USA
Tel: (1) 816 235 2971 (office)
     (1) 913 362 1647 (home)
E-mail: sldriver@cctr.umkc.edu

Urban plans of Madrid, late 19th century; Lucas Mallada, geologist, mining engineer, social commentator; Spanish cartography, late 19th century; landscape imagery in writings of the Generation of 1898; maps used in 16th-century Mexico

'The Veracruz-Mexico City routes in the sixteenth century and the study of pre-industrial transport in historical geography', *Geografía y desarrollo; revista de Colegio Mexicano de Geografía* **6**:12 (1995): 5-18.

'The significance of Sorian landscapes in Antonio Machado's *Campos de Castilla*', *Isle: Interdisciplinary Studies in Literature and the Environment* **4**:1 (1997): 41-70.

DRYBURGH, Paula S.
Todhunter Allen Collection
Map Room
Bodleian Library
Broad Street
OXFORD OX1 3BG
UK
Tel: (44) 01865 277013
Fax: (44) 01865 277139
E-mail: psd@bodley.ox.ac.uk

British cartography, 1570-1900

'The Todhunter-Allen Collection : a little-known treasure trove', *Mercator's World* **2**:1 (1997): 52-55.

DUBREUIL, Lorraine
Map Curator
Dept. of Rare Books & Special
    Collections
McLennan Library
McGill University
3459 McTavish Street
MONTREAL, Quebec H3A 1Y1
Canada
Tel: (1) 514 398 4707
Fax: (1) 514 398 7184
E-mail: dubreuil@lib1.lan.mcgill.ca

Canadian fire insurance plans; early Canadian maps; Canadian county atlases

(with Marcel Fortin and Cheryl A. Woods), *Canadian Fire Insurance Plans in Ontario Collections, 1876-1973* (Ottawa: Association of Canadian Map Libraries and Archives, 1995).

DUKEN, Albert John
Albrecht-Dürer-Str. 2
D-31675 BUCKEBURG
Germany

Unravelling old charts, mapping procedures and old measures

DUNBABIN, John P.D.
St Edmund Hall
OXFORD OX1 4AR
UK
Tel: (44) 01865 279017

The fixing of (what is now) the United States-Canadian border, a process clearly influenced by the available maps

'Red lines on maps: the impact of cartographical errors on the border between the United States and British North America, 1782–1842', *Imago Mundi*, **50** (1998): 105-125.

DUNNIGAN, Brian Leigh
Curator of Maps
William L. Clements Library
909 South University
ANN ARBOR,
Michigan 48109-1190
USA
Tel; (1) 734 764 2347 (office)
(1) 517 423 9232 (home)
Fax: (1) 734 647 0716
E-mail: briand@umich.edu

17th to 19th century Great Lakes region maps of military posts; military cartography and plans, 1750-1815; early maps and images of Detroit, Michigan, and the posts of Michilimackinac and Niagara

DUPONT, Henrik
Map Curator
The Royal Library
Chr Brygge 8
DK 1219 KØBENHAVN K
Denmark
Tel: (45) 33 93 01 11 (office)   (45) 42 25 43 08 (home)
E-mail: hd@kb.dk

Danish cartography 1750-1950; using GIS to analyze and arrange for public GIS and historical cartography in general

'Mercators Atlas fra 1595', *Fund og Forskning* 36 (1997): 45-70.

'Verden set fra Palma' [The world seen from Palma], *Sfinx* 20:2 (1997): 68-75.

DÜRST, Arthur (Prof)
Promenadengasse 12
CH-8001 ZÜRICH
Switzerland
Tel: (41) 1 266 20 55
Fax: (41) 1 266 20 50
E-mail: arthur@duerst.ch
Web: http://www.duerst.ch

Catalogues of unique and rare maps in Swiss archives and libraries, of early globes in Switzerland, of facsimiles of Swiss maps and plans, of mapmakers in Switzerland; bibliographiy on the history of cartography

'La carte de l'Europe', in Marcel Watelet (ed), *Gerardi Mercatoris: Atlas Europae. Facsimilé des cartes de Gérard Mercator contenues dans l'Atlas de l'Europe, vers 1570-1572* (Antwerp: Fonds Mercator, 1994), 31-42. [English edition: *The Mercator Atlas of Europe* (Pleasant Hill, Oregon: Walking Tree Press, 1997).]

'Die *Chorographia et Topographia* von 1566 des Sebastian Schmid (1533-1586)', *Cartographica Helvetica* 19 (1996).

'Jos Murers Planvedute der Stadt Zürich von 1576. Dokumentation zu den Original-Abzügen von den vierhundertjährigen Holzdruckplatten', *Anlass des 100-Jahr-Jubiläums des Vermessungsamtes der Stadt Zürich* 29 (1996).

'Die Katalanische Estense-Weltkarte, um 1540', *Cartographica Helvetica* 14 (1996): 42-44.

(editor), *Sebastian Schmid: 'Chorographia et Topographia'* (facsimile; (Murten, 1996).

'Die Tabula Cosmographica des Johann Baptist Cysat, S.J. (1586-1657). Eine Weltkarten-Unikat von ca.1618', *Duisburger Forschungen* (1996): 73-90.

'Die Weltkarte von Albertin de Virga von 1411 oder 1415', *Cartographica Helvetica* 13 (1996): 18-21.

Jos Murers Planvedute der Stadt Zürich von 1576 (Zürich, 1997) [4 A2-size plans and a 12-page brochure].

'Die Planvedute der Stadt Zürich von Jos Murer, 1576', *Cartographica Helvetica* 15 (1997): 23–37.

Das Zürcher Karten von Hauptmann Andreas Hefti aus den Jahren 1895/1896 (Murten, 1997).

EDNEY, Matthew H.
Osher Map Library and Smith Center
    for Cartographic Education
University of Southern Maine
P.O. Box 9301
314 Forest Avenue
PORTLAND, ME 04104-9301
USA
Tel: (1) 207 780 4850
Fax: (1) 207 780 5310
E-mail: edney@usm.maine.edu

Theoretical examination of the modern modes of cartography as technological, social and cultural practices; mapping Maine and New England, 1750-1900; development of systematic government mapping in the United States

'Theory and the history of cartography', *Imago Mundi* 48 (1996): 185-191.

'Defining a unique city: surveying and mapping Bombay after 1800', in Pauline Rohatgi et al (eds), *Bombay to Mumbay: Changing Perspectives* (Mumbai: Marg Publications, 1997), 40-57.

Mapping an Empire: The Geographic Construction of British India, 1765-1843 (Chicago and London, University of Chicago Press, 1997).

'The Basel 1494 Columbus letter' [14 October 1996], http://www.usm.maine.edu/~maps/columbus/.

'The cartographic creation of New England' [5 December 1996], http://www.usm.maine.edu/~maps/exhibit2/.

'The Mitchell map: an irony of empire' [21 April 1997], http://www.usm.maine.edu/~maps/mitchell/.

EDSON, Evelyn (Dr)
Professor of History
Piedmont Virginia Community
   College
501 College Drive
CHARLOTTESVILLE, Virginia 22902
USA
Tel: (1) 804 961 5257 (office)   (1) 804 286 3466 (home)
Fax: (1) 804 971 8232
E-mail: ee2d@jade.pvcc.cc.va.us

Medieval cartography; maps in computus manuscripts; use of instruments in making early maps

'World maps and Easter tables', *Imago Mundi* **48** (1996): 25-42.

Mapping Time and Space: How Medieval Mapmakers Viewed Their World (London: British Library, 1997).

EGMOND, Marco van (Drs)
Explokart Faculteit Ruimtelijke
   Wetenschappen
Disciplinegroep Kartografie
Postbus 80115
3508 TC UTRECHT
Netherlands
Tel: (31) 30 253 2044 (office)
   (31) 71 402 0814 (home)
Fax: (31) 30 254 0604 (office)
   (31) 71 402 0814 (home)
E-mail: m.vanegmond@geog.uu.nl

Maps in Dutch parliamentary papers; Dutch polders; maps and atlases from the publishing house of Covens & Mortier; 18th-century production of maps and atlases in the Netherlands

'Kaarten voor kamerleden' [Maps for parliamentarians], *KB-Centraal, Journal of the Royal Library, The Hague* 24:5 (1995): 15-17.

EHRENBERG, Ralph
Geography and Map Division
Library of Congress
WASHINGTON, DC 20540-4650
USA
Tel: (1) 202 707 8530 (office)   (1) 301 299 5469 (home)
Fax: (1) 202 707 8531
E-mail: rehr@loc.gov

Exploration and mapping of North America; development of geological maps; military cartography

Library of Congress Geography and Maps: An Illustrated Guide (Washington, D.C.: Library of Congress, 1996).

'Mapping the northern Trans-Mississippi West', *IMCoS Journal* 63 (1996): 13-15.

EHRENSVÄRD, Ulla (Prof Dr)
Banérgatan 10
S-11523 STOCKHOLM
Sweden
Tel & fax: (46) 8 662 11 75

Mapping the Swedish realm; sea charts

'Great-grandpa's Pacific Ocean. Erik W. Dahlgren and geographical history', in Sten Hedberg (ed), *Serving the Scholarly Community. Essays ... Presented to Thomas Tottie* (Uppsala: University Library, 1995), 375-380.

Introductory notes to Peter Gedda and Werner von Rosenfelt, *General Hydrographisk Chart-Book öfwer Östersiön och Katte-Gatt* [1695] (Uppsala: Gullersbild, 1995).

(with Juha Nurminen and Pellervo Kokkonen), *Mare Balticum: 2000 vuotta Itämeren historiaa (Rinnakkaispainokset: Mare Balticum: The Baltic: 2000 Years; Mare Balticum: 2000 år av Östersjöns historia; Mare Balticum: 2000 Jahre der Geschichte der Ostsee)* (Helsinki: John Nurminen Säätiö, 1995, 1996).

'Die Schwedische Landaesaufnahme von Pommern in den Jahren 1758-1763', in Joachim Neumann (ed), *Karten hüten und bewahren. Festgabe für Lothar Zögner* (Gotha: Justus Perthes Verlag, 1995), 51-55.

(with Kurt Zilliacus), *Farlederna berättar: gamla sjökartor över Finlands skägårdar* [Old sea charts of the Finnish archipelago] (Helsinki: Konstsamfundet-Söderströms, 1997; 2nd ed 1998).

'Das Schwedische Projekt zur Verbesserung der Seekarten im 18. Jahrhundert', in M. Stelmach (ed), *Mapy poludniowego Baltyku* (Szczecin: Uniwersytet, 1997), 53-66.

EISENSTEIN, Herbert (Prof Dr)   Islamic cartography
Institut für Orientalistik der
    Universität Wien
Universitätsstrasse 7/V
A-1010 WIEN
Austria
Tel: (43) 1 4277 43421 (office)   (43) 1 798 2369 (home)
Fax: (43) 1 4277 9434

'Die arabische Kartographie unter besonderer Berücksichtigung
von Nordeuropa und Schleswig', in Dagmar Unverhau and Kurt
Schietzel (eds), *Das Danewerk in der Kartographiegeschichte
Nordeuropas* (Neumünster, 1993), 79-94.

'Die Darstellung Europas auf mittelalterlichen arabischen
Weltkarten', in Wolfgang Scharfe (ed), *6. Kartographiehistorisches
Colloquium Berlin 1992. Vorträge und Berichte* (Berlin 1994), 119-
127.

'Islamische Weltkarten des 16. Jahrhunderts', *Cartographica
Helvetica* 15 (1997): 39-43.

ELKHADEM, Hossam (Prof)   History of cartography in
Curator   Belgium; 16th-century car-
Section des Cartes et Plans   tography; 19th-century
Bibliothèque Royale de Belgique   cartography in Belgium
Boulevard de l'Empereur 4
1000 BRUXELLES
Belgium
Tel: (32) 2 519 57 15 (office)   (32) 2 465 44 47 (home)
Fax: (32) 2 519 57 42
E-mail: elkhadem@kbr.be

(with A. Vanrie), 'Aspect technique et typologique' [Analysis of
MS plans of *c.*1550-1554 (J. Deventer), 1582 (P. Le Poivre), 1611
(anon.), & of 1622 (anon.)], in Françoise Thomas et Jacques Nazet
(eds), *Tournai: une ville, un fleuve (XVIe-XVIIe siècle)* (Bruxelles:
Crédit Communal, 1995), 81-97.

La cartographie céleste arabe (Bruxelles: Centre de Documentation
Pédagogique, Université Libre de Bruxelles, 1997).

'Gérard Mercator', in Marie-Thérèse Isaac (ed) *La Bibliothèque de
l'Université de Mons-Hainaut, 1797-1997* (Mons: Université de
Mons-Hainaut, 1997), 152-161.

ENGSTROM, Kathryn L.   Historical cartography;
Reference Team Leader   American cartography,
Geography and Map Division   digital resources
Library of Congress
WASHINGTON, DC 20540-4650
USA
Tel: (1) 202 707 8545
Fax: (1) 202 707 8531
E-mail: keng@loc.gov

ENTERLINE, James   Knowledge about America
144 West 95th Street   in medieval European
NEW YORK, N.Y. 10025   world maps
USA
Tel & fax: (1) 212 865 9648
E-mail: jenterli@concentric.net   kv2z@amsat.org

ESPENHORST, Jürgen   German 'Hand-Atlases'
c/o Pangaea Verlag   1800-1945; hypsometric
Villigster Str. 32   maps; maps of Osnabrück;
D-58239 SCHWERTE   history of German rural
Germany   settlement using analysis of
Tel: (49) 02304 72284   large-scale maps and other
Fax: (49) 02304 78010   sources down to the Middle
E-mail: pangaea@cww.de   Ages

Nachtrag zur Bibliographie der Handatlanten (Schwerte: Pangaea
Verlag, 1995).

'Die "Urenkel" von Mercators Atlanten: die Handatlanten des
deutschen Sprachraums', in W. Scharfe (ed), *Gerhard Mercator und
seine Zeit. 7. Kartographiehistorisches Colloquium Duisburg 1994*
(Duisburg: Braun, 1996), 241-248.

FAGIOLO, Marcello (Prof)   Rome, Lecce (southern
Centro Studi Cultura e Immagine di   Italy), Latin America;
    Roma   iconography of the city
Via della Lungara 10   (Europe, Latin America);
00165 ROME   director of series
Italy   'L'Immagine Storica delle
Tel & Fax: (39) 06 689 3758   Città'

FALCHETTA, Piero (Dr)
Biblioteca Nazionale Marciana
Piazzetta S. Marco, 7
30124 VENEZIA
Italy
Tel: (39) 041 240 7224 (office)
      (39) 041 528 9946 (home)
Fax: (39) 041 523 8803 (office)
E-mail: falchetta@marciana.venezia.sbn.it

Portolan charts, 13th to 15th centuries; urban cartography (plans and views) to 18th century; geography of Africa before 1500; Vincenzo Coronelli

'Elementi di semantica cartografica', in *Sul libro antico* (Viterbo: Betagamma, 1995), 33-44.

(with Marino Zorzi, ed), *Guerre veneto-turche. Carte e piante per la guerra della Morea* (Venezia: Arsenale editrice, 1995).

'Marinai, mercanti, cartografi, pittori. Ricerche sulla cartografia nautica a Venezia, sec. XIV-XV', in *Ateneo Veneto* **182** (1995): 7-109.

L'atlante di Battista Agnese (1552-1554), Edizione facsimile in CD-ROM, con introduzione e note di Piero Falchetta (Venezia: Canal Multimedia, 1996).

FELDMANN, Hans-Uli
Swiss Federal Office of Topography
Seftigenstrasse 264
CH-3084 WABERN
Switzerland
Tel: (41) 031 963 2327 (office)
      (41) 026 670 1050 (home)
Fax: (41) 031 963 2459 (office)
      (41) 026 670 1050 (home)
E-mail: hans-uli.feldmann@lt.admin.ch

Chief editor, *Cartographica Helvetica*; Swiss cartography, 18th to 20th centuries; cartographic techniques

(with Thomas Wallner), Documentation for facsimile edition of *Die Topographische Karte des Kantons Solothurn von Urs Josef Walker, 1832* (Murten: Cartographica Helvetica, 1995).

(with Madelena Cavelti Hammer and Markus Oehrli), *Fabre, Licht und Schatten. Die Entwicklung der Reliefkartographie seit 1660* (Murten: Cartographica Helvetica, 1997). [Exhibition catalogue.]

(with Wolfgang Scharfe and Ingrid Kretschmer), *6è curs: La Cartografia dels països de parla alemanya: Alemanya, Àustria, Suïssa* (Barcelona: Institut Cartogrfic de Catalunya, 1997).

FERGUSON, Paul
Map Library
Trinity College Library
College Street
DUBLIN 2
Ireland
Tel: (353) 1 608 2087
Fax: (353) 1 691 9003
E-mail: pfrguson@tcd.ie

Bibliography and guide to secondary works on Irish map history 1850-; carto-bibliography of the printed maps, city and county of Dublin

FERN, William H. (Dr)
4 Edgewater Hillside
WESTPORT, Connecticut 06880
USA
Tel: (1) 203 222 1879
Fax: (1) 203 221 0318

Pepys Island

FILLIOZAT, Manonmani
   Dominique
31 rue Joséphine
27000 EVREUX
France
Tel: (33) 02 32 31 34 03
E-mail: pfilliozat@magic.fr

French maritime explorations and charts of the Indian Ocean, 17th and 18th centuries

'D'Après de Mannevillette, captain and hydrographer to the French East India Company', *Indian Journal of History of Science* **29**:2 (1994): 329-342.

(with Jean Deloche and Pierre-Sylvain Filliozat), *Anquetil Duperron. Voyage en Inde, 1754-1762. Relation du voyage en préliminaire à la tradition du Zend-Avesta, présentation, notes et bibliographie* (Paris: École française d'Extrême-Orient, Maisonneuve et Larose, 1997).

FINCOEUR, Michel Benoit
Scientific Associate
Bibliothèque Royale de Belgique
Boulevard de l'Empereur 4
1000 BRUXELLES
Belgium
Tel: (32) 02 519 57 40
E-mail: savants.belges@kbr.be

19th-century cartography; Philippe Vandermaelen (with Marguerite Silvestre)

FIORANI, Francesca (Dr)
McIntire Department of Art
Fayerweather Hall
University of Virginia
CHARLOTTESVILLE, VA 22903
USA
Tel: (1) 804 924 3117 (office)
Fax: (1) 804 924 3647
E-mail: ff6f@virginia.edu

Renaissance map murals;
Renaissance mapmaking,
map users, map display;
Renaissance historical maps

(1) 804 977 9729 (home)

'The multimedia format of Renaissance maps', *Bulletin of the Society for Renaissance Studies* (May 1995): 7-12.

'Post-tridentine "Geographica sacra": the Galleria delle Carte Geografiche in the Vatican Palace', *Imago Mundi* **48** (1996): 124-148.

FISCHER, Hanspeter (Dipl-Ing)
Schenkendorfstrasse 3
D-70193 STUTTGART
Germany
Tel: (49) 0711 651646

Historical maps and surveying in south-western Germany

'Die Landtafeln von Wangen im Allgäu und Lindau im Bodensee', in *Erläuterungen zu Reproduktionen Alter Karten* (Stuttgart: Landesvermessungsamt Baden-Württemberg, 1995).

'Frühwerk südwestdeutscher Vermessung und Kartographie: die Landtafeln von Wangen im Allgäu und Lindau im Bodensee', in W. Scharfe (ed), *Gerhard Mercator und seine Zeit. 7. Kartographiehistorisches Colloquium Duisburg 1994* (Duisburg: Braun, 1996), 147-166.

'Werke der Tiroler Bauernkartographen – Vermessungen in Vorderösterreich vor etwa 200 Jahren', *Beiträge zur Landeskunde* (regelmässige Beilage zum Staatsanzeiger für Baden-Württemberg) 5 (1997): 8-15.

FISCHER, Karl (Dr)
Wiener Stadt- und Landesarchiv
Kartographische Sammlung
Rathaus
A-1082 WIEN
Austria
Tel: (43) 1 406 89 61 41 or (43) 1 4000 84843
Fax: (43) 1 406 89 61 43
E-mail: fis@m08.magwien.gv.at

Town plans of Vienna;
Austrian maps

(editor), *Das ist die stat Wienn. Wanderung durch ein halbes Jahrtausend Wiener Stadtkartographie: Vom Albertinischen Plan bis zur Computerstadtkarte* (Ausstellung des Wiener Stadt- und Landesarchivs und des Historischen Museums der Stadt Wien, 204. Sonderausstellung, Historisches Museum der Stadt Wien, Karlsplatz; Wien, 1995; Wiener Geschichtsblätter Beiheft 4/1995).

'Blickpunkt Wien. Das kartographische Interesse an der von den Türken bedrohten Stadt im 16. Jahrhundert', in *Studien zur Wiener Geschichte. Jahrbuch des Vereins für Geschichte der Stadt Wien* **52/53** (1996/1997): 101-116.

Contributions to *Wien-Edition* (a loose-leaf collection of reproductions of different materials, including maps): Plan der Stadt Wien und der Vorstädte 1707/1712; Die Gasbeleuchtung Wiens 1851/1862; Vogelschauplan der Wiener Gemeindebauten; Plan der neuen Bezirkseinteilung, 1850 (all published 1996); Karte des Wald- und Wiesengürtels, 1905; Plan der Wiener Innenstadt, 1799; Vogelschauansichten der Wiener Vorstädte, um 1734 (all published 1997).

'Stadtpläne', and 'Suttinger Daniel', in Felix Czeike, *Historisches Lexikon Wien*, vol. 5 (Wien 1997), 297f, and 402.

FISHER, Susanna
Spencer
Upham
SOUTHAMPTON SO32 1JD
UK
Tel: (44) 01489 860 291
Fax: (44) 01489 860 638
E-mail: 106236.2626@compuserve.com

History of Imray, Laurie, Norie & Wilson, chart publishers; life and surveys of Capt. Joseph Huddart (1741-1816)

'The Blue Back Charts', *Antique Collecting* 32:4 (1997): 47-51.

FITCH, Richard
Old Maps & Prints & Books
2324 Calle Halcon
SANTA FE, New Mexico 87505
USA
Tel: (1) 505 982 2939
Fax: (1) 505 982 3148
E-mail: oldmaps@swcp.com

Decorative borders in 19th-century American atlases as an aid to dating and identifying individual maps

FITZGERALD, Joseph H. (Dr)
Historical Museum of Southern
  Florida
101 West Flagler Street
MIAMI, FL 33130
USA
Tel: (1) 305 446 8129 (office)
Fax: (1) 305 446 9377

Mapping the Caribbean
and Florida; chairman,
Miami International Map
Fair

(1) 305 856 5114 (home)

FITZPATRICK, Gary
Geography and Map Division
Library of Congress
WASHINGTON, DC 20540-4761
USA
Tel: (1) 202 707 8542
Fax: (1) 202 707 8531
E-mail: gfit@loc.gov

History of Hawaiian car-
tography (with Riley M.
Moffat); history of mapping
of the Pacific

(with Riley Moore Moffat), *Surveying the Mahele: Mapping the
Hawaiian Land Revolution* (Vol 2 of Palapala'aina; Honolulu:
Editions Limited, 1995).

FLATNESS, James A
Geography and Map Division
Library of Congress
WASHINGTON, D.C. 20540
USA
Tel: (1) 202 707 8533
Fax: (1) 202 707 8531

18th and 19th century
mapping of the northwest
coast of North America

'Geography and Map Division', in P. Frazier (ed), *Many Nations: A
Library of Congress Resource Guide for the Study of Indian and Alaska
Native Peoples of the United States* (Washington, DC: Library of
Congress, 1996), 186-223.

FLEET, Christopher James
Map Library
National Library of Scotland
33 Salisbury Place
EDINBURGH EH9 1SL
UK
Tel: (44) 0131 226 4531
Fax: (44) 0131 668 3472
E-mail: c.fleet@nls.uk

Scanning and digital imaging of early cartographic
materials; Pont manuscript
maps of Scotland

FLEISCHMANN, Peter (Dr)
Staatsarchiv Nürnberg
Archivstr 17
D-90408 NÜRNBERG
Germany
Tel: (49) 0911 935 1921
Fax: (49) 0911 935 1999

Manuscript and printed
maps of Nürnberg and
Franconia, 16th to 18th
centuries

'Hans Bien', 'Hieronymus Braun', 'Johann Carl/Peter Carl', in
*Allgemeines Künstlerlexikon: Die bildenden Künstler aller Zeiten und
Völker* 10, 14, 16 (München/Leipzig: Saur-Verlag, 1995-1997).

'Das Schultheißenamt Neumarkt – Eine historische Karte im
Pfinzing-Atlas (1594)', *Jahresbericht des Historischen Vereins für
Neumarkt in der Oberpfalz* 21 (1996): 27-40.

(with W. Heinz and C. Heistermann, ed), Commentary to *Das
Pflegamt Hersbruck. Eine Karte des Paul Pfinzing mit Grenzbeschreibung
von 1596* (facsimile; Nürnberg: Alt-nürnberger Landschaft, 1997).

Die handgezeichneten Karten des Staatsarchivs Nürnberg bis 1806 (=
Bayerische Archivinventare 49; München: Staatliche Archive Bayerns,
1998).

FLETCHER, David (Dr)
London Guildhall University
Old Castle Street
LONDON E1 7NT
UK
Tel: (44) 0171 320 1025
Fax: (44) 0171 320 1157
E-mail: fletcher@lgu.ac.uk

Public boundary mapping
in Britain; the role of maps
in estate management; the
emergence of map con-
sciousness in early modern
England

'The Careswell Atlas: working tool and work of art', *The Map
Collector* 73 (1995): 34-37.

The Emergence of Estate Maps: Christ Church, Oxford 1600 to 1840
(Oxford, Oxford University Press, 1995).

'Map or terrier? The example of Christ Church Oxford, estate
management 1600-1840', *Transactions of the Institute of British
Geographers* 23:2 (1998): 221-237.

FLINT, Valerie Irene Jane (Prof)   The Hereford mappa
Department of History   mundi
University of Hull
HULL HU6 7RX
UK
Tel: (44) 01482 466128 (office)   (44) 01482 881333 (home)
Fax: (44) 01482 466126
E-mail: v.i.flint@hist.hull.ac.uk

'The medieval world of Christopher Columbus', *Parergon* **12**:2 (1995): 9-27.

FOGUET, Rafael   Organization and study of
Llusanés, 10 3° A   a Catalonian map library;
08022 BARCELONA   studies in comparative car-
Spain   tography, especially
Tel: (34) 93 330 61 11 (office) Catalonia and Barcelona
    (34) 93 211 83 84 (home)   prints (general views) to
Fax: (34) 93 490 61 75   1900
E-mail: rfoguet@ferrer-int-grupo.es

FORSTNER, Gustav G.   Spatial accuracy of old
Peter Tunnergasse 17   maps; investigation of
A8605 KAPFENBERG   interdependency of old
Austria   maps by mathematical/sta-
Tel: (43) 03862 22012   tistical methods; zero
                                meridians

FOX-FRIEDMAN, Jeanne (Dr)   Monumental world maps in
215 West 90th Street Apt. 6-D   medieval northern Italy
NEW YORK, NY 10024
USA
Tel: (1) 212 799 4579
Fax: (1) 212 799 4659
E-mail: jfried1@idt.net

'Messianic visions: Modena cathedral and the Crusades', *Res. Anthropology and Aesthetics* **25** (Spring 1994): 77-95.

FRANCO, Loredana   Critical analysis of volumes
Via Dante 14   5 to 8 and Additamentum
GORIZIA 43170   of Theodore de Bry's *De*
Italy   *America*
Tel: (39) 0481 533887

'Vincenzo Coronelli: vita e opere: aggiorniamenti', *Nuncius: Annali di Storia della Scienza* **9**:2 (1994): 517-541.

FREDRIKSON, Erkki Onni Volter   Finnish cartography
Fredrikson Map Collection
Institute of History
Jyväskylä University
Seminakriniaiu 15
40100 JYVÄSKYLÄ
Finland
Tel: (358) 14 624917 (office)   (358) 14 612896 (home)
Fax: (358) 14 624933

Finljandija 500 ljet na karte Jevrophyi (Laukaa, Finland, 1996); also in Icelandic, Hungarian, Portuguese, Swedish, Dutch.

'Karjalan karttakuvan vaiheet' [The stages of Carelian cartography], in Lassu Heininen (ed), *Kuhmo Euroopan unionin ja Venäjän, Kuhmon kesäkatemia, 1996* (Finland, 1996).

Finlandia Latina chartographica (Jyväskylä, 1997).

Finnland im Wirkungsbereich der Ostsee und Deutschlands (Jyväskylä, 1997).

'Maps', in *Finland: A Cultural Encyclopedia* (Helsinki, 1997).

Päijännw. Päijänteen karttakuva [Old Maps of Päijänne Lake] (Jyväskylä, 1998).

'Suomenmaa, Suomi Euroopan kartalla' [Finland on the map of Europe] (Helsinki: Reader's Digest, 1998).

FREEMAN, Gordon   Mapping a large stone-age
    Russel (Prof Emeritus)   religious and habitation site
Chemistry Department   in southern Alberta
University of Alberta
EDMONTON, Alberta T6G 2G2
Canada
Tel: (1) 403 492 3468 (office)   (1) 403 486 5522 (home)
Fax: (1) 403 492 8231
E-mail: k.np@ualberta.ca

FREITAG, Ulrich Max (Prof Dr)
Fachrichtung kartograpie
Freie Universität Berlin
Malteser Str. 74-100 Haus H
D-12249 BERLIN
Germany
Tel: (49) 030 779 2329
Fax: (49) 030 7670 6451

History of cartography of Thailand and Southeast Asia; principles of development of global mapping

FRENCH, Josephine Ruth
Map Collector Publications Ltd
48 High Street
TRING, Herts HP23 5BH
UK
Tel: (44) 01442 891004
Fax: (44) 01442 827712

General research for, and updating of, *Tooley's Dictionary of Map Makers*, with Valerie Scott and Mary Alice Lowenthal

FRIEDMAN, Anna Felicity
History of Astronomy Department
Adler Planetarium & Astronomy
    Museum
1300 South Lake Shore Drive
CHICAGO, Illinois 60622
USA
Tel: (1) 312 322 0527
Fax: (1) 312 341 9935
E-mail: anna_friedman@orbit.adler.uchicago.edu

Celestial cartography, 16th to 20th centuries

Awestruck by the Majesty of the Heavens (Chicago: Adler Planetarium & Astronomy Museum, 1997).

FRIEDMAN, David Hodes (Prof)
History, Theory and Criticism
    Section
Department of Architecture,
    room 10-303
Massachusetts Institute of Technology
77 Massachusetts Avenue
CAMBRIDGE, MA 02139
USA
Tel: (1) 617 253 7572
Fax: (1) 617 258 9455
E-mail: dhfriedm@mit.edu

The representation of cities, with a special interest in 15th through 18th century European images, both maps and views

'Palaces and the street in late medieval and Renaissance Italy', in J. Whitehand and P. Larkin (eds), *Urban Landscape: International Perspectives* (London: Routledge, 1992), 69-113.

FRÖMELT, Hubert (Dr)
Neuhauserstrasse 39b
CH-8500 FRAUENFELD
Switzerland
Tel: (41) 52 724 29 74 (office)
    (41) 52 722 26 10 (home)
E-mail: hubert.froemelt@arp.tg.ch

Problems of survey and map making since the 16th century; early cadastral plans (17th-18th centuries)

(with Michel Guisolan), 'Topographische Aufnahme des Kantons Thurgau von Johann Jakob Sulzberger, 1830 bis 1838', *Cartograhica Helvetica* 17 (1996): 3-17.

(with Michel Guisolan), *J.J. Sulzberger: Karte des Kantons Thurgau von 1830-1838* (Dokumentation zur Faksimilierung der Originalzeichnungen; Langnau am Albis, 1997).

FROSTICK, Raymond C.
425 Unthank Road
NORWICH, Norfolk NR4 7QB
UK
Tel & Fax: (44) 01603 452937
E-mail:
raymond.frostick@btinternet.com

Cartobibliography of Norfolk maps, 1574-1840; cartobibliography of Norwich plans and prospects, 1558-1840; British maps in van der Aa atlases; James Corbridge's survey

'English county maps in Jansson's *Atlas Minor*', *IMCoS Journal* 68 (1997): 45-50.

GALERA MONEGAL, Montserrat
Institut Cartogràfic de Catalunya
Cartoteca de Catalunya
Parc de Montjuïc
08036 BARCELONA
Spain
Tel: (34) 3 425 2900
Fax: (34) 3 426 7442
E-mail: mgalera@icc.es

Cartobibliography 'raisonée' of the drawings and engravings of Antoon Van den Wijngaerde, painter of cities and war facts in 16th-century Europe and a reconstruction of his pictorial work

'Estructura y organización de una cartoteca', in *El documento cartográfico como fuente de información* (1997), 119-133.

'La Pobla de Lillet i el seu entorn geogràfic vist a través de la cartografia de Catalunya dels segles XVIII i XIX', *L'Erol* 53 (1997): 37-44.

(with Pau Alegre and Concepció Isern), 'Tres cartoteques catalanes', in Montserrat Galera Monegal (ed), 'Història i cartografia', *L'Avenç* (abril 1998), 23-28.

GALLEZ, Paul (Pablo Jorge) (Prof Dr)
Director, Patagonic Institute
calle Peru 339
RA-8000 BAHÍA BLANCA
Argentina
Tel: (54) 91 52 23 20
E-mail: lgallez@criba.edu.ar

Pre-Columbian cartography of South America; cartography of 16th-century America

'Goeree en Zelandia y Tiera del Fuego' [The toponym Goeree in Zeeland and in Tierra del Fuego], *De Schakel* 380 (Buenos Aires 1995).

'Cómo Cristóbal encontró el Paraiso' [How Christopher Columbus found the Paradise], *Ideas/Imágenes* 226 (Bahía Blanca 1997).

'La protocartografia, ciencia latinoamericana' [Protocartography, a Latin American Science], *Ideas/Imágenes* 236 (Bahía Blanca 1998).

GALLIANO, Graziella (Prof)
Dipartimento Dissgell
Università di Genova
Lungoparco Gropallo 3-6
16122 GENOVA
Italy
Tel: (39) 10 209 5321 (office)   (39) 143 888 423 (home)
Fax: (39) 10 209 5347 (office)   (39) 143 888 423 (home)
E-mail: geoge@unige.it

Italian cartography; religious cartography

'Alcune osservazioni sulla carta anonima catalana della Biblioteca Estense di Modena', in *Atti del Convegno Momenti e problemi della geografia contemporanea* (Roma: Dip. St. Storici della Terza Università, 1995), 477-491.

'L'ecumene di Claudio Tolomeo', *Geografia nelle Scuole* 1 (1995): 37-38.

'La geografia negli scritti di Francesco Borghero', in Claudio Cerreti (ed), *Colonie africane e cultura italiana fra ottocento e novecento: le esplorazioni e la geografia (Roma, 1994)* (Rome, Istituto Italo-Africano-CISU, 1995), 151-162.

'Leggere il Mediterraneo attraverso le carte antiche', *Mondodomani* 4 (1995): 16-18.

'L'Oltre Suez secondo Battista Agnese', *Geografia nelle Scuole* 2 (1995): 103-104.

(with Luciano Lago), *La Terrra Santa e la sua immagine nella cartografia antica* (Trieste: Tip. Adriatica, 1995). {Exhibition catalogue.}

'Note intorno all'immagine dell'Italia fra antichità e medioevo', *Notiziario del Centro Italiano per gli studi storico-geografici* 2:3 (1996): 14-20.

'Sinclair, Colombo, Zeno e la scoperta dell'America', in Graziella Galliano (ed), *Atti del Convegno Rappresentazioni e pratiche dello spazio in una prospettiva storico-geografica* (Genova: Brigati, 1997), 259-266.

GAMBIN, Marie-Thérèse (Prof)
Université de Paris VII - Denis Diderot
UFRG.H.S.S.
Case Courrier 7001, tour 34/44, 3e ét
2 place Jussieu
75251 PARIS
France
Tel: (33) 01 43 54 86 46
Fax: (33) 01 43 29 40 41

Ancient Greek cartography: celestial maps; the 'planisphaerium' of Ptolemy translated from Latin into French; impact of Ptolemy's maps on Renaissance cartography; map projection systems in the Renaissance; history of cartography in 18th-century France

GANADO, Albert (Dr)
1 M.A. Vassalli Street
VALETTA VLT 13
Malta
Tel: (356) 247 109 (office)
     (356) 236 941 (home)
Fax: (356) 247 170

Mapping the Maltese islands; 16th-century plans of Valetta; Maltese cartographers; map holdings of the Malta National Library

GARVER, John B. (Dr)
6777 Surrywood Lane
BETHESDA, Maryland 20817
USA
Tel & fax: (1) 301 469 9398
E-mail: jbgarver@aol.com

Mapping the American West, 1804-1861

'The President's map cabinet', *Imago Mundi* 49 (1997): 153-157.

GASSET ARGEMÍ, Josep
Gran de Gràcia 93, 5ᵉ, 1ª
E-08012 BARCELONA
Spain
Tel: (34) 3 237 06 67

Cartobibliography of
printed maps of Catalonia
and of printed plans and
views of Barcelona before
1900

(with A.M. Adroer and M.D. Florensa), *Catàleg del Fons Cartogràfic de l'Institut Municipal d'Història. II. Mapes antics de la Península Ibèrica i de la resta del mon (segles XVI-XIX)* (Barcelona: Ajuntament de Barcelona, 1995).

GAUTIER DALCHÉ, Patrick
      (Prof Dr)
Institut de Recherche et
      d'Histoire des Textes
40 Avenue d'Iéna
75116 PARIS
France
Fax: (33) 01 45 96 04 39

Medieval geography and
cartography; perception
and use of maps in the
Middle Ages; catalogue of
mappaemundi prior to
1200

'Notes sur la "carte de Théodose II" et sur la "mappemonde de Théodulf d'Orleans"', *Geographia antiqua* 3 (1994-1995): 91-108.

Carte marine et portulan au XIIe siècle: le 'Liber de existencia riviarum et forma maris nostri Mediterranei' (Pise, circa 120) (Collection de l'Ecole Française de Rome 203; Rome: Ecole Française de Rome, 1995).

'Cartes', 'Découvertes', 'Portulan', in A. Vauchez (ed), *Dictionnaire encyclopédique du Moyen Age chrétien* (Paris: Éditions du Cerf, 1996).

'Limite, frontière et organisation de l'espace dans la géographie et la cartographie de la fin du Moyen Age', in Guy P. Marchal (ed), *Grenzen und Raumvorstellungen (11.-20. Jh) / Frontières et conceptions de l'espace (11e-20e siècles)*, *Clio Lucernensis* 3 (Zürich: Chronos, 1996): 93-122.

'L'organisation du monde', et 'L'espace cosmologique', in O. Guyotjeannin et E. Poulle (eds), *Autour de Gerbert d'Aurillac, la pape de l'an Mil* (Paris: Ecole des Chartes, 1996), 2-6, 330-334.

'Pour une histoire du regard géographique. Conception et usage de la carte au XVᵉ siècle', *Micrologus. Natura, scienze e società medievali* 4 (1996): 77-103.

L'usage des cartes marines aux XIVᵉ et XVᵉ siècles', in *Spazi, tempi, misure e percorsi nell'Europa del Bassomedioevo. Atti del XXXII*

Convegno storico internazionale, Todi, 8-11 ottobre 1995 (Spoleto: Centro italiano di studi sul basso Medioevo-Accademia Tudertina, 1996), 97-128.

Géographie et culture. La représentation de l'espace du VIe au XIIe siècle (London: Variorum, Collected Studies Series, 1997).

'*Mappae mundi* antérieures au XIIIᵉ siècle dans les manuscrits latins de la Bibliothèque nationale de France. Un inventaire codicologique', *Scriptorium* 52 (1998).

'Le renouvellement de la perception et de la représentation de l'espace au XIIᵉ siècle', in *Renovación intelectual del Occidente europeo (siglo XII)*, (XXIV Semana de Estudios Medievales, Estella 1997; Pamplona, 1998).

GAVISH, Dov (Dr)
Aerial Photography Curator
Department of Geography
Hebrew University of Jerusalem
JERUSALEM, 91905
Israel
Tel: (972) 2 588 3369 (office)   (972) 2 671 8678 (home)
Fax: (972) 2 582 0549
E-mail: msgavish@pluto.mscc.huji.ac.il

Cartography and aerial
photography of Israel and
Palestine; military, cadastral and topographical
mapping

'As yesterday meets tomorrow: map and photographic consciousness', in Y. Gradus and G. Lipshitz (eds), *The Mosaic of Israeli Geography* (1996), 511-516.

'Foreign intelligence maps: offshoots of the 1:100,000 topographic map of Israel', *Imago Mundi* 48 (1996): 174-184.

GERMANN, Thomas
Zentralbibliothek Zürich
Kartensammlung
Zähringerplatz 6
CH-8025 ZÜRICH
Switzerland
Tel: (41) 01 268 3100 (office)   (41) 01 713 1578 (home)
Fax: (41) 01 268 3290

Historic town plans of
Zürich; panoramas; history
of panoramas; panorama
catalogues and cataloguing

Georg Meyer (1814-1895), Landschaftsmaler und Panoramenkünstler. Kommentar zu seiner 1878 gezeichneten Rundsicht vom Nollen (Frauenfeld: Huber, 1996).

'Johann Gottfried Ebel und sein Panorama von der

Albishochwacht', *Cartographica Helvetica* 13 (1996): 23-30.

Zürich im Zeitraffer. Von der Römerzeit bis zum Schanzenbau 1642 (Zürich: Werd-Verlag, 1997).

GILMARTIN, Patricia
Department of Geography
University of South Carolina
COLUMBIA, SC 29208
USA
Tel: (1) 803 777 2989 (office)
Fax: (1) 803 777 4972
E-mail: gilmartin-pat@sc.edu

Maps for propaganda; history of cartographic symbolization techniques

(1) 803 733 5605 (home)

GLOVER, Sarah Rose
McIntire Department of Art
University of Virginia
Fayerweather Hall
CHARLOTTESVILLE, Virginia
22903
USA
Tel: (1) 804 296 9702
E-mail: srg9s@virginia.edu

Medieval mappaemundi: Last Judgement iconography and the Hereford mappamundi

GODLEWSKA, Anne Marie Claire
Geography Department
Queen's University
KINGSTON, Ontario K7L 3N6
Canada
Tel: (1) 613 531 9864
Fax: (1) 613 545 6122
E-mail: godlewsk@qsilver.queensu.ca

History of Napoleonic mapping; history of geographic thought; mapping, geography and imperialism; mapping and literature

'Jomard, the geographic imagination and the first great facsimile atlases', in Joan Winearls (ed), *Editing Early and Historical Atlases* (Toronto: University of Toronto Press, 1995), 109-135.

'Map, text and image. The mentality of enlightened conquerors: a new look at the Description de l'Egypte' *Transactions of the Institute of British Geographers* 20:1 (1995): 5-28.

'The fascination of Jesuit cartography', in *Jesuit Encounters in the New World* (Rome: Jesuit Historical Institute 'Bibliotheca Instituti Historici S.I.' series, 1997).

'The idea of the map', in Susan Hanson (ed), *Geographical Ideas That Have Changed the World* (New Brunswick, N.J.: Rutgers University Press, 1997), 15-39.

GOEBL, Hans (Prof)
Institut für Romanistik
Universität Salzburg
Akademiestrasse 24
A-5020 SALZBURG
Austria
Tel: (43) 662 8044 4450

Linguistic maps (ie, maps showing the distribution of lesser used languages); reprints of old linguistic maps

GOFFART, Walter A. (Prof)
Department of History
University of Toronto
TORONTO, Ontario M5S 3G3
Canada
Tel: (1) 416 978 8468
Fax: (1) 416 978 4810
E-mail: w.goffart@utoronto.ca

Historical atlases; maps to illustrate history

'The map of the barbarian invasions: a longer look', in Marc A. Meyer (ed), *The Culture of Christendom: Essays in Medieval History in Commemoration of Denis L. T. Bethell* (London: Hambledon Press, 1993), 1-27.

'Breaking the Ortelian pattern: historical atlases with a new program, 1747-1830', in Joan Winearls (ed), *Editing Early and Historical Atlases, Papers Given at the Twenty-Ninth Conference on Editorial Problems, University of Toronto, 5-6 November 1993* (Toronto: University of Toronto Press, 1995), 49-81.

'The first venture into "medieval geography": Lambarde's map of the Saxon Heptarchy (1568)', in Jane Roberts and Janet L. Nelson (eds), *Alfred the Wise, Festschrift for Janet Bately* (Woodbridge, Suffolk, 1997), 53-60.

'What's wrong with the map of the barbarian invasions?' in Susan J. Ridyard and Robert G. Benson (eds), *Minorities and Barbarian in Medieval Life* (Sewanee, Tennessee: University of the South Press, 1997), 159-177.

GOGATE Prasad P.
Department of Geography
University of Mumbai
VIDYANAGARI, Mumbai 400098
India
Tel: (91) 22 811 8016

Indigenous maps of India

(with B. Arunachalam), 'Area maps in Maratha cartography: a study in native maps of Western India', *Imago Mundi*, **50** (1998): 126-140.

GOLASKI, Janusz (Prof Dr)
Katedra Geodezji Akademii Rolniczej
ul. Wojska Polskiego 71f
60-625 POZNAŃ
Poland
Tel: (48) 61 487 778

Land-use changes during the last two centuries; genesis of cartographic forms of topographic information and its connection with non-cartographic forms (written documents and painted landscapes)

GOLE, Susan
3 Aylesbury Road
Wing
LEIGHTON BUZZARD LU7 0PD
UK
Tel: (44) 01296 681071
Fax: (44) 01296 682671

India: indigenous cartography

'I went to Hondius's shop to buy some maps', *IMCoS Journal* 61 (1995): 19, 21, 23, 25, 27.

Cyprus on the Table: Maps of Cyprus in British Government Papers 1878-1920 (Nicosia: Bank of Cyprus Cultural Foundation, 1996).

Maps of the Mediterranean Region Published in British Parliamentary Papers 1801-1921 (Nicosia: Bank of Cyprus Cultural Foundation, 1996).

'When we get there: Bombay in early maps', in Pauline Rohatgi et al (eds), *Bombay to Mumbai: Changing Perspectives* (Mumbai: Marg Publications, 1997), 20-39.

GÓMEZ GÓMEZ, Antonio Agustín
Biblioteca Publica Provincial de
    Huelva
C/ Duque de la Victoria, 23
HUELVA 21.001
Spain
Tel: (34) 959 24 72 62
Fax: (34) 959 25 04 69
E-mail: antonio.gomez1@sauce.pntic.mec.es

Manuscripts maps and plans in the high lawcourt of the Real Chancilleria de Granada (18th-19th centuries)

GOODRICH, Thomas D.
    (Prof Emeritus)
History Department
Indiana University of Pennsylvania
INDIANA, PA 15705-1087
USA
Tel: (1) 724 357 2284 (office)   (1) 724 463 7935 (home)
Fax: (1) 724 357 6478 (office)
E-mail: goodrich@grove.iup.edu

Ottoman maps

'Early Islamic and Ottoman maps at Yale', *Yale University Library Gazette* **72** (1997): 27-40.

'Eureka! A scholar shares an Ottoman cartographic high', *Mercator's World* **2**:3 (1997): 26-31.

GOODWIN, Katherine R.
Special Collections Division
University of Texas at Arlington
    Libraries
P O Box 19497
ARLINGTON, Texas 76019-0497
USA
Tel: (1) 817 273 3393
Fax: (1) 817 794 5797
E-mail: goodwin@library.uta.edu

Texas cartography and cartobibliography from 1492 to 1900; 19th-century railroad maps of the western United States; promotional maps of the United States

GOREN, Haim (Dr)
Tel-Hai Academic College
UPPER GALILEE 12210
Israel
Tel: (972) 6 690 0858 (office)
     (972) 6 693 8665 (home)
Fax: (972) 6 690 2019 / 690 0856
     (972) 6 693 5625 (home)
E-mail: goren@telhai.ac.il

19th-century cartography of Israel's seashores and lakes; Heinrich Kiepert in the Holy Land, 1870; international cooperation in early Holy-Land cartography; Frederick H. Robe's map of the sources of the Jordan; Charles Gaillardot's map of the Ledja

'Titus Tobler's legacy: two sources', *Bulletin of the Anglo-Israel Archaeological Society* 14 (1994-95): 57-62.

'An imaginary European concept of Jerusalem in a late sixteenth-century model', *Palestine Exploration Quarterly* 127 (1995): 106-121.

(with Rehav Rubin), 'Conrad Schick's models of Jerusalem and its monuments', *Palestine Exploration Quarterly* 128 (1996): 103-124.

GOSS Josephus Johannes Sydney
Sanders of Oxford
104 High Street
OXFORD OX1 4BW
UK
Tel: (44) 01865 242590
Fax: (44) 01865 721748
E-mail: info@sanders_oxford.co.uk

Cartobibliography; atlas publications; Oxford town plans, 16th-20th centuries

Blaeu's the Grand Atlas of the 17th Century World (2nd ed; London, 1997).

GOW, Andrew Colin (Prof Dr)
Department of History and Classics
2-28 Tory Bldg.
University of Alberta
EDMONTON, AB T6G 2H4
Canada
Tel: (10 403 492 0853; message x3270 (office)
     (1) 403 439 5071 (home)
Fax: (1) 403 492 9125
E-mail: andrew.gow@ualberta.ca

Legendary peoples on world maps; cosmographical maps; Vienna-Klosterneuberg school; Fra Mauro's mappamundi

'Gog and Magog on mappaemundi and early printed maps: orientalizing ethnography in the apocalyptic tradition', *Journal of Early Modern History* 2:1 (1998): 1-28.

'Kartenrand, Gesellschaftsrand, Geschichtsrand: Die legendären judei clausi/inclusi auf mittlelalterlichen und frühneuzeitlichen Weltkarten', in Helwig Schmidt-Glinzer (ed), *Fördern und Bewahren. Studien zur europäischen Kulturgeschichte der Frühen Neuzeit* (Wolfenbütteler Forschungen, 70; Wiesbaden: Harrassowitz, 1996), 137-155.

(with Jolanta Pekacz), Mappaemundi and Early World Maps, 1200-1500: A Bibliography of Historical Scholarship (MapHist [1997] and on CD-ROM by MapHist [1998 archive]). Available in part via website: http://www.ualberta.ca/~agow/index.html

GRABOWSKI, Piotr
Map Curator, Scientific Library
W. Kętrzyński's Research Institute
Partyzantow 87
10-402 OLSZTYN
Poland
Tel: (48) 089 527 66 18 (office)
     (48) 089 523 50 09 (home)
Fax: (48) 089 527 66 19

East Prussian maps, atlases, cartographic materials, 16th to 20th centuries; cartobibliography of East Prussia; cartographical materials in the Archbishops' and State Archives in Olsztyn

'Obraz terytorium Prus Wschodnich w kartografii XVI-XX wiek.' [Picture of the territory of East Prussia in cartography between 16th and 20th centuries], [*History of Cartography*] 8:10 (1995): 19-49.

'Prezentacja zbioru kartograficznego w Ośrodku Badań Naukowych im W. Kętrzyńskiego w Olsztynie' [Cartographic collection at the Kętrzyński's Research Centre in Olsztyn, against the background of the general resources thereof', [*Proceedings from the 16th All-Polish Conference of the Historians of Cartography – 1995 Olsztyn*] 8:11 (1995): 129-139.

'Ziemie dawnych Prus Wschodnich w Kartografii' [Territory of the ancient East Prussia in cartography], in [*From the History of Cartography*], vol. 8 (Olsztyn, 1997).

GREEN, David Richard
Centre for Remote Sensing and
    Mapping Science (CRSMS)
Department of Geography
University of Aberdeen
Elphinstone Road
ABERDEEN AB9 3UF
UK
Tel: (44) 01224 272324
Fax: (44) 01224 272331
E-mail: d.r.green@abdn.ac.uk
Web: http://www.abdn.ac.uk/geospatial

Applications of computer
technology to map study;
journalistic cartography;
map design, colour; marine
cartography

GREINER, Piotr (Dr)
Institut Historii
Uniwersytet Śląski
ul. Bankowa 11
PL-40007 KATOWICE
Poland
Tel: (48) 32 580 412 (office)   (48) 32 254 6013 (home)
E-mail: greinerp@saba.wns.us.edu.pl

The history of official
multi-scale cartography in
Silesia (to 1945)

'Kartographische Quellen zur Geschichte der oberschlesischen
Städte bis zum Ende des 18. Jahrhunderts' [Cartographic sources
for the history of the towns in Upper Silesia to the end of the 18th
century], in Thomas Wünsch (ed), *Stadtgeschichte Oberschlesiens.
Studien zur städtischen Entwicklung und Kultur einer ostmitteleuropäischen Region vom Mettelalter bis zum Vorabend der Industrialisierung*
(Berlin: Gebr. Mann Verlag, 1995), 239-252.

'Stadtpläne von Oppeln (bis 1945). Plany miasta Opola (do 1945
roku)' [Town plans of Opole/Oppein], in Peter Mrass (ed),
*Oppeln/Opole. Stadtpläne, graphische Ansichten, Fotografien (bis 1945).
Plany miasta, widoki graficzne, fotografie (do 1945 roku)* (Opole,
Ratingen-Hösel: Oberschlesische Landesmuseum, Muzeum Śląska
Opolskiego, 1995), 9-23.

'Dwie serie planów miast górnośląskich z połowy XVIII wieku'
[Two series of town plans of Upper Silesian towns from the middle
of the 18th century], in Idzi Panic (ed), *Ojczyzna Wielka i Mała
Księga pamiątkowa wydana z okazji 40-lecia PTH Oddział Cieszyn*
(Cieszyn: Polskie Towarzystwo Historyczne, Oddział w Cieszynie,
1996), 94-98.

'Militär-Topographische Karte Preussens – analiza na przykładzie

sekcji z obszaru Górnego Śląska z lat 1824-1928' [Militär-
Topographische Karte Preussens: analysis on the basis of the sections from Upper Silesia 1824-1928], in Stanisław Alexandrowicz,
et al (eds), *Kartografia wojskowa krajów strefy bałtyckiej XVI-XX w.*
(Toruń: Uniwersytet Mikołaja Kopernika w Toruniu, 1996), 119-
124.

(with Roland Banduch), 'Plany miasta Katowic (do 1945 roku)'
[Town plans of Katowice (til 1945)], *Kronika Katowic* 6 (1996):
107-117.

(with Roland Banduch), Źródła kartograficzne do dziejów
Wielkich Hajduk (do 1939 r.)' [Cartographic sources for the history of Wielkie Hajduki (til 1939)], in Jacek Kurek (ed), *Z dziejów
tradycji, historii i kultury Wielkich Hajduk. Materiały z sesji popularnonaukowej 4-5 października 1995 r* (Chorzów: Miejski Dom Kultury
'Batory', 1996), 47-52.

*Kartografia górnicza na Śląsku od XVI do pierwszej połowy XIX wieku.
Zarys historyczny, katalog map, bibliografia* [Mining cartography in
Silesia from the 16th century to the first half of the 19th.
Historical sketch, map catalogue, bibliography] (Wrocław:
Centrum Badań Śląskoznawczych i Bohemistycznych, Uniwersytet
Wrocławski, 1997).

GRIFFITHS, Ieuan
School of African and Asian Studies
University of Sussex
FALMER, BRIGHTON BN1 9QN
UK
Tel: (44) 01273 606 755

African political boundaries
and maps

GRIM, Ronald E. (Dr)
Specialist in Cartographic History
Geography and Map Division
Library of Congress
WASHINGTON, DC 20540-4650
USA
Tel: (1) 202 707 8532 (office)
        (1) 301 596 2354 (home)
Fax: (1) 202 707 8531
E-mail: rgrim@loc.gov

United States landowner-
ship maps and US General
Land Office records, 17th
to 19th centuries; immi-
grant and ethnic settlement
patterns in 18th and 19th
century Virginia; place-
names; the Mullan Road
and Gustavus Sohon

(with John A. Wolter, ed), *Images of the World: The Atlas through
History* (Washington, DC: Library of Congress; New York:

INTERNATIONAL
MAP COLLECTORS' SOCIETY

The society for people who like maps

~

UK and international meetings,

Quarterly Journal,

Visits to famous map collections,

Largest annual international map fair

~

Contacts

Membership Secretary
Samantha Pearce
7 East Park Street, Chatteris, Cambridge PE16 6LA, UK
Tel: +44 (0) 1354 692023   Fax: +44 (0) 1354 692697

Chairman
Jenny Harvey
E-mail: jeh@harvey27.demon.co.uk

Web site
http://www.harvey27.demon.co.uk/imcos/

McGraw-Hill, 1996).

(with Paul D. McDermott), 'The mapmaker as artist', *Mercator's World* 1:1 (1996): 28-33.

GRÓF, László
3 Oxford Military College
Temple Cowley
OXFORD OX4 2UG
UK
Tel & fax: (44) 01865 771477

Maps of Hungary, especially by Ortelius; Hungarian surveyors and cartographers; Oxfordshire, 18th-century

'Marsigli gróf élete' [The life of Count Marsigli], *Cartographica Hungarica* 5 (1996): 12-17.

'Maps of Hungary in the Ortelius atlases 1570-1612'. *IMCoS Journal* 72 (1998): 7-18.

GRUBER, Mayer Irwin (Dr)
Deptartment of Bible & Ancient
    Near East
Ben-Gurion University
P.O. Box 653
BEERSHEVA
Israel
Tel: (972) 7 646 1015
Fax: (972) 7 647 2913
E-mail: gruber@bgumail.bgu.ac.il

Maps in ancient Near Eastern and biblical texts; maps in ancient and medieval commentaries on those texts

GUNASENA, Diana Patricia
    Huntingdon
70 Kenilworth Court
Lower Richmond Road
LONDON SW15 1EN
UK
Tel: (44) 0181 788 0730

Early 17th century cartographers and land surveyors

GUTHORN, Peter Jay
514 North Lakeside Drive
LAKE WORTH, Florida 33460
USA
Tel: (1) 407 588 1565

Mapping of the American Revolutionary War; 18th and 19th century charting of the US coastal waters

HABEL, Rudolf (Dr-Ing)
Gartenstrasse 40
D-99867 GOTHA
Germany

Structure and contents of world atlases, 17th to first half of the 20th century

HADSEL, Fred Latimer
106 White Street
LEXINGTON, Virginia 24450
USA
Tel: (1) 703 463 5767

History of the map of Africa, 15th to 19th centuries

HAFT, Adele J.
Department of Classical and
    Oriental Studies
Hunter College, City University of
    New York
695 Park Avenue
NEW YORK, NY 10021
USA
Tel: (1) 212 772 5063 (office)   (1) 718 852 2699 (home)
E-mail: ahaft@shiva.hunter.cuny.edu

Maps in poetry, especially 20th-century poetry in English

'Maps, mazes, and monsters: the iconography of the library in Umberto Eco's *The Name of the Rose*', *Studies in Iconography* 14 (1995): 9-50.

HAMELEERS, Marc (Drs)
Municipal Archives
P.O. Box 51140
1007 EC AMSTERDAM
Netherlands
Tel: (31) 20 572 0300 (office)   (31) 346 561 428 (home)
Fax: (31) 20 675 0596

Maps of Amsterdam; Dutch polder mapping; teaching, curatorship, theory

(with Erik Schmitz), 'Amsterdamse uitgiftekaarten, 1586-1769' [Amsterdam lot-issue plans], *Amstelodamum 1996* **88**te Jaarboek (1997): 44-64.

'De muurkaart op het huis van "de bakker op de hoek" met de weg naar het Amsterdamse kledingmagazijn Oostmeijer' [The wall map painted on the house of 'the bakery at the corner' with the route to the Oostmeijer clothing shop], *Caert-Thresoor* 16:3 (1997): 61-65.

HANLE, Adolf (Prof Dr)
Mozartsr. 7
D-68549 ILVESHEIM
Germany
Tel: (49) 0621 494 523

19th-century atlas cartography; cartography of the Bibliographisches Institut AG; Nicolaus Cusanus

HANNAH, Robert
Department of Classics
University of Otago
P.O. Box 56
DUNEDIN
New Zealand
Tel: (64) 3 479 8711
Fax: (64) 3 479 9029
E-mail: robert.hannah@stonebow.otago.ac.nz

Mappaemundi; early celestial charts; iconography of Greek and Roman constellations; early navigation

'The image of Cautes and Cautopates in the Mithraic tauroctony icon', in *Religion in the Ancient World: New Themes and Approaches* (Amsterdam: Hakkert, 1996), 177-192.

'Is it a bird? Is it a star? Ovid's kite and the first swallow of spring', *Latomus: Revue d'Etudes Latines* **56** (1997): 327-342.

'Odysseus's navigation', *Prudentia* **29** (1997); 15-33.

'The tethering of Meskhetiu', *Göttingen Miszellen* **160** (1997): 33-39.

HARVEY, Paul D.A. (Prof)
Lyndhurst
Farnley Hey Road
DURHAM DH1 4EA
UK
Tel: (44) 0191 386 9396

Medieval local and regional maps from Europe and Palestine

'Cartography and its written sources', in F.A.C. Mantello and A.G. Rigg (eds), *Medieval Latin: An Introduction and Bibliographical Guide* (Washington, D.C.: Catholic University of America Press, 1996), 386-394.

'English estate maps: their early history and their use as historical evidence', in D. Buisseret (ed), *Rural Images: Estate Maps in the Old and New Worlds* (Chicago: University of Chicago Press, 1996), 27-61.

Mappa Mundi: The Hereford World Map (London: Hereford Cathedral and British Library; Toronto: Toronto University Press, 1996).

'The Sawley map and other world maps in twelfth-century England', *Imago Mundi* **49** (1997): 33-42.

'The thirteenth-century map of the world in Hereford Cathedral', *Israeli Map Collectors' Society Journal* **15** (1997): 1-6.

HASEGAWA, Koji (Prof)
Institute of Letters
Faculty of Letters
Kobe University
1-1, Rokkodai-cho, Nada-ku
KOBE 657
Japan
Tel: (81) 78 803 0474 (office)   (81) 6 971 3814 (home)
Fax: (81) 78 803 0486 (office)   (81) 6 971 3814 (home)

Social history of atlases (16th-17th centuries); history of disaster maps; British cartography (16th-17th centuries)

'Ortelius *Sekai no Butai* timei taiso hyo N.V.V.' [List of ancient and modern place-names in Ortelius's Theatrum Orbis Terrarum], *The Kobe City University Journal* **45**:4,5,6 (1994): 71-91, 71-96, 83-104.

'Mercator's Atlas no sougo-teki kenkyu' [Comprehensive studies on Mercator's Atlas], *Annals of Fukutake Science and Culture Foundation* (1996): 120-124.

Kindai Chizu-Cho no Tenjo [The birth of the modern atlas: Translation of C. Koeman's The History of Abraham Ortelius and His Theatrum Orbis Terrarum] (Kyoto: Rinsen Shoten, 1997).

HATANO, Masataka
1-23-302, Minami 4-Nishi 25
Chuo-ku
SAPPORO 064
Japan

Spatial perception in historical ages and regional reconstruction

HÉBERT, John R. (Dr)
Hispanic Division
Library of Congress
WASHINGTON, DC, 20540
USA
Tel: (1) 202 707 1992 (office)
     (1) 703 978 1553 (home)
Fax: (1) 202 707 2005
E-mail: jheb@loc.gov

Spanish colonial maps; Spanish hydrographic charts, 1715-1820; D. Gutiérrez's map of America 1562; Vicente S. Pintado, Spanish surveyor-general, Spanish West Florida, 1806-1817

(editor), *The 1531 Huexotzinco Codex* (Washington: Library of Congress; Mexico: Ediciones de Multiarte, 1995).

Library of Congress Hispanic and Portuguese Collections, An Illustrated Guide (Washington: Library of Congress, 1996).

'Rare Book and Special Collections Division' and 'Early Contacts with Europeans', in *Many Nations: A Library of Congress Resource Guide for the Study of Indian and Alaska Native Peoples in the United States* (Washington: Library of Congress, 1996), 35-71.

(with Abby Forgang), 'Small particulars: variant titles and dates to the manuscript of Fray Diego Durán', *The Americas* (Winter 1997).

HEIDENREICH, Conrad E.
Department of Geography
York University
4700 Keele Street
TORONTO, Ontario M3J 1P3
Canada
Tel: (1) 416 736 5107
Fax: (1) 416 736 5735
E-mail: cheidenr@yorku.ca

Mapping of Canada, 1500-1800

HEIJDEN, Henk A.M. van der (Dr)
Lange Reen 2
NL-5524 AJ STEENSEL
Netherlands
Tel: (31) 0497 514 637

Maps of the Netherlands in the French period, 1795-1815

'The development of cartography in the Low Countries', *IMCoS Journal* 51 (1994): 6-10.

'Atlas Iprensis, 1570-1639', *Caert-Thresoor* no 2 (1995): 25-34.

'Kaart als Kunst' [Map as a product of art], *Caert-Thresoor*, no 4 (1995): 77-84.

'De minuutkaart van Middelburg in Vlaanderen van Jacob van Deventer teruggevonden' [The original map of Middelburg in Flanders by Jacob van Deventer found again], *Caert-Thresoor*, no 4 (1996): 107-108.

'Het oudste kaartje van het Hertogdom Brabant?' [The oldest map of the Duchy of Brabant?], *Caert-Thresoor*, 16:3 (1997): 67-69.

'Een Spaans lesje in Nederlandse historische kartografie' [A Spanish lesson in Dutch history of cartography], *Caert-Thresoor* 16:2 (1997): 42-43.

'Heinrich Bünting's Itinerarium Sacrae Scripturae, 1581: a chapter in the geography of the Bible', *Quaerendo* 28:4 (1998): 1-23.

Old Maps of the Netherlands, 1548-1598 (Utrecht 1998).

HEINZ, Markus
Malplaquetstrasse 7
D-13347 BERLIN
Germany
E-mail:
markus.heinz@sbb.spk-berlin.de

Catalogue and analysis of the maps published by J.B. Homann, Homann Heirs and Fembo (Nuremberg, 1702-1852); atlas history, history of copperplate printing

'Die Atlanten der süddeutschen Verlag Homann und Seutter (18. Jahrhundert)', in Hans Wolff (ed), *400 Jahre Mercator, 400 Jahre Atlas* (Bayerische Staatsbibliothek München, Aussfellungskatalog 65; Wissenhorn: Anton H Conrad, 1995), 81-94.

(with Elisabeth Zeilinger), 'Ordnung auf der Kugel? Die Abfolge von Karten in Atlanten (16.-18. Jahrhundert)', in W. Scharfe (ed), *Gerhard Mercator und seine Zeit. 7. Kartographiehistorisches Colloquium Duisburg 1994* (Duisburg: Braun, 1996), 217-223.

'A programme for map publishing: the Homann firm in the eighteenth century', *Imago Mundi* 49 (1997): 104-115.

HELGERSON, Richard (Prof)
Department of English
University of California
SANTA BARBARA, CA 93106
USA
Tel: (1) 805 893 2988 (office)
    (1) 805 965 2628 (home)
Fax: (1) 805 893 4622
E-mail:
rhelgers@humanitas.ucsb.edu

Maps and contemptus mundi in early modern Europe; maps in 17th-century Dutch genre painting; literature and geography (special issue of the on-line journal *Early Modern Literary Studies* [EMLS] – co-edited with Joanne Woolway)

'Soldiers and enigmatic girls: the politics of Dutch domestic realism, 1650-1672', *Representations* 58 (1997): 49-87.

HELLWIG, Fritz (Dr)
Klosterbergstrasse 117c
D-53117 BONN 2
Germany
Tel: (49) 0228 322 017

Functional cartography (history of trade and traffic, hydrography); Italian mapmakers of 16th and 17th centuries

HERBERT, Francis
Curator of Maps
Royal Geographical Society
1 Kensington Gore
LONDON SW7 2AR
UK
Tel: (44) 0171 591 3050
Fax: (44) 0171 591 3001
E-mail: f.herbert@rgs.org

Census of extant cartographic wood-blocks, copper-plates, and lithographic stones; subscribers lists to cartographic products; firms of Arrowsmith (Aaron, Samuel, John) and Stanford (Edward and William); Lt-Col Sir William Thorn (ie, Grossbritannischer Obristleutnant Wilhelm Thorn)

'Imago Mundi bibliography', *Imago Mundi* 47 (1995): 209-225; **48** (1996): 236-261; 49 (1997): 199-227; **50** (1998): 232-269.

HERNANDO, Agustín (Prof Dr)
Geography Department
Faculty of Geography and History
University of Barcelona
08026 BARCELONA
Spain
E-mail: agustin@trivium.gh.ub.es

Cartography of Spain and the regions of Spain; atlases produced in Spain or for Spanish people

'Los cosmografos de la Casa de Contratación y la cartografía de Andalucía', in *Miscelanea geográfico en homenaje al Profesor Luis Gil Varon* (Córdoba: Servicio de Publicaciones de la Universidad de Córdoba, 1994), 125-143.

'La cartografia Mallorquina de la Baixa Edat Mitjana', in Agustín Hernando et al, *Cartografia Mallorquina* (Barcelona: Diputació de Barcelona, 1995), 11-69.

El mapa de España, siglos XV-XVIII (Madrid: Instituto Geográfico Nacional, Ministerio de Fomento, 1995).

La imagen de un país. Juan Bautista Labaña y su mapa de Aragón (1610-1620) (Zaragoza: Institución Fernando el Católico, 1996).

HERTERICK, E.J.
141 Pale Ivy Lane
IRMO, South Carolina 29063
USA
Tel: (1) 803 781 4366

Early American road maps; cartography and the American automobile

HILL, Sharon L.
American Geographical Society Collection
Golda Meir Library
University of Wisconsin-Milwaukee
P.O. Box 399
MILWAUKEE, WI 53201
USA
Tel: (1) 414 229 6282 (office)
Fax: (1) 414 229 3524
E-mail: slh@gml.uwm.edu

Map samplers of Great Britain; Bible maps/pilgrimage maps; travel patterns of Amish people

(1) 414 291 9800 (home)

HILLS, Helen (Dr)
Department of Art History & Archaeology
University of Manchester
Oxford Rd.
MANCHESTER, M13 9PL
UK
Tel: (44) 0161 275 3318 (office)
    (44) 01457 766534 (home)
Fax: (44) 0161 275 3331
E-mail: h.m.hills@.man.ac.uk

Images of the city in southern Italy in the early modern period; cartography of Palermo and Naples; cartographic images used in festivals in Italian cities; cartographic images used in conjunction with patron saints; Italian cities of 17th and 18th centuries

'Mapping the early modern city', *Urban History* 23:2 (1996):145-162.

HILLS, Richard Leslie (Rev Dr)
Stamford Cottage
47 Old Road
MOTTRAM, Hyde
Cheshire SK14 6LW
UK
Tel: (44) 01457 763104

James Watt, 1736-1819

'James Watt at Campbeltown', *Kintyre Antiquarian and Natural History Society Magazine* 41 (1997): 3-8; 42 (1997): 3-8.

'John Watt's map of the Clyde', *Notes and Records of the Royal Society* (January 1998).

HINDLE, Brian Paul (Dr)
Department of Geography
University of Salford
SALFORD M5 4WT
UK
Tel: (44) 0161 295 5000
Fax: (44) 0161 295 5015
E-mail: b.p.hindle@geography.salford.ac.uk

Maps as evidence of British landscape change; depiction of roads and rights of way on maps

HODSON, Arundel Yolande (Dr)
16 Hertford Road
TEWIN, Herts. AL6 0JY
UK
Tel & fax: (44) 01438 717825

Preparation of a catalogue raisonné of King George III's military maps in the Royal Collection; Ordnance Survey maps and plans; mapping of Palestine in the 19th century

(with Alan Gordon), *An Illustrated History of 250 Years of Military Survey* (London: Military Survey Defence Agency, 1997).

'Mapping it out: in the field with the PEF surveyors', *ERETZ: The Geographical Magazine from Israel* 52 (1997): 43-50.

HODSON, Donald
16 Hertford Road
TEWIN, Herts. AL6 0JY
UK
Tel & fax: (44) 01438 717825

Road-books and itineraries of England and Wales to 1850

County Atlases of the British Isles Published after 1703. Vol III: *Atlases Published 1764-1789 and Their Subsequent Editions* (London: The British Library, 1997).

HOFMANN, Catherine
Map Curator
Département des cartes et plans
Bibliothèque National de France
58, rue de Richelieu
75002 PARIS
France
Tel: (33) 01 47 03 83 59 (office)
Fax: (33) 01 47 03 83 61
E-mail: catherine.hofmann@bnf.fr

French cartographical editions in the 18th century; cartography as the 'eye of history'

(33) 01 47 00 38 58 (home)

(with Ève Netchine), 'Connaissance du monde, vanité du monde: le globe, image du savoir, image de la Création (XVIe-XVIIIe siècle)', in D. Lecocq, E. Netchine, M. Pelletier, *Le Globe et son image* (Paris: Bibliothèque nationale de France, 1995), 49-69.

'Un géographie sur les traces du mythe grec: Jean-Denis Barbié du Bocage (1760-1825)', in Christian Huetz de Lemps (ed), *La Découverte géographique à travers le livre et la cartographie* (Bordeaux: Société des bibliophiles de Guyenne, 1997), 135-154.

HÖHENER, Hans-Peter (Dr)
Zentralbibliothek Zürich
Kartensammlung
Zähringerplatz 6
CH-8025 ZÜRICH
Switzerland
Tel: (41) 1 268 3100 (office)
(41) 1 482 8432 (home)
Fax: (41) 1 286 3290
E-mail: hoehener@zb.unizh.ch

History of cartography of Switzerland

(41) 1 268 3165 (direct)

(with A. Dürst, H.-U. Feldmann and M. Oehrli), *Die Ostschweiz im Bild der Frühen Kartenmacher: Karten und Vermessungsinstrumente aus fünf Jahrhunderten* (Murten: Verlag Cartographica Helvetica, 1994).

'La Suisse', in *Gérard Mercator cosmographe, le temps et l'espace* (Antwerp: Fond Mercator Paribas, 1994), 361-367.

'Zur Geschichte der Kartendokumentation in der Schweiz', in Joachim Neumann (ed), *Karten hüten und bewahren: Festgabe für Lothar Zögner* (*Kartensammlung und Kartendokumentation* 11; Gotha: Verlag Justus Perthes, 1995), 57-66.

*d'***HOLLANDER**, Raymond
Association française de Topographie
13 Avenue Emile Laurent
75012 PARIS
France
Tel: (331) 46 28 34 60

Geographical sciences in antiquity and in the Muslim world; history of the loxodrome; history of cartography at IGN-Institut géographique (1940-1990)

HOLLÓ, Szilvia Andrea (Dr)   City maps in Europe
Map Curator
Kiscelli Muzeum-Budapest History Museum
Kiscelli Utca 108
1037 BUDAPEST
Hungary
Tel: (36) 1 250 0304 (office)   (36) 1 332 9868 (home)
Fax: (36) 1 368 7917 (office)
E-mail: h13455hol@ella.hu

'Collections of early maps in Hungary', *IMCoS Journal* 71 (1997): 10-14.

HOLZHEIMER, Arthur
1145 Lincoln Avenue South
HIGHLAND PARK, Illinois 60035
USA
Tel: (1) 312 255 3711 (office)
      (1) 847 433 1129 (home)
E-mail: janart-maps@worldnet.att.net

Maps of the world and North America to 1700; 19th-century maps of the trans-Mississippi West, discovery and exploration

HOLZER, Gerhard (Mag)
Librarian, Österreichische Akademie
      der Wissenschaften
Kommission für Geschichte der
      Naturwissenschaften
Postgasse 7-9 /St 1
1010 WIEN
Austria
Tel: (43) 0222 51581 400 (office)   (43) 0222 280 9450 (home)

Maps of New Zealand; routes on old maps (to 1900)

Cartographic Rarities of the Woldan Collection (Vienna: Austrian Academy of Sciences, 1995). [Exhibition catalogue.]

'Österreichische Akademie der Wissenschaften: Bibliothek der Kommission für Geschichte der Mathematik, Naturwissesnchaften und Medizin', in Helmut W. Lang (ed), *Handbuch der historischen Buchbestände in Österreich* (Hildesheim: Gerog Olims Verlag, 1995).

(editor), *Sammlung Woldan: Bestandskatalog, Abteilung A: Cartographica*: Teil I: *Gesamte Erde und Außereuropa* (Veröffentlichungen der Kommission für Geschichte der Mathematik, Naturwissenschaften und Mediziin, 50; Wien: Österreiche Akademie der Wissenschaften, 1995).

HOOK, Colin M. (Dr)
5 Hendriks Court
HIGHTON, Victoria 3216
Australia
Tel: (61) 3 5243 7075
E-mail: colin@deakin.edu.au

Italian town maps and views; urban cartography of the Renaissance; art and cartography

'Renaissance man and artist: figures of ambiguity and ambivalence', *Exedra* 6:2 (1995): 38-43.

HOOKER, Brian
9 Amorino Drive
Red Beach, OREWA
New Zealand
Fax: (64) 09 42 6497

New Zealand printed maps by James Wyld; a catalogue of New Zealand printed maps to 1840; cartographical aspects of Tasman's voyage 1642-1643

'La carte du monde de W.J. Blaeu of 1604', *Mappemonde* (Montpellier, 1997), 4: 5-8.

'Raphael Clint's map of Auckland, 1839', *Auckland-Waikato Historical Journal* 69 (April 1997): 37-39.

'In the name of the son', *Mercator's World* 3:4 (1998): 44-49.

HOPKINS, Daniel P.
Department of Geosciences
University of Missouri-Kansas City
KANSAS CITY, MO 64110
USA
Tel: (1) 816 822 0274
E-mail: dhopkins@cctr.umkc.edu

Danish colonial mapping

HORNER, Arnold (Dr)
Department of Geography
University College Dublin
Belfield
DUBLIN 4
Ireland
Tel: (353) 1 706 8382
Fax: (353) 1 269 5597

Thematic mapping in Ireland; cartographical responses to partition in Ireland, 1920-1930; the land capability maps of Sir Robert Kane (1809-1890)

HOROWITZ, Wayne B. (Dr)
Department of Assyriology
Hebrew University
Mount Scopus
JERUSALEM
Israel
Tel: (972) 02 881181

Ancient Mesopotamian cartography, geography, astronomy

HOU Renzhi (Prof)
Institute of Historical Geography
Peking University
100871 BEIJING
China
Tel: (86) 1 250 2602
Fax: (86) 1 256 4095

History of Chinese cartography and geographical thought; historical atlas of Beijing

†HOWSE, Humphrey Derek (Cdr)
12 Barnfield Road
Riverhead
SEVENOAKS, Kent TN13 2AY
UK

Sea charts and navigation

Greenwich Time and the Longitude (London: Philip Wilson, 1997).

HRENKÓ, Pál
Alkotás u. 25.3ep. V/38
BUDAPEST H 1123
Hungary
Tel: (36) 1 563785

Hungarian maps, mapping history, biography

'A *Hármas Kis Tükör* téképei' [Maps of "Tripartition Little Mirror"], *Geodézia és Kartográfia* (Budapest), 48:3 (1996): 25-29; and *Cartographica Hungarica* 5 (1996): 22-29.

'Térképészetünk millecentenáris tükre' [Surveying and mapping highlights of Hungary's 11 centuries], *Geodézia és Kartográfia* 48:8 (1996): 19-25.

HSU, Mei-Ling (Prof Dr)
Department of Geography
University of Minnesota
414 Social Science Building
267 19th Avenue South
MINNEAPOLIS, MN 55455
USA
Tel: (1) 612 625 7375
Fax: (1) 612 624 1044

Chinese cartographic development; Chinese population and urban-development maps

'An inquiry into early Chinese atlases through the Ming Dynasty', in John A. Wolter and Ronald E. Grim (eds), *Images of the World: The Atlas through History* (New York: McGraw-Hill, 1997), 31-50.

HU, Bangbo
Department of Geography
Liberal Arts Center 304
Villanova University
VILLANOVA, Pennsylvania 19085-1699
USA
Tel: (1) 610 519 4640

Chinese administrative gazetteer maps of the Song Dynasty (960-1279)

HUBBARD, Jason Clyde
P.O. Box 338
LINCOLN, Massachusetts 01773
USA
Tel & fax: (1) 781 259 3117

European printed maps of Japan (with Lutz Walter); printed charts of the East Indies showing Japan before 1700

HUDSON, Alice
Chief, Map Division
New York Public Library
5th Avenue & 42nd Street
NEW YORK, NY 10018-2788
USA
Tel: (1) 212 930 0589 (office)
     (1) 212 222 2835 (home)
Fax: (1) 212 921 2546
E-mail: ahudson@nypl.org

John Seller; 17th and 18th century English mapping and charting of the Middle Atlantic colonies (Carolinas to New York); pre-20th-century women mapmakers; pre-20th-century New York City mapmakers; pre-20th-century maps of western North America

'The Library's Map Division goes to war, 1941-45', *The New York Public Library Biblion* 3:2 (1996): 126-147.

'Putting Appalachia on the map: or, Appalachia: its perception as a barrier on maps to 1733', *The Portolan* **40** (Fall 1997): 26-33.

'A brief history of the New York Public Library Map Division', *Meridian*, no. 13 (Spring 1998): 5-6.

'The Map Division in press: more than fifteen seconds of fame', *Meridian*, no. 13 (Spring 1998): 61-62.

HUGHES, Paul
106 High Street
AIRMYN, Yorkshire
DN14 8LB
UK

Early river ports

HÜHNEL, Helga (Dr)
Österreichische Nationalbibliothek
Kartensammlung und Globenmuseum
Josefsplatz 1
A-1015 WIEN
Austria
Tel: (43) 1 53 410 302
Fax: (43) 1 53 410 319
E-mail: helga.huehnel@onb.ac.at

Maps in travel books

(with Franz Wawrik, Jan Mokre, Elisabeth Zeilinger, eds), *Kartographische Zimelien. Die 50 schönsten Karten und Globen der Österreichischen Nationalbibliothek* (Wien: Holzhausen, 1995).

(with Johannes Dörflinger), *Österreichische Atlanten 1561-1918* (2 vols. = *Atlantes Austriaci*, 1.2; Wien: Böhlau, 1995).

'Österreichische Globenhersteller: ein biographischer Streifzug durch die Jahrhundert', in Peter E. Allmayer-Beck (ed), *Modelle der Welt. Erd- und Himmelsgloben* (Kulturerbe aus österreichen Sammlungen; Wien: Verlag Christian Brandstätter, 1997), 88-104.

HUIDEKOPER, Fay
c/o Rezayat Company Limited
P.O. Box 90
ALKHOBAR 31952
Saudi Arabia
Tel & fax: (966) 3 895 4686

Cartography of the Arabian peninsula, 15th to 19th centuries

HYDE, Ralph
Keeper of Prints & Maps
Guildhall Library
Aldermanbury
LONDON EC2P 2EJ
UK
Tel: (44) 0171 332 1864 (office)   (44) 0181 317 0525 (home)
E-mail: ralph.hyde@ms.corpoflondon.gov.uk

Prospects and panoramas of British towns; parish maps of London; town plans by John Wood

IACOVOU, Maria (Prof)
The Bank of Cyprus Cultural
    Foundation
P.O. Box 1995
1515 NICOSIA
Cyprus
Tel: (357) 2 467 134 (office)   (357) 2 780 475 (home)
Fax: (357) 2 472 898
E-mail: info@cultural.bankofcyprus.com

History of cartography of Cyprus; map collection of the Cultural Foundation of the Bank of Cyprus

'The map collections of the Bank of Cyprus Cultural Foundation', *The Map Collector* **71** (1995): 2-7.

16th Century Rare Maps of Cyprus: Twelve Facsimiles from the Map Collection of the Bank of Cyprus Cultural Foundation (2nd ed; Nicosia, 1997).

'The European cartographers of Cyprus 16th-19th c.', in Dimitra Papanicola Bakirtzi and Maria Iacovou (eds), *Byzantine Medieval Cyprus* (Nicosia, 1998), 289-293.

IBARRA GRASSO, Dick Edgar
Av. Rivadavia 2183, 7' 63
BUENOS AIRES
1034
Argentina
Tel: (54) 1 953 6087

The representation of America in pre-Columbian maps (Arabic and Roman) and the real discoveries of Columbus

INGRAM, Elizabeth Morley
1200 Brooklyn Ave
ANN ARBOR, Michigan 48104
USA
Tel: (1) 313 769 0250

Maps of the Holy Land, 16th and 17th centuries (with Catherine Delano Smith)

(with Ruth S. Luborsky, ed), *A Guide to English Illustrated Books, 1536-1603* (Tempe: Arizona Center for Medieval & Renaissance Texts & Studies, 1998).

JAATINEN, Stig (Prof Dr)
Department of Geogrphy
University of Helsinki
Brändö parkväg 42 B
00570 HELSINGFORS
Finland

History of thematic and
atlas cartography; cadastral
mapping of the 17th and
18th centuries in relation
to historical and regional
geography

JACOB, Christian
Centre Louis Gernet
10 rue Monsieur-le-Prince
75005 PARIS
France
Tel: (33) 1 44 41 46 50 (office)
Fax: (33) 1 43 31 37 22 (home)
E-mail: cjacob@ehess.fr

Ancient Greek and Roman
cartography; astronomical
maps (moon, Mars); theo-
retical approach to the history of cartography;
comparative studies in the
history of cartography

'Cartographies. Entretien avec Christian Jacob', *Les Cahiers de la Villa Médicis / Revue de l'Académie de France à Rome* 9:1 (1995): 74-83.

'L'Inde imaginaire des géographie alexandrins', in J.-C. Carrière et al, *Inde, Grèce ancienne. Regards croisés en anthropologie de l'espace* (Annales de l'Université de Besançon, 576 (Paris 1995): 61-80).

'Littérature et géographie en Grèce ancienne', in Ernst Leonardy et Hubert Roland, *Descriptions et créations d'espaces dans la littérature* (Université de Louvain-la-Neuve, *Recueil de Travaux d'Histoire et de Philologie* (1995): 11-29).

'La géographie', in J. Brunschwig et al, *Les savoirs grecs* (Paris: Flammarion, 1996), 338-351.

'Quand les cartes réfléchissent', *Espaces/Temps* **62-63** (1996): 36-49.

'Towards a cultural history of geography', *Imago Mundi* **48** (1996): 191-198.

'De la terre à la lune: les débuts de la sélénographie au XVIIe siècle', in Marie-Ange Brayer (ed), *Cartographiques* (Paris: Seuill, 1997), 9-43.

'Lieux de la carte, espace du savoir', in Philippe Antoine (ed), *Cahiers de la Villa Gillet 'Lieux ou espaces de la mémoire?'* (1997), 67-99.

'Premières géographies. Poésie, cartes et périégèse en Grèce (VIIIe-fin VIe siècle avant J.-C.)', in *Des Sumériens aux Romains d'Orient. La perception géographique du monde. Espaces et territoires au Proche-Orient*

ancien (Actes de la Table ronde du 16 novembre 1996; Paris: Jean Maisonneuve, 1997), 157-176.

JAEGER, Eckhard (Dr)
c/o Antiquariat Ruthild Jaeger
Postfach 1861
D-21308 LÜNEBURG
Germany
Fax: (49) 04131 42798

Pomerania, Mecklenburg,
Lüneburg, Baltic States

'Johannes Mellinger und die erste Landesvermessung des Fürstentums Lüneburg: ein Beitrag zur Renaissancekartographie im norddeutschen Raum', in W. Scharfe (ed), *Gerhard Mercator und seine Zeit. 7. Kartographiehistorisches Colloquium Duisburg 1994* (Duisburg: Braun, 1996), 121-136.

JANKOWSKA, Maria (Dr ing)
Katedra Geodezji Akademii Rolniczej
ul. Wojska Polskiego 71f
60-625 POZNAŃ
Poland
Tel: (48) 61 487 778

Land-use changes since
1800 on middle-scale
maps; develpment of cartographic form of topographical information and its
connection with written
documents

JARMAN, Robert
Bahrain National Museum
c/o 28 Kepplestone, Staveley Road
EASTBOURNE, East Sussex
    BN20 7JZ
UK
Tel: (44) 01323 723681

Historic maps of Bahrain,
Arabia and the
Persian/Arabian Gulf

JAVORSKY, Irene
Österreichische Nationalbibliothek
Kartensammlung
Josefsplatz 1
A-1015 WIEN
Austria
Tel: (43) 1 53 410 297
Fax: (43) 1 53 410 319

Bibliography of atlases in
the Austrian National
Library

Cartographica Helvetica

Journal on the history of cartography

Since 1990 the working group "History of Cartography" of the Swiss Society of Cartography publishes a *journal on the history of cartography* - as a means of communication between map collectors, researchers and dealers. It aims to provide information on every aspect of early maps, their history as well as production methods. These collected journals amount to a valuable reference library.

- information on present and future map facsimile projects
- reviews on books, exhibits and conferences
- information on forthcoming auctions and events
- reader's forum
- map quiz
- dealers' catalogues, market prices at auctions
- classified advertising section for map dealers and collectors on map sales and exchanges

Format of Cartographica Helvetica
56 pages, with superb illustrations, some in colour. Size: 21 x 29.7 cm (A4)

Publishing dates
The journal is published bi-annually (January and July). The first issue appeared in January 1990.

Contents of each issue
- feature articles in German, written by leading experts on various subjects of the history of cartography
- summaries in English and French

Subscription rate
Switzerland: SFr.35.-, overseas SFr.38.- (per year) Single issue: SFr.20.- Postage included

Editorial Board
Cavelti Hammer Madlena, Horw
Cavelti Alfons, Köniz
Feldmann Hans-Uli, Murten
Hohener Hans-Peter, Zürich
Klöti Thomas, Bern
Oehrli Markus, Wabern

Editor and Publisher
Verlag Cartographica Helvetica
Untere Längmatt 9,
CH-3280 Murten

World map by Oronce Fine 1536

Facsimile of the map of the Bibliothèque Nationale, Paris (BNF, Rés. Ge DD 2987[63])

Size: 59x51cm
Reproduction: 4 colour offset printing
Paper: $200g/m^2$
Documentation (German/French): 20 p. with illustration by Monique Pelletier, Paris
Price: SFr.65.-(plus shipping)

Verlag Cartographica Helvetica
Untere Längmatt 9, CH-3280 Murten

JOHNSTON, Stephen Andrew
Museum of the History of Science
Broad Street
OXFORD OX1 3AZ
UK
Tel: (44) 01865 277 283
Fax: (44) 01865 277 288
E-mail: stephen.johnston@mhs.ox.ac.uk

16th-century practical mathematics; scientific instruments

(with J.A. Bennett), *The Geometry of War, 1500-1750* (Oxford: Museum of the History of Science, 1996).

JONES, Derek Charles (Prof)
Department of Economics
Hamilton College
198 College Hill Road
CLINTON, New York 13323
USA
Tel: (1) 315 859 4381
Fax: (1) 315 859 4632
E-mail: djones@hamilton.edu

Statistical atlases and school atlases and geographies, their changing scope and nature; the economic organization of the map trade

JONES, Ieuan Evans
15 Middle Park Road
BIRMINGHAM BQ9 4BE
UK
Tel: (44) 0121 475 1710

John Blair's chronology and history of the world, 1754-1834

JOPPEN, Petrus W.A.
Paulus Swaen Old Maps & Prints
POB 129
5590 AC HEEZE
Netherlands
Tel: (31) 0495 599050
Fax: (31) 0495 599051
Email: paulus@swaen.com
Web: http://www.swaen.com

Map colourists active in the Netherlands in the 17th and 18th centuries

KAIN, Roger James Peter (Prof)
Department of Geography
University of Exeter
EXETER EX4 4RJ
UK
Tel: (44) 01392 263 333
Fax: (44) 01392 263 342 (office)
      (44) 01395 223 754 (home)
E-mail: r.j.p.kain@ exeter.ac.uk

Government and large-scale mapping of parishes in England and Wales before the Ordnance Survey; boundaries of ancient parishes of England and Wales; historical atlases of south-west England; mapping urban England

A Socio-Economic Survey of Land Use: The 1836 National Tithe Files Database (Marlborough, Adam Matthew, 1995) [with CD-rom].

(with Richard Oliver), *The Tithe Maps of England and Wales: A Cartographic Analysis and County-by-County Catalogue* (Cambridge: Cambridge University Press, 1995).

(with Catherine Delano Smith), *English Cartography* (Cicle de conferències sobre Història de la Cartografia 7è curs, La Cartografia Anglesa; Barcelona: Institut Cartogràfic de Catalunya, 1997).

'The tithe maps of England and Wales: a national land use survey?' *Cartographic Journal* 34:1 (1997): 31-37.

(with Richard R. Oliver), 'Maps and the assessment of parish rates in nineteenth-century England and Wales', *Imago Mundi*, **50** (1998): 156-173.

KALLENBACH, Helga (Dr)
Staatsbibliothe zu Berlin
Kartenabteilung
Postfach 1407
D-10 772 BERLIN
Germany
Tel & fax: (49) 030 266 2726

Geological maps; cartouches; Youssuf Kamal and his atlas; cartobibliography

Alphabetisches Bestands-Verzeichnis der Geologischen Karte von Deutschland 1:25 000 (Berlin: Staatsbibliothek zu Berlin, 1993).

KANAZAWA, Kei (Prof ret)
1-21-5, Shin-Toride
TORIDE-SHI 302-0031
Japan
Tel & fax: (81) 3 297 74 1070
E-mail: kanazawk@olive.ocn.ne.jp

History of cartographic technology

KARAMUSTAFA, Ahmet
Targon (Dr)
Department of ANELL
Center for the Study of Islamic
Societies and Civilizations
Washington University
One Brookings Drive
ST LOUIS, Missouri 63130
USA
Tel: (1) 314 935 4446
Fax: (1) 314 935 7462
E-mail: akaramus@artsci.wustl.edu

Pre-18th-century Islamic maps

'Islamic terrestrial maps and mapmaking', in Helaine Selin (ed), *The Encyclopedia of the History of Science, Technology and Medicine in Non-Western Cultures* (Dordrecht: Kluwer Academic Publishers, 1997), 573-577.

KARK, Ruth (Prof)
Department of Geography
Faculty of Social Sciences
Hebrew University of Jerusalem
Mt. Scopus
JERUSALEM 91905
Israel
Tel & fax: (972) 2 643 4820
E-mail: mskark@pluto.mscc.huji.ac.il

Cartographic history of Palestine, 19th and 20th centuries

'Land purchase and mapping in a mid-nineteenth century Palestinian village', *The Palestine Exploration Quarterly* **130** (1997): 150-161.

'Mamluk and Ottoman cadastral surveys and early mapping of landed properties in Palestine', *Agricultural History* **71** (1997): 46-70.

KARROW, Robert W.
Curator of Maps
The Newberry Library
60 W. Walton Street
CHICAGO, Illinois 60610-3380
USA
Tel: (1) 312 255 3554
Fax: (1) 312 255 3513
E-mail: karrowr@newberry.org

Cartographic revolution, 1400-1600

KAWAMURA, Hirotada (Prof Dr)
503-17 Nagatani-nishi
Ogohiri-cho
YAMAGUCHI 754
Japan
Tel: (81) 0832 56 1111 (office)   (81) 0839 73 2354 (home)
Fax: (81) 0832 56 9577 (office)   (81) 0839 73 2354 (home)

History of cartography in Japan, 16th to 19th centuries

'Provincial maps (Kuniezu) of the early Edo period which are considered to be the reduced copies of the Kanei provincial maps', *Historical Geographic Review* 37:5 (1995): 1-9.

'A papier-mâché relief map: the Bocho-dozu from the Edo Era in Japan', *Imago Mundi* 49 (1997): 83-89.

Research on the History of Cartography in Bocho (Yamaguchi: Sakura Print, 1997).

KAWAMURA, Katsunori
Archivist
Yamaguchi Prefectural Archives
Ushiro-gawara
YAMAGUCHI 753-0083
Japan
Tel: (81) 0839 24 2116
Fax: (81) 0839 24 2117

East Asian cartography

'Hayashi-shihei "chosen-koku-zen-zu" no naiyo to sono keito bon' [A study of the map of Korea 'Chosen-koku-zu' produced by Hayashi-shihei], *Area Yamaguchi: Journal of Yamaguchi Geograhpical Association* 26 (1997): 15-21.

KELLY, Jan I.
Department of Geography
University of Auckland
Private Bag 92019
AUCKLAND 1
New Zealand
Tel: (64) 9 373 7599 ext 8447 (office)   (64) 9 415 9034 (home)
Fax: (64) 9 373 7434
E-mail: j.kelly@auckland.ac.nz

Visions of the world; mental maps; Maori maps; Pacific voyaging

'Cartography, map-making, and GIS', Society of Cartographers, *Bulletin* 28:2 (1995).

'Tuki's map of New Zealand in 1793', *New Zealand Map Society*

Journal 9 (1995): 11-18.

(with Brian Marshall), *Atlas of New Zealand Boundaries* (Auckland: Auckland University Press, 1996).

KEPSU, Saulo Juhani
Veräjäkallionkatu 10
02600 ESPOO 60
Finland
Tel: (358) 0 513525

Old maps of Ingria and cadastral maps of southern Finland

KERSHAW, Kenneth Andrew
442 Wilson Street East
ANCASTER, Ontario L9G 2C3
Canada
Tel: (1) 905 648 1991
Fax: (1) 905 304 1037

Printed maps of Canada, 1540-1799

KIMURA Hiroshi (Prof emeritus)
Kyoto Junior College of Foreign Languages
Kasame-Chō, Saiin
Ukyō-Ku
KYŌTO 615-8558
Japan
Tel: (81) 075 322 6032 (office)   (81) 075 391 7614 (home)
Fax: (81) 075 322 6247

Historical cartography of East and South-east Asia

'Kyōto Gaikokugo Daigaku fuzoku Toshokan shozō no Seiyōkokan Chizu (Europe hen) to Kaisetsu (2)' [The European antique maps in the library of KUFS (Kyoto University of Foreign Studies) and their explanations (Europe part 2)], *KUFS Academic Bulletin* 44 (1995): 393-414.

[European antique maps in the library of KUFS and their explanations (Asia part 1)], *KUFS Academic Bulletin* 46 (1996): 217-238; [Asia part 2], **48** (1997): 268-289; [Asia part 3], **50** (1998): 369-389.

KINNIBURGH, Ian A.G.
Eredene, Huntly Road
ABOYNE, Aberdeenshire
     AB34 5HE
UK
Tel: (44) 013398 86484

William Roy: early influences; the Pont manuscript maps of Scotland; techniques of cartography in the recent past

KING, David Anthony (Prof)
Institute of History of Science
IGN – FBI3
Frankfurt University
D-60054 FRANKFURT AM MAIN
Germany
Tel: (49) 69 798 22754 (office)   (49) 69 597 0872 (home)
Fax: (49) 69 798 23275 (office)   (49) 69 596 4286 (home)
E-mail: king@em.uni-frankfurt.de

Medieval Islamic and European cartography and mathematical geography

'The orientation of medieval Islamic religious architecture and cities', *Journal for the History of Astronomy* 26 (1995): 253-274.

'Islamic astronomy', in Christopher Walker (ed), *Astronomy before the Telescope* (London: British Library, 1996), 143-174.

'Two Iranian world maps for finding direction and distance to Mecca', *Imago Mundi* 49 (1997): 62-82.

KITCHEN, Frank (Dr)
130 Downside
SHOREHAM BY SEA
W. Sussex BN43 6HB
UK
Tel: (44) 01273 441248

Techniques and vision: early modern English cartography; life and work of John Norden

'John Norden (c.1574-1625): estate surveyor, topographer, county mapmaker and devotional writer', *Imago Mundi* 49 (1997): 43-61.

KIVELSON, Valerie A. (Prof)
Department of History
1029 Tisch Hall
University of Michigan
ANN ARBOR, MI 48109-1003
USA
Tel: (1) 734 763 2049 (office)   (1) 734 996 0364 (home)
Fax: (1) 734 647 4881
E-mail: vkivelso@umich.edu

Russian cartography in the early-modern period, religious meaning and identity

KLEMP, Egon
Staatsbibliothek zu Berlin
Unter den Linden 8
10117 BERLIN
Germany
Tel: (49) 030 2015 1235
Fax: (49) 030 2015 1392

Cartobibliography; Berlin cartography

(with Lothar Zögner and Gudrun Maurer), *Verzeichnis der Kartensammlungen in Deutschland* (Wiesbaden: Harrassowitz, 1998).

KLÖTI, Thomas (Dr)
Stadt- und Universitätbibliothek
Postfach
CH-3000 BERN 7
Switzerland
Tel: (41) 031 320 32 48
Fax: (41) 031 320 32 99
E-mail: kloeti@stub.unibe.ch

Johann Friedrich von Ryhiner map collection

'Die Kartensammlung als Forschungsstätte: Die Sammlung Ryhiner, ein wisssenschaftliches Erschliessungsprojekt', *Unipress* 87 (1995): 24-28.

'Die Landtafel des Standes Luzern aus der Werkstatt der Malerfamilie Wägmann', *Vermessung, Photorammetrie, Kulturtechnik* 10 (1995): 619-621.

'Der virtuelle Atlas: Die Sammlung Ryhiner sowie weitere kartengeschichtlich interessante Anlegestellen im Internet', *Cartographica Helvetica* 12 (1995): 45-47.

'Die Vorherrschaft der holländischen und französischen Kartenkunst – Karten im bernischen 17. Jahrhundert', in *Im Schatten des Goldenen Zeitalters. Künstler und Auftraggeber im bernischen 17. Jahrhundert* (Bern: Kunstmuseum, 1995), I: 319-341.

'Kartographische Kostbarkeiten in der Stadt- und Universitätsbibliothek', *Berner Geographische Mitteilungen 1995* (1996): 10.

'Die Welt – eine Augenweide: Transparente Landschafts- und Sternbilder von Franz Niklaus König', in *Sensationen, Welt-Schau auf Wanderschaft = Schriftenreihe des schweizerischen PTT-Museum* (Bern, 1996), 35-40.

'Die Zollkarte der Schweiz (1825) von Johann Kaspar Zellweger und Heinrich Keller', *Zoll-Rundschau* 2 (1996): 39-42, and

Cartographica Helvetica 14 (1996): 25-34.

'Das Probeblatt zum "Atlas Suisse" (1796)', *Cartographica Helvetica* 16 (1997): 23-30.

KOEPP, Donna P.
Govenment Documents & Map Library
University of Kansas
6001 Malott Hall
LAWRENCE, Kansas 66045
USA
Tel: (1) 785 864 4660 (office)
Fax: (1) 785 864 5154
E-mail: dkoepp@ukans.edu

19th-century US government produced or sponsored mapping

(1) 785 748 9863 (home)

(editor), *Index and Carto-bibliography of Maps 1789-1996*, Part 14 of 16 volume *CIS U.S. Serial Set Index* (Bethesda, Maryland, Congressional Information Service, 1995-1997).

KOKKONEN, Pellervo (Dr)
Vilkaharjuntie 1
FIN 58700 SULKAVA
Finland
Tel: (358) 15 471 239 (office)
Fax: (358) 15 471 239 (office)
E-mail: pkokko@netti.fi
pellervo.kokkonen@helsinki.fi

Marine and coastal cartography; 18th century Baltic Sea; missionary cartography in Africa; cartographical theory and methodology; Russian archival cartographical sources concerning Finland (with Alexei V. Postnikov)

(with Ulla Ehrensvärd and Juha Nurminen, *Mare Balticum: 2000 vuotta Itämeren historiaa (Rinnakkaispainokset: Mare Balticum: The Baltic: 2000 Years; Mare Balticum: 2000 år av Östersjöns historia; Mare Balticum: 2000 Jahre der Geschichte der Ostsee)* (Helsinki: Otava ja John Nurmisen Säätiö, 1995).

A.E. Nordenskiöld and the Discovery of History (Finnish Science Center Heureka 1996). [World Wide Web: http://www.heureka.fi].

'Kartan sosiaalinen todellisuus', in *Tila, paikka ja maisema* (Vastapaino, Tampere, 1997), 53-73.

'Practice of marine cartography and the Russian representation of the Baltic Sea in the eighteenth century', *Fennia* 175:1 (1997): 1-96.

KOKS, Frans
345 Laurier Avenue East, Apt 804
OTTAWA, Ontario K1N 6RS
Tel: (1) 613 565 9151
E-mail: koks0001@algonquinc.on.ca

Cartography and history of Old Regime Canada; cartography of the Delisle family

KÖNIG, Gebhard (Dr)
Director
Niederösterreichische
   Landesbibliothek
Landhausplatz 1
A-3109 SANKT PÖLTEN
Austria
Tel: (43) 2742 200 2843 (office)   (43) 2236 46767 (home)
Fax: (43) 2742 200 3860
E-mail: gebhard.koenig@noel.gv.at

Lower Austria; life and works of G.M. Vischer

Alte Landekarten aus Niederösterreich: eine Ausstellung aus den Sammlungen der NÖ Landesbibliothek, 8 April - 3 September 1995 (Haitzendorf: Schloss Grefenegg, 1995).

Niederösterreich im alten Kartenbild: ein Ausstellung aus den Sammlungen der NÖ Landesbibliothek, 21 September 1995 bis 5 Juli 1996 im Foyer der NÖ Landesbibliothek, Wien (Wien, 1995).

'Die Sondersammlungen', in *Festschrift zur Eröffnung des Neubaues der Niederösterreichischen Landesbibliothek* (NÖ Schriften 99; Sankt Pölten, 1997), 107-112.

'Niederösterreich im Bild alter Karten', in *Tradition und Fortschrift: Festschrift cür Hermann Riepl zum 60. Geburtstag* (Jarhbuch für Landaeskunde von Niederösterreich, NF 63/64, 1998).

KONOPSKA, Beata (Dr)
Polskie Przedsiebiorstwo Wydawnictij
   Kartograficznyck S.A.
ul. Św. Jadwigi 12
50-266 WROCŁAW
Poland
Tel: (48) 71 343 8461 (office)   (48) 71 341 2310 (home)
Fax: (48) 71 343 7545

History of cartography of Poland and Silesia; Polish historical cartography since 1848

Polskie atlasy historyczne – koncepcje i realizacje (Warszawa: Whnit Pan, 1994).

'Motywy kartograficzne w medalierstwie polskim', *Z Dziejów*

Kartografii 7 (Warszawa 1995), 99-124 [with co-author].

'Wystawa "Zimia Kłodzka w dawnej kartografii" w Muzeum Ziemi Kłodzkiej', *Polski Przegląd Kartograficzny* 27:4 (1995): 228-229.

'Ziemia Kłodzka w dawnej kartografii – wystawa map w Muzeum Ziemi Kłodzkiej', *Śląski Labirynt Krajoznawczy* 7 (1995): 189-191.

'Kartografia Śląska w dorobku wydawniczym Karola Flemminga', *Czasopismo Zakladu Narodowego im Ossolińskich* 7 (1996): 57-67.

'Problematyka górska w dawnej kartografii na przykładzie Sudetów', in Wieslawa A. Wójcik, *Góry w kartografii* (Kraków: COTG PTTK, 1996), 23-38.

KONVITZ, Josef W. (Dr)
Urban Affairs Division
OECD
2 rue André-Pascal
75775 PARIS
France
Tel: (33) 1 45 24 97 47
Fax: (33) 1 45 24 16 68

France, 1660-1870; urban cartography

KOSTET, Juhani (Dr)
Provincial Museum of Turku
Tuureparinkatn 12 B 20
FIN-20110 TURKU
Finland
Tel: (358) 921 2620250

Helsinki; Cartographia urbium Finnicarum

KOZÁK, Jan (Dr)
Hradešínská 64
100 00 PRAHA 10
Czech Republic

History of cartography of Czech lands; history of geomagnetism maps and earthquake maps

(with Krystyna Szykuła), *Das Prager Stadtpanorama aus dem Jahre 1562 von Jan Kozel und Michael Peterle nach dem Exemplar der Universitätsbibliothek Wroclaw/Breslau* (Wissenhorn: Konrad, 1995).

(with Rudolf Dusek), 'Gerard Mercators Karte von Boehmen (1585) und ihre Quellen', in W. Scharfe (ed), *Gerhard Mercator und seine Zeit. 7. Kartographiehistorisches Colloquium Duisburg 1994* (Duisburg: Braun, 1996), 89-94,

KRAACK, Detlev (Dr)
Institut für Geschichtswissenschaft
Technische Universität Berlin
Sekr. Tel 18/1
Ernst-Reuter-Platz 7
D-10587 BERLIN
Germany
Tel: (49) 30 3142 2018 (office)
    (49) 30 8950 3887 (home)
Fax: (49) 30 3147 9438
E-mail: kraaocci@mailszrz.zrz.tu-berlin.de

Ancient, medieval and early modern cosmology and cartography; early-modern cartography of northern Europe, Scandinavia and the territories of Schleswig-Holstein

(editor), Der Flensburger 'Atlas Major': ein Sammelatlas zum Großen Nordischen Krieg und zu den Türkenkriegen (Flensburg: Landeszentralbibliothek Schleswig-Holstein, 1997).

'Der Flensburger 'Atlas Major' und die historische Kartensammlung aus der Bibliothek des Alten Gymnasiums Flensburg. Ein Editionsprojekt der Landeszentralbibliothek Schleswig-Holstein', Zeitschrift für Geschichtswissenschaft 46:1 (1998): 63-66.

KRAACK, Gerhard (Dr)
Landeszentralbibliothek
Waitzstr. 5
D-24937 FLENSBURG
Germany
Tel: (49) 0461 1860 6200 (office)
    (49) 0461 1964 73 (home)
Fax: (49) 0461 1860 6220
E-mail: lzb.flensburg@t-online.de

Map collection in the Landeszentralbibliothek, especially maps from the Jordt family dating from before 1795 (with Detlev Kraack)

'Eine bisher unbekannte Kartensammlung in Flensburg', Cartographica Helvetica 17 (1998): 20-24.

KREJČÍ, Zdeněk
Ministerstvo zahranivčních věcí
    České republiky
Loretánské náměstí 5
118 00 PRAHA 1
Czech Republic
Tel: (420) 2 2418 2597
Fax: (420) 2 2418 2037
E-mail: krejci@mzv.cz

Military cartography of Czech lands and Slovakia

'Německé mapy území ČSR v předvečer a v dobe 2. světové války' [German maps of the ČSR's territory on the eve and in the time of World War II], in 'Historické mapy', Zborník z vedeckej konferencie (Bratislava, 1997), 192-207.

KRETSCHMER, Ingrid (Prof Dr)
Department of Geography
University of Vienna
Universitätsstrase 7
A-1010 WIEN
Austria
Tel: (43) 1 4277 48640 (office)
    (43) 1 817 3966 (home)
Fax: (43) 1 4277 9486

Topographic and thematic maps of Austria and Central Europe; 'Atlantes Austriaci' (with Johannes Dörflinger); Austrian cartography overseas

'Die Eigenschaften der "Mercatorprojektion" und ihre heutige Anwendung', in I. Hantsche (ed), Mercator – ein Wegbereiter neuzeitlichen Denkens (Referate des 2. Mercatorsymposiums; Bochum: Universitätsverlag Brockmeyer, 1994), 141-169.

(with Christa Binder), 'La projection mercatorienne', in Marcel Watelet (ed), Gérard Mercator, cosmographe (Antwerp: Fonds Mercator, 1994), 193-207.

(with Johannes Dörflinger), Atlantes Austriaci. Österreichische Atlanten 1561-1994 (2 vols; Wien-Köln-Weimar: Böhlau Verlag, 1995).

'Zur Entwicklung thematischer Atlanten im 19. und 20. Jahrundert', in Hans Wolff (ed), 400 Jahre Mercator, 400 Jahre Atlas (Weissenhorn: Konrad, 1995), 231-263.

'Kartenprojektionen in Gerhard Mercators Atlas', in H.-H. Blotevogel and R. Vermij (eds), Gerhard Mercator und die geistigen Strömungen des 16. und 17. Jahrhunderts (Bochum: Universitätsverlag Brockmeyer, 1995), 65-85.

'Arbeits-, Forschungs- und Projektbereich "Kartographiegeschichte"', in Ingrid Kretschmer and Karel Kriz (eds), Kartographie in Österreich '96 (Wein: Institut für Geographie der Universität Wien, 1996), 153-164.

'Frühe Alpenpanoramen aus Österreich', Kartographische Nachrichten 46:6 (1996): 213-218.

'Kartographische Arbeiten Friedrich Simonys', Geographischer Jahresbericht aus Österreich 53 (1996): 43-61.

'History of cartography: present and future', in Ferjan Ormeling and Bernard Köbben (eds), *Proceedings of the Seminar on Teaching the History of Cartography III held at the Nationalbibliothek, Vienna, Austria, September 10, 1995* (Utrecht, 1996), 5-7.

(with Wolfgang Scharfe and Hans-Uli Feldmann), *6è curs: La Cartografia dels països de parla alemanya: Alemanya, Àustria i Suïssa* (Barcelona: Institut Cartogrfic de Catalunya, 1997).

KREUER, Johannes Werner (Dr Prof)
Institute of Geography
Universität GH Essen/Ruhr
Universitätsstr. 5
D-45117 ESSEN
Germany
Tel: (49) 0201 183 3105 (office)   (49) 02254 7410 (home)
Fax: (49) 0201 183 2811

Early maps of Germany and Europe; world maps; maps of Martellus and Rosselli

Imagines et Tabulae, Europäische Stadtbilder und Kartentafeln an der Schwelle zur Neuzeit (Essen: Institut für Geographie, 1996). [Exhibition catalogue.]

Monumenta cartographica, 1490-1525. Kartographische Denkmäler, ein Triumph über die Zeit. 6 Original faksimiles mit Kommentarband (Essen: Institut für Geographie, 1996).

KROGT, Peter C.J. van der (Dr)
Explokart Research Project
Faculty of Geographical Sciences
University of Utrecht
P.O. Box 80 115
3508 TC UTRECHT
Netherlands
Tel: (31) 30 253 2052
Fax: (31) 30 254 0604 (office)
     (31) 15 212 6063 (home)
E-mail: p.vanderkrogt@frw.ruu.nl

Atlases published in the Low Countries [new edition of Koeman's *Atlantes Neerlandici*]; catalogue of the Atlas Blaeu–van der Hem in the Austrian National Library; globes; Dutch commercial cartography; bibliography of the history of Dutch cartography

'Commercial cartography in the Netherlands with particular reference to atlas production (16th-18th centuries)', in *La Cartografia dels Paises Baixos: Cicle de conferencies sobre Historia de la Cartografia 4rt curs . . .* (Barcelona: Generalitat de Catalunya, Departament de Politica Territorial i Obres Publiques, Institut Cartografic de Catalunya, 1994), 70-140.

'Das "Plenilunium" des Michael Florent van Langren: Die erste Mondkarte mit Namenseinträgen', *Cartographica Helvetica* 11 (1995): 44-49.

'De Amsterdamse atlasproduktie in de jaren 1630: een nachtmerrie voor de bibliograaf', *Kartografisch Tijdschrift* 21:4 (1995): 21-24.

'De foliokaart van de Nederlanden door Filips Galle uit 1579', *Caert-Thresoor* 14 (1995): 63-67.

(with Heleen Hayes), 'De Wereld in het klein', *Fibula: Tijdschrift van de Nederlandse Jeugdbond voor Geschiedenis* 36:2 (1995): 7-12.

'Het verhoudingsgetal als schaal en de eerste kaart op schaal 1:10000', *Kartografisch Tijdschrift* 21:1 (1995) = *Nederlands Geodetisch Tijdschrift/Geodesie* 37:1 (1995): 3-5.

'Mercators Atlas: Geschichte, Editionen, Inhalt', in H.H. Blotevogel and R. Vermij (eds), *Gerhard Mercator und die geistigen Strömungen des 16. und 17. Jahrhunderts: Duisburger Mercator-Studien* Band 3 (Bochum: Brockmeyer, 1995), 49-64.

'Wereldatlasjes', *Kartografisch Tijdschrift* 21:4 (1995): 33-38.

'Amsterdam atlas production in the 1630s: a bibliographer's nightmare', *Imago Mundi* 48 (1996): 149-160.

(with Erlend de Groot), *The Atlas Blaeu–van der Hem of the Austrian National Library: Volume I: Spain, Portugal and France, Descriptive Catalogue of Volumes 1-8 of the Atlas* ('t Goy-Houten: HES, 1996).

'Boek van het jaar: De Atlas (1595) van Gerard Mercator', *Jaarboek van het Nederlands Genootschap van Bibliofielen 1995* (Amsterdam: De Buitenkant, 1996), 19-46.

'De Mercatorjaren 1994 en 1995: een terugblik', *Kartografisch Tijdschrift* 22:3 (1996): 17-25, and *Caert-Thresoor* 15 (1996): 89-97.

'De Vrede van Munster en de atlaskartografie', *Kartografisch Tijdschrift* 22:4 (1996): 30-36.

'"Der neue Koeman" Koemans "Atlantes Neerlandici" Edito IIa', in W. Scharfe (ed), *Gerhard Mercator und seine Zeit. 7. Kartographiehistorisches Colloquium Duisburg 1994* (Duisburg: Braun, 1996), 95-101.

'From "Atlas" to atlas', *Mercator's World* 1:1 (1996): 61-63, 93.

'Gemeente versus uitgeverij: een kwestie over auteursrecht', *Kartografisch Tijdschrift* 22:3 (1996): 27-31.

'Gerard Mercator, the father of modern cartography', *Mercator's World* 1:4 (1996): 34-41.

SHEPPARD'S
INTERNATIONAL DIRECTORY OF
PRINT AND MAP SELLERS

- Full details of over 1,600 print and map dealers
- Dealers listed by country, state or county & town
- Speciality Index with over 170 classifications
- Covering more than 40 countries worldwide
- Indexes of Business & Proprietor Name
- 3rd Edition 440 Pages Hardback £24.00

OTHER SHEPPARD'S DIRECTORIES

Book Dealers in the British Isles *22nd Edn, 2,625 entries, 572 pages*	£24
Book Dealers in Australia & New Zealand *3rd Edn, 627 entries, 280 pages*	£24
Book Dealers in Europe *10th Edn, 1,541 entries, 384 pages*	£27
Book Dealers in North America *13th Edn, 3,350 entries, 676 pages*	£27
Book Dealers in Japan *1st Edn, 400 entries, 200 pages*	£24
Book Dealers in India & the Orient *2nd Edn, 550 entries, 221 pages*	£24
International Ephemera Dealers *2nd Edn, 971 entries, 324 pages*	£24
Dealers in Collectables (UK) *2nd Edn, 1,235 entries, 432 pages*	£18
Dealers in Collectibles (North America) *1st Edn (September 1998)*	£24

SHEPPARD'S DIRECTORIES ON CD-ROM

Richard Joseph Publishers and Book Data have joined forces to produce a CD-Rom which contains half a million records of out-of-print books and information from Sheppard's Directories.

RICHARD JOSEPH PUBLISHERS LTD
UNIT 2, MONKS WALK, FARNHAM, SURREY GU9 8HT
TEL: 01252 734347 FAX: 01252 734307 E-MAIL: RJOE01@AOL.COM
HTTP://MEMBERS.AOL.COM/RJOE01/SHEPPARDS.HTM

'De Catalogus van de Atlas Blaeu–van der Hem,' *Questa: periodiek van de Faculteit Ruimtelijke Wetenschappen* 11:3 (Jan. 1997): 10-13.

'Delft portrait: no stamp of approval', *Mercator's World* 2:2 (1997): 82.

Koeman's Atlantes Neerlandici New Edition: Volume 1: The Folio Atlases by Gerard Mercator, Jodocus Hondius, Henricus Hondius, Joannes Janssonius and their successors ('t Goy-Houten: HES, 1997).

'Mercator—seine Atlanten und seine Zeitgenossen', in Rienk Vermij (ed), *Gerhard Mercator und seine Welt* (Duisburg: Mercator Verlag, 1997), 110-131.

KRYGIER, John
Department of Geography
State University of New York at
    Buffalo
105 Wilkeson Quad
BUFFALO, NY 14261
USA
Tel: (1) 716 645 2722, ex. 23 (office)
    (1) 716 832 0047 (home)
Fax: (1) 716 645 2329
E-mail:
jkrygier@geog.buffalo.edu
Web:
http://www.geog.buffalo.edu/~jkrygier/

Maps, images, panoramas of the American West in the 19th century; history of academic cartography; native (non-western) representations of space; maps and other visual representations in environmental conflicts; relations between maps and text, images, and other visual representations (specifically in travel and exploratory narratives)

'Cartography as an art and a science', *Cartographic Journal* 32:6 (1995): 3-10.

'Envisioning the American West: maps, the representational barrage of 19th century expedition reports, and the production of scientific knowledge', *Cartography and Geographic Information Systems* 24:1 (1997): 27-50.

KUDRNOVSKÁ, Olga (Dr)
Holečkova 36
150 00 PRAHA 5
Czech Republic
Tel: (420) 2 538 922

Karel Kořistka, life and work; the Josephinian mapping of Czech lands

'Reminiscenses of the work of Professor Karel Kuchař', *Acta Universitatis Carolinae/Geographica* (Praha 1996), 1: 97-111.

KUPČÍK, Ivan (Dr)
Kiliansplatz 2
80339 MUNICH
Germany
Tel: (49) 89 2180 2487 (office)
    (49) 89 503212 (home)
Fax: (49) 89 2179 465
E-mail:ghw@lrz.uni-muenchen.de
also: Hlavatého 618
149 00 PRAHA 4
Czech Republic

History of cartography of Czech lands; catalogue of early Bohemian maps preserved outside Czech lands; military cartography of Central Europe; development of European pilgrim maps; portolan charts

Mappae Bavariae. Thematische Karten von Bayern bis zum Jahre 1900 (Weissenhorn, Konrad, 1995).

'Nález rukopisné předlohy tisku Müllerovy mapy Čech, pohřešovaného rukopisu mapy Moravy a tiskové desky mapy okolí Chebu' [New discoveries: manuscript of the map of Bohemia by J.K. Müller, manuscript of the map of Moravia and plates of the map of Cheb's Environs], *Sborník České geografické spolačnosti* 100: 1 (Praha 1995): 25-34.

'Vývoj mapového zobrazení českých zemí na mapách poutnických cest do poloviny 16 století', *Z dějin geodézie a kartografie* (8 Rozpravy Národního technického muzea v Praze 136; Praha: NTM, 1995), 34-39.

'Bayern à la carte. Entwicklung der thematischen Kartographie in Bayern bis 1900', *Kultur & Technik* 20:1 (1996): 54-57.

'The development of thematic maps in Bavaria up to the year 1900' *Acta Universitatis Carolinae: Geographica* (Praha, 1996), 1: 113-137.

'Entdeckung und Restaurierung der Landkartengalerie in der Salzburger Residenz', in W. Scharfe (ed), *Gerhard Mercator und seine Zeit. 7. Kartographiehistorisches Colloquium Duisburg 1994* (Duisburg: Braun, 1996), 137-146.

'Geschichte der thematischen Kartographie. Von globaler zu regionaler Forschung. Freundenskreis für Cartographica in der Stuftung Preussischer Kulturbesitz e V., *Mitteilungsblatt* 10 (Weissenhorn: Konrad, 1996): 26-31.

'Pařížské kopie pohřešovaných mnichovských portulánů z počátku 16. století' [Paris copies of reproductions of early 16th-century portolan charts in Munich], *Kartographie na přelomu tisíciletí* (Sborník příspěvků 12. kartografické konference, Olomouc, 1997), 201-207.

'První tematické mapy českých zemí do r. 1918', *Z dějin geodézie a kartografie* (9 Rozpravy Národního muzea v Praze 150; Praha: NTM, 1997), 129-134.

'Úřední mapy ke slovenskému území z let 1918-1945' [Official maps of the Slovak territory, 1918-1945], in *'Historické mapy', Zborník z vedeckej konferencie* (Bratislava, 1997), 182-191.

'Handgezeichnete Kopie der Apianschen Karte von Bayern von Dominicus Franciscus Calinus (um 1661)', *Cartographica Helvetica* 17 (1998): 32-34.

KUPFER, Marcia
3611 Patterson St NW
WASHINGTON DC 20015
USA
Tel: (1) 202 363 2240

Medieval mappaemundi in the context of monumental art

'The lost wheel of Ambrogio Lorenzetti', *Art Bulletin* **78**:2 (1996): 286-310.

KUSOV, Vladimir S.
Faculty of Geography and Geodesy
Moscow State University
Vorobjevy Gory
119899 MOSCOW
Russia
Tel: 7 095 198 0575 (home)

History of Russian cartography; retrospective mapping of Russian land

[The discovery of a new 17th-century Russian geographical diagram of lands in present-day Moscow], *Bulletin of Schools of Higher Education: Geodesy*, No 1 (1997): 169-177.

[An early cartographic representation of Moscow lands near the Vorobyov Bluffs], *Bulletin, Moscow University Geography*, no. 4 (1997): 20-24 [in Russian].

[Moscow and the first steps of the Chief Geodesic Administration], *Geodesy and Cartography*, No 9 (1997): 17-20.

[Three new 17th-century Russian geographical diagrams], *Archaeological Annual 1997* (Moscow: Nauka, 1997), 120-127.

LAFRENZ, Jürgen
Hans Robert (Prof Dr)
Institut für Geographie
Universität Hamburg
Bundesstrasse 55
D-20146 HAMBURG
Tel: (49) 040 4123 4953
Fax: (49) 040 4123 5270

Topographical areas of northern Germany; historical mental maps; historical atlases of European towns

'Die "Pracktische Kriegsbaukunst" von Zacharias Wolff: ein Kartenwerk zum Festungswesen', in W. Scharfe (ed), *Gerhard Mercator und seine Zeit. 7. Kartographiehistorisches Colloquium Duisburg 1994* (Duisburg: Braun, 1996), 167-193.

LAGARDE, Lucie
8 rue du Général Camou
75007 **PARIS**
France

French cartography in the 18th century

'Philippe Buache, 1700-1773, cartographe ou géographe', in Danielle Lecoq and Antoine Chambard (eds), *Terre à découvrir, terres à parcourir, éléments pour une histoire de la découverte de la Terre et de la géographie* (Paris: Publications de l'Université Paris 7–Denis Diderot, 1996), 147-165.

LAGUARDA TRIAS,
Rolando A. (Prof)
Instituto de Historia y Geografía del Uruguay
8 de octubre 3255
MONTEVIDEO 11600
Uruguay
Tel: (598) 2 247 0868/1810
Fax: (598) 2 247 0868

Early 16th century maps showing the Río de la Plata to determine who discovered it (Amerigo Vespucci, João de Lisboa, Juan Díaz de Solís)

'El descubrimiento de las Islas Malvinas en 1520 y su predescubrimiento presunto', *Revista de Historia de America* (Mexico), **118** (1994): 51-81.

LAING, William (Dr)
Glenesk
Montgomerie Ave.
FAIRLIE, Ayrshire KA29 0EE
UK
Tel: (44) 01475 568402

Marine cartography of the Firth of Clyde, with special reference to the Watt family (c.1720-1760) and coastal Admiralty surveys (c.1830-1860); John Marr, mariner of Dundee (c.1650-1700); collation of maritime information relating to Scotland to the mid-17th century (Brouscon, Lindsay, Munro, Martin, Pont)

LANE, Christopher W.
The Philadelphia Print Shop, Ltd.
8441 Germantown Avenue
PHILADELPHIA, PA 19118
USA
Tel: (1) 215 242 4750
Fax: (1) 215 242 6977
E-mail: philaprint@philaprintshop.com

Mapping non-existent places; Hugh Anderson (1782-1866), engraver and mapmaker; Philadelphia mapmakers

'The color of old maps', *Mercator's World* 1:6 (1996): 50-57.

LANNON, John
Boston Athenaeum
10½ Beacon Street
BOSTON, Massachusetts 02108
USA
Tel: (1) 617 227 0270
Fax: (1) 617 227 5266
E-mail: lannon@bostonathenaeum.org

New England, 17th to 20th centuries

LAURETI, Lamberto (Prof)
Dipartimento di Scienze della Terra
Università di Pavia
Via Abbiategrasso 209
27100 PAVIA
Italy
Tel: (39) 0382 505858
Fax: (39) 0382 505890

19th and 20th century history of cartography; evolution of thematic mapping (mainly geological and population maps); cartobibliography of Italian atlases; cartographic sources for reconstructing past landscapes

LAXTON, Paul
Department of Geography
University of Liverpool
P.O. Box 147
LIVERPOOL L69 3BX
UK
Tel: (44) 0151 794 2845 (office)
Fax: (44) 0151 794 2866
E-mail: laxton@liv.ac.uk

English large-size county mapping; urban maps as plans 1700-1850

(44) 0151 639 3872 (home)

LAYLAND, Michael Franklin
2922 Phyllis Street
VICTORIA, British Columbia,
   V8N 1Y9
Canada
Tel: (1) 250 727 0727 (office)
Fax: (1) 250 727 3153 (office)
E-mail:baytext@islandnet.com

Exploration and mapping of the Amazon region; history of mapping of British Columbia

(1) 250 477 2734 (home)
(1) 250 477 2716 (home)

'"Sales from the Map Room" or collecting "modern" cartography', *The Map Collector* 73 (1995): 30-32.

'A land that is uncultivated, insane, impassable and largely unknown...' *Mercator's World* 1:5 (1996): 44-49.

'The line that divided the world', *Mercator's World* 1:1 (1996): 34-36, 88-89.

'Teixeira's act of possession', *Mercator's World* 1:2 (1996): 24-29.

'Devious diplomacy: three large maps of South America' *Mercator's World* 3:1 (1998): 14-25.

LECOQ, Danielle
13 rue Christiani
75018 PARIS
France
Tel: (33) 01 42 58 27 15

Cosmography; medieval astronomy; mappaemundi and cartography in the Middle Ages; history of cartography and geography

'Images médiévales du monde', in *A la rencontre de Sinbad* (Catalogue de l'exposition, *La route maritime de la soie*, Musée de la Marine, Paris, 1994), 56-62.

(editor), *Paulmiers, Roumieux, Jacquaires* (Paris: Université Paris 7–Denis Diderot, 1994).

(with Catherine Hofmann, Ève Netchine et Monique Pelletier), *Le globe et son image* (Paris: Bibliothèque nationale de France, 1995).

'Gog et Magog, peuples de la fin des temps', *Le Monde de la Bible: Archéologie et Histoire* **94** (1995): 36-37.

'Mathieu Paris: de l'itinéraire à la représentation du monde', in Catherine Bosquet-Bressolier (ed), *L'oeil du cartographe* (Paris: C.T.H.S., 1995), 19-38.

(editor), *De l'empyrée à la sphère de l'air troublé: les hommes et le ciel au Moyen Âge* (Paris: Publications de l'Université Paris 7–Denis Diderot, 1996).

'Plate ou sphérique? La conception de la Terre au Moyen Âge' *Comité français de cartographie* (juin 1996): 19-38.

'Les premières cartes de la Terre sainte', *Le Monde de la Bible: Archéologie, Art, Histoire* **100** (1996): 65-71.

(with Antoine Chambard, ed), *Terre à découvrir, terres à parcourir, éléments pour une histoire de la découverte de la Terre et de la géographie* (Paris: Publications de l'Université Paris 7–Denis Diderot, 1996).

'Les îles aux confins du monde', in Daniel Reig (ed), *Îles des merveilles. Mirage, miroir, mythe* (Paris: L'Harmattan, 1997).

LEISERACH, Michael   Sheldon tapestry maps
4 Thames Court
Thames St.
EYNSHAM OX8 1JW
UK
Tel: (44) 01865 882464

LEMOINE-ISABEAU, Claire   Cartography of Belgian ter-
Musée royale de l'Armée   ritory, 1550-1916; military
3, Parc du Cinquantenaire   cartography
1040 BRUXELLES
Belgium
Tel: (32) 2 733 44 93
Fax: (32) 2 734 54 21

'Evolution topographique de Tournai', in F. Thomas (ed), *Tournai: une ville, un fleuve (XVIe-XVIIe siècle)* (Brussels: Crédit Communal, 1995), 35-67.

LEWIS, G. Malcolm   Cartography in traditional
9 Derriman Avenue   societies (especially North
SHEFFIELD S11 9LA   American)
UK
Tel & fax: (44) 0114 236 5145

'Communiquer l'espace: malentendus dans la transmission d'information cartographique en Amérique du Nord', in Laurier Turgeon et al (eds), *Transferts culturels et métissages Amérique/Europe XVIe-XXe siècle* (Québec: Les Presses de l'Université, 1996), 357-375.

'An early map on skin of the area to become Indiana and Illinois', *British Library Journal* **22**:1 (1996): 66-87 (also in Karen Severud Cook (ed), *Images and Icons of the New World: Essays on American Cartography* (London: The British Library, 1996), 66-87).

'Maps and mapmaking in native North America', in Helaine Selin (ed), *Encyclopaedia of the History of Science, Technology, and Medicine in Non-Western Cultures* (Dordrecht, Boston and London, 1997), 592-594.

'Native North Americans' cosmological ideas and geographical awareness: their representation and influence on early European exploration and geographical knowledge', in John Logan Allen (ed), *North American Exploration, vol. 1: A New World Disclosed* (Lincoln and London: University of Nebraska Press, 1997), 71-126.

(editor), *Cartographic Encounters: Non-Native Perspectives on Native North Americans' Maps, Mapmaking, and Map Use* (Chicago: University of Chicago Press for the Newberry Library, 1998).

LI Xiaocong (Prof)   Cartobibliography of China
Department of History   before 1949; pre-1900
Peking University   Chinese maps abroad
100871 BEIJING
China
Tel: (86) 10 6275 1656 (office)   (86) 10 6256 0099 (home)
Fax: (86) 10 6275 1650
E-mail: lixc@public.fhnet.cn.net

'Survey and study of the pre-1900 Chinese maps kept in Europe', *Studies in Sinology* **3** (Beijing: Peking University Press, 1995): 489-523.

A Descriptive Catalogue of Pre-1900 Chinese Maps in Europe (Beijing: International Culture Publishing Corp., 1996) [in Chinese and English].

'Cartography and culture', in *The Vanishing Border: A Retrospective of China and Hong Kong through Maps* (Hong Kong: Credit Lyonnais Securities (Asia) Ltd, 1997).

'Father Matteo Ripa and the complete map of the empire during the Emperor Kangxi era: dissemination and influence of the Chinese maps in Europe since the 16th century', *Soochow Journal of History*, no 4 (Taipei, Taiwan, 1998).

LICINI, Patrizia Anna (Prof Dr)
via T. Grossi 10
21047 SARONNO (VA)
Italy
E-mail: licinice@tin.it

Mappaemundi and illuminated initials; perception of the world in the Chrsitian Middle Ages

'Cartografando l'immaginabile', *Notiziario del Centro Italiano per gli Studi Storico-Geografici* 3:1 (1995): 10-27.

'Da questo punto in poi ci sono i leoni', in *MUSIS* [Museo della Scienza e dell'informazione scientifica] *GEO-grafie. Un mondo e le sue rappresentazioni* (Roma: EUroma, 1995), 29-39.

'L'enigma. l'etnia, la pergamenia', in Associazione Geografi Italiani (ed), *Geotema I: l'officina geografica/teorie e metodi tra moderno e post-moderno* (Bologna: Pàtron, 1995), 75-90.

'La Georgia del sec. XVII vista dall'Archivio Generale di S. Andrea della Valle', *Regnum Dei. Collectanea Theatina* 121 (1995): 221-237.

'Confini nel tempo: l'Europa orientale. I territori dell'ecx-URSS oggi: considerazioni introduttive', in E. Squarcina (ed), *Temi e problemi di Geografia* (Milano: Associazione Italiana Insegnanti di Geografia – Sez. di Milano, 1996), 32-34.

'La rotta di Nord-Est: dal mito alla realtà' in C. Cerreti (ed), *Atti del XXVI Congresso Geografico Italiano, Genova 4-9 maggio 1992* (Roma: Istituto dell'Enciclopedia Italiana, 1996), 2: 714-724.

'Dalle carte nautiche di Wagenaar (1584) a due pratiche divergenti dello spazio: il mondo latino e il mondo anglosassone', in M. Quaini (ed), *Rappresentazioni e pratiche dello spazio in una prospettiva storico-geografica (28-30 sett. 1995 San Faustino)* (Genova: Brigati, 1997), 297-323.

'Parlare dalla mappa: la carta geografica come palinsesto dell'arte del dire', in Associazione Geografi Italiani (ed), *Geotema 8: Il viaggio come fonte di conoscenze geografiche* (Bologna: Pàtron, 1997), 11-43.

'The Ottoman conquest of Armenia in progress from an Italian portolan chart (Jesi, XVth c.)', *Environmental Design* (1998): 34-59.

LIEBENBERG, Elizabeth Catharina
Department of Geography
University of South Africa
P O Box 392
PRETORIA 0003
South Africa
Tel: (27) 12 429 6013 (office)
Fax: (27) 12 429 3221 (office)
E-mail: liebeec@alpha.unisa.ac.za

History of surveying and mapping in South Africa during the 19th and 20th centuries

(27) 12 47 1987 (home)

'Mapping British Africa: the case of G.S.G.S. 2230', *Imago Mundi* 49 (1997): 129-142.

LIERZ, Wolfgang
Asylstrasse 66
CH-8708 MAENNEDORF
Switzerland
Tel: (41) 1 79018 61
Fax: (41) 1 79018 62
E-mail: lierz@library.ethz.ch
Web: /www:http://www.ethbib.ethz.ch/lierz/

19th and 20th century atlases, railway maps, cycling maps, road maps, relief maps, profiles, curiosities

'Zur Rolle der Mercatorprojektion in deutschsprachigen Atlanten des 19. und 20. Jahrhunderts', in *Gerhard Mercator und seine Zeit. 7. Kartographiehistorisches Colloquium, Duisburg 1994* (Duisburg: Walter Braun, 1996): 195-201.

LINDGREN, Uta (Prof Dr)
Universität Bayreuth
Wissenschaftsgeschichte
Postfach 10 12 51
D-95440 BAYREUTH
Germany
Tel: (49) 0921 55 50 33
Fax: (49) 0921 55 50 53

Problems of map making in the Middle Ages and the early modern epoch

'Die Bedeutung Philipp Melanchthons (1497-1560) für die Entwicklung einer naturwissenschaftlichen Geographie', in *Gerhard Mercator und seine Zeit. 7. Kartographiehistorisches Colloquium, Duisburg 1994* (Duisburg: Walter Braun, 1996), 1-12.

LINDNER, Klaus (Dr)
Staatsbibliothek zu Berlin
Preussischer Kulturbesitz
Kartenabteilung
Potsdamer Strasse 33
D-10785 BERLIN
Germany
Tel: (49) 030 266 2725 (office)
Fax: (49) 030 266 3010 (office)

History of cartography of
Silesia; town plans of Berlin

(49) 030 781 8804 (home)
(49) 030 782 7387 (home)

'Begrenzung und Wachstum. Berliner Stadtentwicklung im
Spiegel von Karten', in *Begrenzung und Wachstm. Berliner
Stadtentwicklung im Spiegel von Karten* (Berlin: Ausstellung des
Landesarchivs Berlin, 1995), 4-72.

*Zwischen Oder und Riesengebirge. Schlesische Karten aus fünf
Jahrhunderten* (Staatsbibliothek zu Berlin – Ausstellungskataloge
29; 2nd ed., Weissenhorn 1995).

'Johann David Schleuens Schlesien-Atlas mit den Randansichten
von Friedrich Bernhard Werner', in *Jarhbuch der Schlesischen
Friedrich-Wilhelms-Unversität zu Breslau* **38/39** (1997-1998)).

Zwischen Ems und Hunte. Land am Wasser und unter dem Krummstab
(Ausgewählte Karten und Ansichten aus der Staatsbibliothek zu
Berlin; Austellung vom 5. Mai–21. Juni 1998; Gut Altenkamp,
Papemburg Aschendorf (Berlin 1998).

LÍTER MAYAYO, Carmen
Biblioteca Nacional
Servicio de Cartografía
Paseo de Recoletos 20
28071 MADRID
Spain
Tel: (34) 91 580 78 13
Fax: (34) 91 577 56 34

Spanish cartography (16th-
19th centuries); Tomás
López (1730-1802), geog-
rapher to the Spanish king;
atlases in the National
Library of Spain

LIVINGSTONE, David N. (Prof)
School of Geosciences
Queen's University of Belfast
BELFAST BT7 1NN
Northern Ireland
Tel: (44) 01232 335145
Fax: (44) 01232 321280

Cartography and empire;
anthropometric cartogra-
phy in the 19th century;
history of cartography and
history of geography

LOISEAUX, Olivier
Bibliothèque nationale de France
Département des cartes et plans
58 rue de Richelieu
75084 PARIS
France
Tel: (33) 01 47 03 83 56
Fax: (33) 01 47 03 83 61
E-mail: olivier.loiseaux@bnf.fr

19th-century maps of
Africa; topynomy; cartog-
raphy of the 20th century

'Regards des européens sur l'Afrique: acteurs et enjeux de la
toponymie africaine du XVIe siècle au XIXe siècle', in *Séminaire
toponymique franco-africain: UNESCO 3-4-5 juin 1996* (Conseil
national de l'information géographique, Commission nationale de
toponymie; Paris: CNIG, 1997), 245-256.

LONGENBAUGH, Dee
The Observatory
235 Second Street
JUNEAU, Alaska 99801
USA
Tel: (1) 907 586 9676 (office)
Fax: (1) 907 586 9606
E-mail: deelong@alaska.net

History of mapping in
Alaska, Alaska history pre-
1867

(1) 907 586 4144 (home)

'The cold race to chart Alaska', *Mercator's World* **3**:2 (1998): 38-45.

LORCH, Richard Paul (Dr)
Institut für Geschichte der
    Naturwissenschaften
D-80306 MÜNCHEN
Germany
Tel: (49) 089 844588
Fax: (49) 089 21803162

Mathematical sciences in
the medieval Arab world
and their transmission to
the West

MAGALLANES, Luis
Servicio Geográfico del Ejército
Cartoteca Historica
C/ Dario Gazapo 8
28024 MADRID
Spain
Tel: (34) 91 711 50 43, ext. 230
Fax: (34) 91 711 50 32

Cartography of Spain
(1900-1950) in the Army
Geographical Service (catalogue); the border between
Spain and Portugal

MALING, Peter Bromley
1/203 B Clyde Road
Fendalton, CHRISTCHURCH
New Zealand
Tel: (64) 03 351 7714

Pre-1850 New Zealand
charts and maps

Historic Charts & Maps of New Zealand, 1642-1885 (Auckland:
Reed Books, 1996).

MANASEK, Francis John
G.B. Manasek Inc
Box 1204
NORWICH, Vermont 05055-1204
USA
Tel: (1) 802 649 1722
Fax: (1) 802 649 2256
E-mail: manasekinc@aol.com

Microscopic structure of
paper and vellum used in
map making; the micro-
scopic appearance of lines
produced by different map
printing techniques

'Frisland: phantom island of the North Atlantic', *Mercator's World*
2:1 (1997): 14-18.

Collecting Old Maps (Norwich, VT: Terra Nova Press, 1998).

MANGANI, Giorgio (Dr)
Map Curator
Cartoteca Storica delle Marche
P.O. Box 118
I-60100 ANCONA
Italy
Tel: (39) 071 52735 (office)
     (39) 071 2070 605 (home)
Fax: (39) 071 52610

Moral cartography and
Abraham Ortelius: history
and cartography of the
Ecclesiastical State and
Marche region of Italy,
mainly the printed maps

(with Feliciano Paoli, ed.), *Gerardo Mercatore. Sulle tracce di geografi e
viaggiatori nelle Marche* (Le collezoni di Casteldurante dai Della
Rovere agli Ubaldini, Grafica e Cultura Roveresca 4; Urbania:
Edizioni Biblioteca e Civico Museo di Urbania, 1996). [Exhibition
catalogue.]

(with Emanuela Casti Moreschi), *Una geografia dell'Altrove: l'Atlante
d'Africa di Arcangelo Ghisleri*, 1997. [Exhibition catalogue.]

'Abraham Ortelius and the hermetic meaning of the cordiform
projection', *Imago Mundi*, **50** (1998): 59-83.

MARINO, John A.
Department of History
University of California, San Diego
9500 Gilman Drive
LA JOLLA, California 92093-0307
USA
Tel: (1) 619 534 3041
Fax: (1) 619 534 7283
E-mail: jmarino@ucsd.edu

16th-century Italian maps

MARQUES, Alfredo Pinheiro
Faculdade de Letras
Universidade de Coimbra
3049 COIMBRA
Portugal
Tel: (351) 39 410 9900 (office)
     (351) 33 33258 (home)
Fax: (351) 39 36733 (office)
     (351) 33 34450 (home)
E-mail: alfmarq.cemar@mail.telepac.pt

Cartography of geographi-
cal discoveries (13th-18th
centuries); Portuguese cartography (15th-17th cen-
turies); the Fra Mauro and
other 15th century maps;
portolan charts; Portuguese
cartography in Japan; cartography of Brazil

A Cartografia dos Descobrimentos Portugueses [Cartography of the
Portuguese discoveries] ([Mafra]: ELO, [1995]).

'The discovery of the Azores and its first repercussions in cartography', *Arquipélago. Revista da Universidade dos Açores* 1:2 (1995): 7-
16.

'Epilogue: triumph for Da Gama and disgrace for Columbus', in
George Winius (ed.), *Portugal: the Pathfinder. Journeys from the
Medieval toward the Modern World, 1300-ca.1600* (Madison:
University of Wisconsin, 1995).

*A Maldição da Memória do Infante D. Pedro e as Origens dos
Descobrimentos Portugueses* (Figueira da Foz: CEMAR, 1994 [1995]).

'A maldição da memória e a criação do mito. O Infante D. Pedro e
o Infante D. Henrique nos Descobrimentos' [The accursed heritage
and the creation of the myth: Prince Peter and Prince Henry in the
Portuguese discoveries], *Vértice* [Lisbon] 64 (1995): 63-74.

'Prefácio', in Joaquim Ferreira do Amaral, *'Pedro Reinel Me Fez'. À
volta de um Mapa dos Descobrimentos* (Lisbon: Quetzal, 1995), 11-16.

Gravura de Buarcos de c.1638 [An engraving of Buarcos, c.1638]
(Figueira da Foz: Centro de Estudos do Mar, 1996).

'A influência no estrangeiro das técnicas e práticas científicas dos descobrimentios portugueses: a cartografia' [Cartography and other techniques and scientific practices of the Portuguese geographical discoveries: its influence abroad], in Carlos Motta (ed.), *Os Descobrimentos e a Expansão Portuguesa no Mundo. Actas do Curso de Verão 1994* (Lisbon: Universidade Lusíada, 1996), 109-132.

(editor), *Manual do Utilizador da Bibliografia Internacional dos Descobrimentos e Encontros Ultramarinos – International Bibliography of the Discoveries and Overseas Encounters: User's Handbook* (Coimbra-Figueira da Foz, 1996).

'New light on the problem of Cabrillo's origin', in Francis A. Dutra and João Camilo dos Santos (eds), *The Portuguese and the Pacific. Proceedings of the International Colloquium (Santa Barbara 1993)* (Santa Barbara: Center for Portuguese Studies, 1995 [1996]), 17-25.

Vida e obra do Infante Dom Pedro [Life and work of Prince Pedro] (Figueira da Foz: Centro de Estudos do Mar, 1996).

'A cartografia e a definição dos limites do Brasil' [The cartography and definition of the Brazilian borders], in *Memorias del Primer Simposio Panamericano de História* (Quito, Equador, 1988), vol. 1 (Mexico: Instituto Panamericano de Geografia e História, 1997), 179-189.

(with Kenneth Nebenzahl), 'Moreira's manuscript. A newly discovered Portuguese map of the world – made in Japan', *Mercator's World* 2:4 (1997): 18-23.

Vida e obra do 'Príncipe Perfeito' Dom João II [The life and work of the 'Perfect Prince' King João II] (Figueira da Foz: Centro de Estudos do Mar; Mira: Câmera Municipal de Mira, 1997).

MARSHALL, Brian
Geography Librarian
University of Auckland
Private Bag 92019
AUCKLAND
New Zealand
Tel: (64) 9 373 7599 ex 8452
E-mail: bw.marshall@auckland.ac.uz

New Zealand maps in nineteenth-century periodicals; New Zealand maps published by Justus Perthes; history of surveying and mapping in New Zealand

(with Jan Kelly), *Atlas of New Zealand Boundaries* (Auckland: Auckland University Press, 1996).

'Maps of New Zealand published in the journals of the Royal Geographical Society, 1831-1950', *New Zealand Map Society Journal* 10 (1996): 1-9.

MARSHALL, James A.
1828 South Roselle Road
SCHAUMBURG, Illinois 60172-5016
USA
Tel: (1) 708 529 3471

American Indian mathematics and cartography; black African people's scripts, mathematics and cartography

MARTINIC BEROS, Mateo
Academia Chilena de la Historia
Almirante Montt 454
SANTIAGO
Chile
Tel: (56) 2 639 9323

History of cartography of Magellan Strait

MARTIN-MERÁS, Luisa
Map Curator
Museo Naval de Madrid
Montalbán, 2
28071 MADRID
Spain
Tel: (34) 91 379 5052
Fax: (34) 91 379 5056
E-mail: mleras@santandersupemet.com

Spanish nautical cartography; Spanish hydrographical service; cartobibliography of atlases

'Un mapa desconocido de las Islas Canarias', *Revista de Historia Naval* 54 (1996): 97-111.

'La cartografía de los navegantes y de los descubrimientos', in *De la cartografía de los navegantes a la cartografía medioambiental* (Alicante: Universidad de Alicante, 1997).

'Spanish cartographic collection of the northwest coast of America in the Naval Museum in Madrid', in *Nutka, regreso a una historia olvidada* (Madrid: Ministerio de Asuntos Exteriores, 1998), 67-82.

MARTINS, Luciana de Lima
Department of Geography
Royal Holloway, University of London
EGHAM, Surrey TW20 0EX
UK
Tel: (44) 01784 434455 (office)   (44) 0181 840 2526 (home)
Fax: (44) 01784 437520
E-mail: l.martins@rhbnc.ac.uk

19th-century mapping in South America

'Navigating in tropical waters: British maritime views of Rio de Janeiro', *Imago Mundi*, 50 (1998): 141-155.

MASON, Adair Stuart (Dr)
Pelham, 61A Main Road
GILDEA PARK, Essex RM2 5EH
UK
Tel: (44) 01708 744 606

Estate maps of Essex and
their makers

MASON, Roger
Flat 3
189 Woodstock Road
OXFORD
UK
Tel: (44) 01865 552 776

Gough map of Great
Britain; medieval and early
renaissance regional cartography

McCORKLE, Barbara B.
1704 Carmel Drive
LAWRENCE, Kansas 66047
USA
Tel: (1) 785 838 4193
Fax: (1) 785 838 4194
E-Mail: bmccorkl@kuhub.cc.ukans.edu

18th-century English and
American geography; pre-
1800 cartography of New
England

The 16th International Conference on the History of Cartography:
report', *Imago Mundi* **48** (1996): 206-208.

'A mid-continent map collection: early maps at the University of
Kansas', *Meridian: A Journal of the Map and Geography Round Table
of the American Library Association* (Springfield, Missouri; 1997): 11,
23-26.

McELFRESH, Earl Bentley
McElfresh Map Company
P.O. Box 565
OLEAN, New York 14760
USA
Tel: (1) 716 372 8800 (office)
Fax: (1) 716 372 8090

American Civil War mili-
tary maps, mapmakers and
map making, for an atlas of
American Civil War maps

(1) 716 372 1034 (home)

McINTOSH, Gregory C.
19615 Donna Avenue
CERRITOS, California 90703-6436
USA
Tel: (1) 562 924 4348
E-mail: plusultra@hotmail.com

Piri Reis's 1513 map;
medieval and renaissance
maps of the North
Atlantic, Arctic and
America, particularly the
West Indies and
Newfoundland; exploration
and 16th-century mapping
of America

McKEE, Marianne M.
Map Specialist
The Library of Virginia
800 East Broad Street
RICHMOND, VA 23219
USA
Tel: (1) 804 692 3575
Fax: (1) 804 692 3556
E-mail: mmckee@vsla.edu

Virginia cartography;
preparation of an atlas of
Vriginia maps (with
Richard W. Stephenson)

McKENZIE, Stephen John Lynch
English Department
University of Adelaide
NORTH TERRACE, South
    Australia 5005
Australia
Tel: (61) 08 8373 2229
E-mail: smckenzi@arts.adelaide.edu.au

Quadripartite symbolism
on English and related
mappaemundi; develop-
ment of a mythology about
Asia and Africa in medieval
travel literature

McKINNON, Malcolm Arthur (Dr)
Historical Branch
Department of Internal Affairs
PO Box 805
WELLINGTON
New Zealand
Tel: (64) 4 494 0635
Fax: (64) 4 495 7212
E-mail: malcolm.mckinnon@dia.govt.nz

Maps of New Zealand prior
to 1950

(editor), *New Zealand Historical Atlas* (Auckland: David Bateman
Ltd, in association with Historical Branch, Dept of Internal Affairs,
Wellington, 1997).

McLAUGHLIN, Glen
14016 Camino Barco
SARATOGA, California 95070-5661
USA
Tel: (1) 408 867 9161 (office)   (1) 408 867 5366 (home)
Fax: (1) 408 867 5817
E-mail: vla@ix.netcom.com

California as an island maps

(with Nancy H. Mayo), *The Mapping of California as an Island: An Illustrated Checklist* (California Map Society Occasional Paper no 5; Saratoga, CA: California Map Society, 1995).

(with W. Michael Mather and Rosero L. Mayer), 'The island of California: a curious New Spain map of 1727', *Calafia* 8:5 (April 1997): 9-14.

MEER, Sjoerd de
Curator of Maps
Maritiem Museum 'Prins Hendrik'
Leuvehaven 1
3011 EA ROTTERDAM
Netherlands
Tel: (31) 010 413 2680
Fax: (31) 010 413 7342
E-mail: demeer@mmph.nl

Dutch cartography between the 16th and 20th centuries

MERCIER, Raymond Paul (Dr)
11 Ashton Close, Needingworth
ST IVES, Cambs PE17 3UB
UK
Tel: (44) (01480) 494209

Determination of alignments in the star map in Ptolemy's *Almagest*

MERRIMAN, Marcus H. (Dr)
Department of History
University of Lancaster
LANCASTER LA1 4YG
UK
Tel: (44) 01524 592505
Fax: (44) 01524 846102
E-mail:
m.merriman@lancaster.ac.uk

Mapping the Anglo-Scottish frontier, 16th century; Italian 'engineers' in Britain, 16th century; the first ordnance survey?: Scotland in 1549; plattes and the evolution of the 'blueprint'

MESENBURG, Peter (Prof Dr-Ing)
Universität GH Essen
Fachbereich Vermessungswesen
Henri Dunantstr. 65
D-45131 ESSEN
Germany
Tel: (49) 201 183 7336 (office)   (49) 201 738 925 (home)
Fax: (49) 201 183 7379
E-mail: peter.mesenburg@uni-essen.de

Portolan charts; medieval maps; historical cadastral maps; visualization and representation of geo-data

'Netzgeometrie und Abbildungskonzept der Karte des Nicolaus von Cues (Eichstätt 1491)', in D. Klemp and H.J. Lagoda (eds), *Zur Geschichte des Vermessungswesens* (VDV-Schriftreihe Bd **8**; Weisbaden, Chmielorz, 1995), 46-53.

'Germania Universalis: Untersuchungen zur Netzgeometrie der Mercator-Karte aus dem Jahre 1585', in W. Scharfe (ed), *Gerhard Mercator und seine Zeit. 7. Kartographiehistorisches Colloquium Duisburg 1994* (Duisburg: Braun, 1996), 49-66.

'Geschichte vermessen', in H. Koschik (ed), *Archäologie im Rheinland 1996, Landschaftsverband Rheinland* (Bonn: R. Habelt, 1997), 99-102.

MEURER, Peter H.
University of Utrecht
Department of Cartography
Postbus 80 115
NL-3508 TC UTRECHT
Netherlands

Dutch-born mapmakers working outside the Netherlands (pre-1700)

'Ein frühes Landkarten-Autograph Christian Sgrothens in der Trierer Stadtbibliothek?' *Kurtrierisches Jahrbuch* **33** (1993): 123-134.

'Le territoire allemand' (334-349), 'Les territoires de la couronne polonaise' (350-359); 'Les fils et petit-fils de Mercator' (370-385), in Marcel Watelet (ed), *Gérard Mercator cosmographe – Le temps et l'espace* (Antwerp: Fonds Mercator Paribas, 1994).

'De verboden eerste uitgave van de Henegouwen-kaart door Jacques de Surhon uit het jaar 1572', *Caert-Thresoor* **13** (1994): 81-86.

'Widmungsexemplare der Wachtendonk-Pläne Gerhard Stempels von 1588', *Kurtrierisches Jahrbuch* **34** (1994): 129-140.

Cartographica Rarissima II: Willem Janszoon Blaeu, Nova et accurata totius Germaniae tabula (Amsterdam 1612) (Alphen aan den Rijn: Canaletto, 1995).

'Hintergründe und Analysen zu Tobias Mayers "Kritischer Karte von Deutschland"', *Cartogrpahica Helvetica* 12 (1995): 19-26.

'Der kurtrierische Beitrag zum Kosmographieprojekt Sebastian Münsters', *Kurtrierisches Jahrbuch* 35 (1995): 189-225.

'Die "Poliographia Germanica" von Joannes Janssonius (Amsterdam 1616). Zur Editionsgeschichte des ersten Städteatlas von Deutschland', in Joachim Neumann (ed), *Karten hüten und bewahren: Festgabe für Lothar Zögner (Kartensammlung und Kartendokumentation* 11; Gotha: Verlag Justus Perthes, 1995), 97-117.

'Cartographica in den Frankfurter Messekatalogen Georg Willers von 1564 bis 1592', *Cartographica Helvetica* 13 (1996): 31-37.

'Sebastian Münsters Karte der Eifel in quellenkundlicher Sicht', in Friedhelm Burgand (ed), *Beiträge zur mittelalterlichen Geschichte und geschichtlichen Landeskunde (Trierer Historische Forschungen* 28 (1996)), 517-526.

'Eine Rechnung für eine Kartenlieferung des Hauses Fugger an Alonso de Santa Cruz von 1546', *Cartographica Helvetica* 16 (1997): 31-38.

'Die Kölner Jesuiten Franz und Hermann Joseph Hartzheim als Kartographen', *Annalen des Historischen Vereins für den Niederrhein* 200 (1997): 107-133.

'Die "Trevirensis Episcopatus exactissimo descriptio" des Jan van Schilde: Analysen zur ältesten gedruckten Karte von Kurtrier', in Roland Baumhauer (ed), *Aktuelle Forschungen aus dem Fachbereich VI Geographie Geowissenschaften (Trier Geographische Studien* 16 (1997)), 285-300.

'Zwei Briefe Tilemann Stellas von 1558 an Hartmann Beyer. Die frühesten bekannten Belege zu den Arbeiten am ersten systematischen Deutschland-Kartenwerk', *Hessisches Jahrbuch für Landesgeschichte* 47 (1997): 85-104.

'Ein Mercatorbrief an Philipp Melanchthon über seine Globenlieferung an Kaiser Karl V. im Jahre 1554', *Der Globusfreund* 45/46 (1998): 187-196.

MICHEA, Hubert (Captain)
148 rue Lecourbe
PARIS 75015
France
Tel: (33) 01 45 32 29 76
E-mail: hubert.michea@wanadoo.fr

Early medieval nautical maps; DATI maps

'Histoire de la région Brestoise deux anniversaires', *Marine, revue de l'ACROAM* 165 (octobre 1994): 26-29.

'Quelques reflexions à propos de l'anneau astronomique vu à l'exposition "On a retrouvé le San Diego"', *Navigation* (L'Institut Français de Navigation), 43 (no 170, avril 1995): 258-265.

(editor), *Voyage de la mer du Sud aux côtes du Chili et du Pérou* [édition critique de Amédée Frézier d'après l'édition de 1716], Paris: UTZ 1995).

'Frézier, Cassini et la longitude', *Actes du congrès du CTHS*, Nice 1996.

MICHEL-ZAITSU, Wolfgang
Institute of Languages and Cultures
Kyushu University
4-2-1 Roppon Matsu
CHUOKU, FUKUOKA CITY 810
Japan
Tel: (81) 092 771 4161
Fax: (81) 092 731 8745

Maps of Japan and China prior to 1900; map making in Tokugawa, Japan; Romanization of Chinese and Japanese place names on Western maps

MIEKKAVAARA, Leena Kyllikki
Pyörrekuja 12
04300 TUUSULA
Finland
Tel: (358) 09 2756 476 (office)
     (358) 050 590 2756
Fax: (358) 09 2320 052
     (358) 09 8718 3450

Ptolemy's Geography in Nordenskiöld's Facsimile Atlas; catalogue of the maps of Karelia (1550-1968) in the A. Piltz's Collection

MILANESI, Marica (Prof)
Dipartimento Storico-Geografico
Università degli Studi
Strada Nuova 65
27100 PAVIA
Italy

Vincenzo Coronelli; geography and cartography in the 15th century

'Il commento al Dittamondo di Guglielmo Capello (1435-1437)', in Marco Bertozzi (ed), *Alla corte degli Estensi: Filosofia, arte e cultura a Ferrara nei secoli XV e XV* (Ferrara: Università degli Studi, 1994), 365-388.

'Geography and cosmography in Italy from XV to XVII century', *Memorie della Società Astronomica Italiana/Journal of the Italian*

Astronomical Society 65:2 (1994): 443-468.

'A forgotten Ptolemy: Harley Codex 3686 in the British Library', *Imago Mundi* 48 (1996): 43-64.

(with L. Gambi and A. Pinelli), *La Galleria delle Carte geografiche in Vaticano* (Modena: Panini, 1996).

MILLEA, Nick
Map Curator
Bodleian Library
Broad Street
OXFORD, OX1 3BG
UK
Tel: (44) 01865 277013 (office)   (44) 01608 810370 (home)
Fax: (44) 01865 277139
E-mail: nam@bodley.ox.ac.uk
Web: http://www.bodley.ox.ac.uk/guides/maps/

Developing the cartographical collections at the Bodleian Library

All at sea: the story of navigational charts: an exhibition to celebrate two hundred years of the Hydrographic Office (Oxford: Bodleian Library, 1995).

MIŠKOVIĆ, Veselin
National and University Library
Turjaška 1
1001 LJUBLJANA
Slovenia
Tel: (386) 61 125 0141
Fax: (386) 61 125 7293
E-mail:
veselin.miskovic@nuk.umi-lj.si

Slovenian cartography; iconography on maps, in atlases (frontispieces), and in geography and travel literature related to the discovery of America (1492-1850) as a visualization of Western concepts of other lands and peoples

'Imago Sloveniae', in M. Glavan (ed.), *Naša beseda in zemljevidi slovenskega ozemlja: vodnik po razstavi* [Slovenian literature and maps of Slovenian territory: exhibition catalogue] (Ljubljana: Narodna in univerzitetna knjižnica, 1997), 17-37.

MITCHELL, Rose
Map and Picture Department
Public Record Office
KEW, Surrey TW9 4DU
UK
Tel: (44) 0181 876 3444
Fax: (44) 0181 878 8905

Early maps in the PRO; estate maps in the PRO

MIYOSHI Tadayoshi (Dr)
24, Kyo-machi
Chuo-Ku
KOBE 650-0034
Japan
Tel: (81) 078 391 0035
Fax: (81) 078 392 7054

History of Japanese cartography; early cartographical communication between Japan and Europe

MOFFAT, Riley Moore (Prof)
Box 1966
Joseph F. Smith Library
Brigham Young University-Hawaii
LAIE, Hawaii 96762
USA
Tel: (1) 808 293 3884 (office)
     (1) 808 293 1106 (home)
Fax: (1) 808 293 3877
E-mail: moffatr@byuh.edu

Cartography of Hawaii and the Pacific islands, particularly the work of the Hawaiian government survey, c.1870-1900 (with Gary L. Fitzpatrick); western North America; population history of Canada, Australia, New Zealand from 1850

(with Gary L. Fitzpatrick), *Surveying the Mahele: Mapping the Hawaiian Land Revolution* (Vol 2 of Palapala'aina; Honolulu: Editions Limited, 1995).

Population History of Western U.S. Cities and Towns, 1850-1990 (Lanham, Md: Scarecrow Press, 1996).

MOJSKI, Piotr Maria (Mgr)
Foehrliweg 17
CH-8600 DÜBENDORF
Switzerland
Tel: (41) 1 294 6592 (office)   (41) 1 821 8639 (home)
     (41) 79 423 4912 (office)
Fax: (41) 1 294 6506 (office)   (41) 79 606 7064 (home)
E-mail: mojski_piotr@swissonline.ch

Rare maps of Poland

Cartographia Rappersviliana Polonorum: Rare Maps Collection Catalogue (Rapperswil, Switzerland: Polish Museum Rapperswil, 1995).

MOKRE, Jan
Map Curator
Österreichische Nationalbibliothek
Kartensammlung und
    Globenmuseum
Josefsplatz 1
A-1015 WIEN
Austria
Tel: (43) 1 53 410 298
Fax: (43) 1 53 410 319
E-mail: mokre@grill.onb.ac.at

18th and early 19th century maps of Vienna and its environs

'Das große 18. Jahrhundert der Wiener Stadtkartographie', in Karl Fischer (ed), *Das ist die stat Wienn. Vom Albertinischen Plan zur Computerstadtkarte–Ein halbes Jahrtausend Wiener Stadtkartographie* (= *Wiener Geschichtsblätter* 4, 1995): 29-37.

(with Franz Wawrik, Helga Hühnel and Elisabeth Zeilinger), *Kartographische Zimelien. Die 50 schönsten Karten und Globen der Österreichischen Nationalbibliothek* (Wien: Holzhausen, 1995).

'"Die Mitführung einer Landkarte ist unerläßlich": die kartographische Entdeckung der Wiener Gegenden im Biedermeier', in Joachim Neumann (ed), *Karten hüten und bewahren: Festgabe für Lothar Zögner* (*Kartensammlung und Kartendokumentation* 11; Gotha: Verlag Justus Perthes, 1995), 119-139.

'The environs map: Vienna and its surroundings c.1650-c.1850', *Imago Mundi* 49 (1997): 90-103.

'Immensum in parvo–Der Globus als Symbol', in Peter E. Allmayer-Beck (ed), *Modelle der Welt. Erd- und Himmelsgloben. Kulturerbe aus österreichen Sammlungen* (Wien: Brandstätter, 1997), 70-87.

MONMONIER, Mark (Prof Dr)
Department of Geography
Syracuse University
SYRACUSE, NY 13244-1090
USA
Tel: (1) 315 443 2605 (office)
Fax: (1) 315 443 4227
E-mail: mon2ier@syr.edu

History of cartography in the 20th century; map design; map use and mapping policy

(1) 315 446 1508 (home)

'Cartocontroversy: tales of maps of weapons of persuasion and deception', *Mercator's World* 1:1 (1996): 22-25.

'Cartography', in Adam Kuper and Jessica Kuper (eds), *Social Science Encyclopedia* (2nd ed.; London and New York: Routledge, 1996), 74-75.

Eins ze einer Million: Die Tricks und Lügen der Kartographen, Doris Gerstner, trans. (Basel: Birkhaüser Verlag, 1996).

'Graphic narratives for emergency mapping', in Ferdinand Mayer and Karel Kriz (eds), *Kartographie im multimedialen Umfeld* (Wiener Schriften zur Geographie und Kartographie, 5. Wiener Symposium; Wien: Institut für Geographie der Universität Wien, Ordinariat für Geographie und Kartographie, 1996), 186-190.

How to Lie with Maps (2nd ed.; Chicago: University of Chicago Press, 1996).

'Maps that speak for themselves: viewer-friendly multimedia cartography is just around the corner', *Marketing Tools* [an American Demographics/Dow Jones publication] (March 1996): 8-12.

Cartographies of Danger: Mapping Hazards in America (Chicago: University of Chicago Press, 1997).

'The cartography of danger: hazard maps as social constructions', *Mercator's World* 2:3 (1997): 52-56.

'The rise of the national atlas', in John A. Wolter and Ronald E. Grim (eds), *Images of the World: The Atlas through History* (Washington, DC: Library of Congress, 1997).

'Scripting and geographic templates for pattern matching with epidemiological distributions', in Robert Aangeenbrug and others (eds), *Proceedings of the International Symposium on Computer Mapping in Epidemiology and Environmental Health* (Tampa, Florida: World Computer Graphics Foundation, 1997), 96-104.

'The weather map: exploiting electronic telecommunications to forecast the geography of the atmosphere', in Susan Hanson (ed), *Ten Geographic Ideas That Changed the World* (New Brunswick, NJ: Rutgers University Press, 1997), 40-59.

MONTANER GARCIA,
Carme (Dr)
Curator of the Aerial Photo Archive
Institut Cartogràfic de Catalunya
Parc de Montjuic
E-08038 BARCELONA
Spain
Tel: (34) 3 425 29 00 (office)   (34) 3 886 18 22 (home)
Fax: (34) 3 426 74 42
E-mail: cmontaner@icc.es

Catalan cartographers; the map as a political and social symbol; topographical maps of 19th and 20th century

[Cataloger of maps in]: *Portolans procedents de collecions espanyoles* [Portolan charts from Spanish collections] (Barcelona: Institut Cartogràfic de Catalunya, 1995).

MOORE, John Nicholas
Glasgow University Library
Hillhead Street
GLASGOW G12 8QE
UK
Tel: (44) 0141 330 6749
Fax: (44) 0141 330 4952
E-mail: j.n.moore@lib.gla.ac.uk

Scottish cartography, especially the work of John Adair (1660-1718) and John Watt (1684-1737); urban cartography and the work of the early Ordnance Survey in Scotland

'Glasgow surveyors, 1719-1854: an index', University of Glasgow, Department of Geography, *Occasional Papers*, no. 32 (1995).

'The Ordnance Survey 1:500 town plan of Glasgow: a study of large-scale mapping, departmental policy and local opinion', *Cartographic Journal* 32 (1995): 24-32.

'Heritage and mapping: a future for the past? Some thoughts from a distance', *The Globe* (Journal of the Australian Map Circle) 44 (1996): 17-23.

The Maps of Glasgow: A History and Cartobibliography to 1865 (Glasgow: Glasgow University Library, 1996).

'"Many years servant to the town": James Barrie and the eighteenth century mapping of Glasgow, *Scottish Geographical Magazine* 113 (1997): 105-112.

MORRIS, R.J.
Department of Economic and
    Social History
William Robertson Building
University of Edinburgh
George Square
EDINBURGH EH8 9JY
UK
Tel: (44) 0131 650 3834
E-mail: rjmorris@holyrood.ed.ac.uk

Maps in 19th and 20th century urban history in Britain, Ireland and Canada; 19th century maps in computer-based social history teaching projects

MUCHA, Ludvík (Dr)
Pod lípami 58
130 00 PRAHA 3
Czech Republic
Tel: (420) 2 827 8854

History of cartography of Czech lands; catalogue of Czech atlases and globes

(with J Dörflinger and H Hühnel), *Atlantes Austriaci: Österreichische Atlanten 1561-1918* (2 vols.; Wien: Böhlau, 1995).

'Děčínsko na starých mapách' [Tetschenland on old maps], *Sborník České geografické společnosti* 100:4 (1995): 234-238.

'Die Globen des Prager Astronomen Josef Georg Böhm (1807-1868)' *Der Globusfreund* 43/44 (1995): 227-236.

'Ivančicko na starých mapách' [Ivančice country on old maps], *Ivančický zpravodaj* 25:4 (1996): 17-21.

'The life and work of Professor Karel Kuchař', *Acta Universitatis Carolinae–Geographica* 31:1 (1996): 5-20.

'The postal maps of František Jakub Jindřich Kreibich', *Acta Universitatis Carolinae–Geographica* 31:1 (1996): 203-210.

'Slovenská atlasová kartografie 1924-1990' [Slovak atlas cartography 1924-1990], in *Historické mapy* (Bratislava: Kartografická spoločnosť Slovenskej republiky, 1997), 174-181.

MUKERJI, Chandra (Prof)
Department of Communication
University of Calfornia, San Diego
LA JOLLA, CA 92093-0503
USA
Tel: (1) 619 534 3596 (office)   (1) 619 755 3520 (home)
Fax: (1) 619 534 7315
E-mail: cmukerji@ucsd.edu

Comparison of military, scientific, and forestry maps in late 17th to early 18th-century France

Territorial Ambitions and the Gardens of Versailles (Cambridge: Cambridge University Press, 1997).

MÜLLER, Theo (Dipl.-Ing.)
Ruedesheimer Strasse 8
D-53175 BONN
Germany
Tel: (49) 0228 310364

Organization, history and cartobibliography of Germany's official map series, military map series, and MilGeoWesen

MUMFORD, Ian
Brailes
Green Lane
CHESSINGTON KT9 2DS
UK
Tel: (44) 0181 397 2767

Lithography and maps

MUNDY, Barbara E. (Dr)
Department of Art History and
    Music, FMH 447
Fordham University
441 East Fordham Road
BRONX, NY 10458
USA
Tel: (1) 718 817 4897
Fax: (1) 718 817 4829
E-mail: barbaramundy@sprintmail.com

Indigenous cartography, Mexico and Peru, 16th century published maps

The Mapping of New Spain (Chicago: University of Chicago, 1996).
'Mapping the Aztec capital: the 1524 Nuremberg map of Tenochtitlan, its sources and meanings', *Imago Mundi*, **50** (1998): 11-33.

MURRAY, Jeffrey S.
National Archives of Canada
395 Wellington Street
OTTAWA, Ontario K1A 0N3
Canada
Tel: (1) 613 995 9519
Fax: (1) 613 996 8982
E-mail: jmurray@archives.ca

History of Canadian cartography, 19th and 20th centuries; military cartography; cartography and its social contexts

'The face of Armageddon: although maps played a vital role in defeating the German army during the Great War, Britain was initially unprepared for the vast number that would be needed', *Mercator's World* 1:2 (1996): 30-37.

'Mythical seas: Europe's quest for the orient', *Mercator's World* 1:1 (1996): 16-21.

'Selling golden dreams: misleading maps lured prospectors to the Klondike', *Canadian Geographic* 116:6 (1996): 46-47.

'Celestial delights: Europe's early infatuation with the universe', *Mercator's World* 2:1 (1997): 20-27.

'Going for gold: misleading maps lured prospectors to the Klondike," *Mercator's World* 2:4 (1997): 36-42.

MUSALL, Heinz (Prof Dr)
Fachhochschule Karlsruhe
Fachbereich Geoinformations-wesen
Bammentaler Strasse 39
D-69251 GAIBERG
Germany
Tel: (49) 06223 4382

Maps of the Rhine; maps and views of fortifications; world maps (17th-19th centuries); maps of north-west North America (western Canada and Alaska)

MYERS, James Phares, Jr.
Department of English
Gettysburg College
GETTYSBURG,
Pennsylvania 17325
USA
Tel: (1) 717 337 6761 (office)
    (1) 717 677 7420 (home)
Fax: (1) 717 337 6666
E-mail: eremond@gettysburg.edu

Pre-Revolutionary cartography of the Pennsylvania frontier; Thomas Hutchins; the Scull family of cartographers and surveyors (Pennsylvania)

NADAL PIQUE, Francesc (Prof Dr)
Department of Human Geography
University of Barcelona
c/ Baldini Reixac s/n
08028 BARCELONA
Spain
Tel: (34) 93 440 92 00
Fax: (34) 93 333 06 14
E-mail: fnadal@trivium.gh.ub.es

National topographical maps in Spain; contemporary urban and cadastral maps in Catalonia

(with Ignacio Muro and Luis Urteaga), 'Els estudis hidrològics de

Pedro Antonio de Mesa, 1862-1865', *Treballs de la Societat Catalana de Geografia* 40 (Barcelona, 1995): 33-41.

(with Ignacio Muro and Luis Urteaga), *Geografía, estadística y catastro en España, 1856-1870* (Barcelona: Ediciones del Serbal, 1996).

(with Luis Urteaga), 'El Mapa Topogràfic d'Espanya: l'arxiu dels canvis territorials', *L'Avenç* 224 (Barcelona, 1998): 51-54.

NALIS, Henk   Van Doetecum mapmakers
Stadsarchief
Klooster 3
7411 NH DEVENTER
Netherlands
Tel: (31) 0570 693713 (office)   (31) 0570 615981 (home)
Fax: (31) 0570 693437

'Cresfeldts kaart van de "Iselstroom" uit het midden van de 16de eeuw' [Cresfeldt's map of the River Issel from the middle of the 16th century], *Caert-Thresoor* 15:1 (1996): 6-7.

NEBENZAHL, Kenneth   World maps to 1800;
P.O. Box 370   North America to 1900;
GLENCOE, Illinois 60022-0370   southwestern Colorado;
USA   Middle East; Holy Land-
Tel: (1) 847 835 0515   Israel-Palestine; Himalayas;
Fax: (1) 847 835 0519   Rand McNally Christmas
                                card maps, 1948-1997;
                                Buondelmonte manuscript
                                atlases; maps and US
                                Presidents; Great Wall of
                                China

Atlas zum Heiligen Land, Karten der Terra Sancta durch zwei Jahrtausende (Stuttgart: Verlag Katholisches Bibelwork, 1995), first published in the United States as *Maps of the Holy Land* (New York, 1986).

'Zaddiq's Canaan', Israeli Map Collectors' Society *Journal* 13 (1996): 25-35.

(with Alfredo Pinheiro Marques): 'Moreira's manuscript, a newly discovered Portuguese map of the world---made in Japan', *Mercator's World* 2:4 (1997): 18-23.

NEUMANN, Joachim (Prof Dr)   History of German cartog-
Hochschule für Technik (FH)   raphy; history of charts
    Karlsruhe
Moltkestr. 30
D-76012 KARLSRUHE
Germany
Tel: (49) 0721 925 2632 (office)   (49) 07243 61690 (home)
Fax: (49) 0721 925 2591

(editor), *Karten hüten und bewahren: Festgabe für Lothar Zögner* (*Kartensammlung und Kartendokumentation* 11; Gotha: Verlag Justus Perthes, 1995).

'Das Werden des kartographischen Deutschlandbildes', *Mitteilungen, Freundeskreis für Cartographica in der Stiftung Preussischer Kulturbesitz e. V.* 11 (1997), 16-24.

NEWMAN, Alfred William   Early maps of California
1414 Mariposa Street   and the American West
VALLEJO, California 94590
USA
Tel: (1) 707 642 9091

NICHOLSON, Timothy Robin (Dr)   Map publishers' ephemera;
187 Russell Court   Bartholomew maps
Woburn Place
LONDON WC1H 0LR
UK
Tel: (44) 0171 837 6319

NIEWODNICZANSKI,   Cartography of Poland and
    Thomas (Dr)   Eastern Europe
Heinrichstr 24A
D-54634 BITBURG
Germany
Tel: (49) 6561 14212 (office)   (49) 6561 14217 (home)
Fax: (49) 6561 14499 (office)   (49) 6561 940128 (home)
E-mail: dr.t.niewodniczanski@t-online.de

NOLAN, Michael A. (Col)
Tall Trees, Broad Layings
Woolton Hill
NEWBURY, Berks RG20 9TS
UK
Tel: (44) 01635 253167
E-mail: maptnolan@aol.com

Thomas Best Jarvis and the Topographical & Statistical Depot of the War Office 1854-1857; maps of the Topographical Branch of the Intelligence Department 1857-1880; maps of the Crimean and Boer wars, of the Gallipoli, Macedonian, Egypt, Palestine and East African campaigns, of the Ottoman Empire and Turkey

NOVÁK, Václav (Ing-Dr)
Natural Science Faculty
Palacký University
tř. Svobody 26
771 46 OLOMOUC
Czech Republic
Tel: (420) 68 522 2451
Fax: (420) 68 522 3757
E-mail: geogr@risc.upol.cz

History of cartography of Moravia and Upper Silesia

NUTI, Lucia
Dipartimento di Storia delle Arti
Università di Pisa
Pz. S. Matteo 2
I-56127 PISA
Italy
Tel: (39) 050 542345
Fax: (39) 050 580128

Art and cartography (15th to 18th centuries); urban mapping; relationship between verbal and visual description

'I teatri di città e l'Italia del secolo XVII: il ruolo delle imagine', in M.-A.. Brayer (ed), *Cartographiques: Actes du colloque de l'Académie de France à Rome* (Paris: Réunion des Musées nationaux, 1996), 105-123.

O'DEA, Fabian
12 Winter Place
ST JOHN'S,
    Newfoundland A1B 1J6
Canada
Tel: (1) 709 722 2127

Cartography of Newfoundland, 1500-1800

OEHRLI, Markus
Federal Office of Topography
Seftigenstrasse 264
Postfach
CH-3084 WABERN
Switzerland
Fax: (41) 31 963 24 59
E-mail:
markus.oehrli@switzerland.org

Biographical data on Swiss cartographers and map-makers; bibliography on the history of cartography in Switzerland; topographi-cal maps of Switzerland from 1800; co-editor *Cartographica Helvetica*

(with Madlena Cavelti Hammer and Hans-Uli Feldmann, eds), *Farbe, Licht und Schatten. Die Entwicklung der Reliefkartographie seit 1660* (Murten: Cartographica Helvetica, 1997).

(with Pierre Gerber), 'Unsere Bibliothek. Unsere Kartensammlung', *Personalzeitschrift Bundesamt für Landestopographie* **88** (1997): 8-16.

(with Gustav Forstner), 'Graphische Darstellungen der Untersuchungsergebnisse alter Karten und die Entwicklung der Verzerrungsgitter', *Cartographica Helvetica* 17 (1998): 35-43.

OKHUIZEN, Edwin (Drs)
Department of Cartography
Faculty of Geographical Sciences
University of Utrecht
P O Box 80115
3508 TC UTRECHT
Netherlands
Fax: (31) 302 54 06 04

Dutch cartography of Russia and the Baltic Sea (16th-18th centuries); car-tography of the Arctic (15th-19th centuries); car-tobibliography of maps in Dutch books about Russia, 1500-1800

'Nederlandse kartografen in dienst van Tsaar Peter de Grote. Een unieke Nederlandse inbreng van hydrografen en graveurs in het 18e-eeuwse Rusland' [Dutch cartographers in the service of Tsar Peter the Great], *Kartografisch Tijdschrift* **21**:4 (1995): 25-28.

'The cartography of the northern sea route, 15th-19th centuries', in H. Kitagawa (ed), *Northern Sea Route: Future & Perspective. The*

OLD CHURCH
GALLERIES

MATI HARRINGTON

~

ANTIQUE MAPS AND PRINTS OF ALL PARTS OF THE WORLD

~

320 KINGS ROAD, CHELSEA, LONDON SW3 5UH

TEL: 0171 351 4649   FAX: 0171 351 4449

Proceedings of INSROP Symposium Tokyo '95 (1–6 October 1995) (Tokyo, 1996), 567-576.

'Het kaartbeeld van het noordpoolgebied vóór Barentsz' [The mapping of the Arctic up to Willem Barents], *Spiegel Historiael* 31:10 (1996): 383-389.

'De Nederlandse bijdrage aan de kaartenverzameling van Peter de Grote' [The Dutch contribution to the map collection of Peter the Great], in R. Kistemaker et al. (eds), *Peter de Grote en Holland. Culturele en wetenschappelijke betrekkingen tussen Rusland en Nederland ten tijde van tsaar Peter de Grote* [Peter the Great and Holland. Cultural and scientific relations between Russia and the Netherlands in the time of Tsar Peter the Great] (Bussum/Amsterdam, 1996), 108-114.

OLIVER, Richard Ross (Dr)
Department of Geography
University of Exeter
EXETER EX4 4RJ
UK
Tel: (44) 01392 263348
Fax: (44) 01392 263342
E-mail: r.r.oliver@exeter.ac.uk

Enclosure, tithe, rating and other cadastral mapping of England and Wales; mapping urban areas in England and Wales; the Ordnance Survey

'The evolution of the Ordnance Survey National Grid', *Sheetlines* 43 (1995): 25-46.

'Railway revision on Ordnance Survey maps, 1880-1914', *Sheetlines* 42 (1995): 33-36.

'Sheet lines and overlaps of the one-inch Fifth and New Popular editions', *Sheetlines* 44 (1995): 22-44.

(with Roger J.P. Kain), *The Tithe Maps of England and Wales: A Cartographic Analysis and County-by-County Catalogue* (Cambridge: Cambridge University Press, 1995).

'The rivals: notes on some intermediate-scale commercial topographic map series of Britain and Ireland since 1868', *Sheetlines* 47 (1996): 8-36.

'Taking to the water: some examples of Ordnance Survey mapping of the coast', *Sheetlines* 45 (1996): 9-27.

'Cartographic discoveries', *Sheetlines* 49 (1997): 14-24.

'Ordnance Survey One-inch Old Series sheets: some notes on development and dating', *Sheetlines* 50 (1997): 11-31.

(with Roger J. P. Kain), 'Maps and the assessment of parish rates in nineteenth-century England and Wales', *Imago Mundi*, **50** (1998): 156-173.

O'LOUGHLIN, Thomas (Dr)
Department of Theology and
    Religious Studies
University of Wales Lampeter
LAMPETER, Ceredigion, Wales
    SA48 7JP
UK
Tel: (44) 01570 424708 (office)
    (44) 01570 421081 (home)
Fax: (44) 01570 423641
E-mail: o-loughlin@lamp.ac.uk

Maps in works of Isidore of Seville; maps found in connection with scriptural exegesis; whether the concept of mental maps can help in reading medieval religious texts

'"The Gates of Hell": from metaphor to fact', *Milltown Studies* **38** (1996): 89-114.

'The view from Iona: Adomnán's mental maps', *Peritia* 10 (1996): 98-122.

ORLIN, Lena Cowen (Prof)
Executive Director
Shakespeare Association of America
University of Maryland Baltimore
    County
1000 Hilltop Circle
BALTIMORE, MD 21250
USA
Tel: (1) 410 455 6788 (office)
Fax: (1) 410 455 1063 (office)
E-mail: saa@umbc.edu

Conceptual and cartographic mapping of English domestic spaces, 1500-1650

(1) 301 652 5705 (home)
(1) 301 652 5024 (home)

OSTROWSKI, Jerzy
Instytut Geografii i Przestrzennego
    Zagospodarowania PAN
ul. Twarda 51/55
00-818 WARSZAWA
Poland
Tel: (48) 22 697 8731 (office)
    (48) 22 624 8321 (home)
Fax: (48) 22 620 6221
E-mail: jostrow@kki.net.pl

Polish literature on the history of cartography; cartography in the Polish Kingdom, 1815-1915; 18th-century plans of Warsaw (with W. Wernerowa)

(with Jan Szeliga), 'Działalność profesora Stanisława Pietkiewicza w zakresie historii kartografii (w setną rocznicę urodzin)' [The work of professor Stanisław Pietkiewicz in the history of cartography (on his 100th birthday)], and 'Historia kartograffi w 24 tomaach powojennego "Polskiego Przeglądu Kartograficznego"' [The history of cartography in 25 volumes of the postwar 'Polish Cartographical Review'], in J. Ostrowski and W. Wernerowa (eds), *Z Dziejów Kartografii*, vol. 7: *Dwudziestolecie Zespołu Historii Kartografii* (Warsaw: Polska Akademia Nauk Instytut Historii Nauki, 1995), 59-71, 181-205.

(with Wiesława Wernerowa), 'Nieznana wersja wielkiego rękopiśmiennego planu Warszawy z 1771 roku w zbiorach Biblioteki Narodowej w Kijowie: Wiadomość wstępna' [The unknown version of a manuscript map of Warsaw issued 1771 from the collection of the National Library in Kiev], *Polski Przegląd Kartograficzny* 29:1 (1997): 32-35.

OSWALD, Diane L.
15889 Woodlake Drive
COLLEGE STATION, Texas 77845
USA
Tel: (1) 409 690 7251
E-mail: dianeoswald@juno.com

Fire insurance and other 19th and early 20th century commercial maps

'Could you be responsible for an environmental cleanup?' *Business Geographics* 3:6 (1995): 42-45.

'Fire insurance maps: history and uses', *The National Environmental Journal* (July/August 1995): 54-56.

'Geographic technology trends in insurance: an overview', *Business Geographics* 1:5 (1996): 26-28.

Fire Insurance Maps, Their History and Applications (College Station, TX: Lacewing Press, 1997).

PADRÓN, Ricardo A.
Department of Spanish, Italian and
    Portuguese
University of Virginia
Wilson 115
CHARLOTTESVILLE, VA 22903
USA
Tel: (1) 804 924 7543 (office)
Fax: (1) 804 924 7160
E-mail: rp2d@virginia.edu

Cartography and literature in the early modern period; mapping of the Americas; cartography and power; cartography and modernity

(1) 804 977 8929 (home)

PALADINI, Angel (Col)
Servicio Geográfico del Ejército
Cartoteca Historica
C/ Dario Gazapo 8
28024 MADRID
Spain
Tel: (34) 91 711 50 43, ext 252
Fax: (34) 91 711 50 32

Cartographical projection of portolan charts (14th-17th centuries); units of measurement in the Spanish kingdoms; methods of determining scale on old maps

PALSKY, Gilles Stéphane
Centre Géohistoire
9 rue Malher
75181 PARIS
France
Tel: (33) 1 45 17 11 41
Fax: (33) 1 45 17 11 85
E-mail: palsky@univ-paris12.fr

Colour in cartography in 19th-century Europe; thematic mapping in 19th and 20th century Europe

'La cartographie médicale et anthropologique' and 'Un monde fini, un monde couvert', in I. Poutrin (ed) *Le XIXe siècle. Science, politique et tradition* (Paris: Berger-Levrault, 1995), 206-233, 130-145.

(with M. Pelletier and P. Prost), *La cartografia francesa: 5è curs, 21-25 de febrer de 1994* (Barcelona: Institut cartogràfic de Catalunya, 1996).

Des chiffres et des cartes: naissance et développement de la cartographie quantitative française au XIXe siècle (Paris: Comité des travaux historiques et scientifiques, 1996).

PÁPAY, Gyula (Prof Dr)
Universität Rostock
Fachbereich Geschichtswissenschaften
August-Bebel-Str. 28
D-18051 ROSTOCK
Germany
Tel: (49) 0381 498 2730 (office)   (49) 0381 714 810 (home)
Fax: (49) 0381 498 2720
E-mail: gyula.papay@philfak.uni-rostock.de

History of theoretical cartography; history of cartography of Mecklenburg

'A térképtudomány fejlödésének alapvonalai (Grundlinien der Entwicklung der Wissenschaft Kartographie)', in *Kartográfiatörténet (Kartographiegeschichte)* (Budapest: Eötvös Loránd Tudományegyetem, 1995), 33-137 [English version: www http://lazarus.elte.hu].

'Digitale Karten zur Geschichte der Universität Rostock', in *Wissenschaftliche Tagung Universität und Stadt* (Rostock, 1995), 45-54.

'Ein bedeutender Kartograph in Mecklenburg: Tilemann Stella (1525-1589)', in *Stadt und Hof. Schwerin als Residenzstadt im 16. Jahrhundert* (Historisches Museum Schwerin, 1995), 93-98.

Historischer und geographischer Atlas von Mecklenburg und Pommern. Bd 2: Mecklenburg und Pommern: Das Land im Rückblick (Schwerin, 1996).

'Historische und Geo-Informationssysteme für Mecklenburg und Vorpommern', in Ilona Buchsteiner et al (eds), *Mecklenburg und seine ostelbische Nachbarn: Historisch-geographische und soziale Strukturen im regionalen Vergleich* (Schwerin, 1997), 264-361.

PARRY, David Emlyn (Dr)
Demeter House
Station Road
CAMBRIDGE CB1 2RS
UK
Tel: (62) 21 722 3177 (office) [Indonesia]
     (62) 21 750 2810 (home)
Fax: (62) 21 725 0721 (office)   (62) 21 750 2810 (home)
E-mail: dparry@rad.net.id

Cartographical history of Southeast Asia with particular reference to Indonesia and the Spice Islands

PASTOUREAU, Mireille (Dr)
Director
Bibliothèque de l'Institut de France
23, quai de Conti
75006 PARIS
France
Tel: (33) 01 44 41 44 10
Fax: (33) 01 44 41 44 11

French cartography, 16th to 18th centuries

'Entre Gaule et France: la Gallia', in Marcel Watelet (ed), *Gérard Mercator cosmographe* (Antwerp: Fonds Mercator, 1994), 316-333.

'La mappemonde', in Marcel Watelet (ed), *Gerardi Mercatoris Atlas Europae. Facsimilé des cartes de Gérard Mercator contenues dans l'Atlas de l'Europe, vers 1570-1572* (Antwerp: Fonds Mercator, 1994), 79-87. [English edition: *The Mercator Atlas of Europe* (Pleasant Hill, Oregon: Walking Tree Press, 1997).]

'French school atlases: sixteenth to eighteenth centuries', in John A. Wolter and Ronald E. Grim (eds), *Images of the World: The Atlas through History* (Washington, DC: Library of Congress, 1997), 109-134.

PATTON, Jeffrey
Department of Geography
University of North Carolina-
    Greensboro
GREENSBORO, NC 27402
USA
Tel: (1) 336 334 5388 (office)   (1) 336 271 6521 (home)
Fax: (1) 336 334 5864
E-mail: pattonj@durkheim.uncg.edu

Map design for children, development of 18th and 19th century school atlases; 19th-century thematic maps

Nineteenth Century Images of the World for American School Children (Slide Set and Commentary No. 20; Chicago: The Newberry Library, 1997).

PAVIOT, Jacques (Dr)
144 rue de Rennes
75006 PARIS
France
Tel: (33) 01 45 49 36 56

Medieval cartography

PAYNE, Anthony
c/o Bernard Quaritch Ltd
5-8 Lower John St.
Golden Square
LONDON W1R 4AU
UK
Tel: (44) 0171 734 2983 (office)   (44) 0181 947 2680 (home)
Fax: (44) 0171 437 0967 (office)   (44) 0181 947 2680 (home)
E-mail: rarebooks@quaritch.com

Bibliography of Richard Hakluyt (1552-1616), including the maps contained in his books

'Richard Hakluyt and his books', and (with P.A. Neville-Sington), 'An interim census of surviving copies of Hakluyt's *Divers Voyages* and *Principal Navigations*', Hakluyt Society *Annual Talk 1996* (London: Hakluyt Society 1997).

PEARCE, Margaret Wickens (Dr)
Department of Geography
Humboldt State University
ARCATA, California 95521
USA
Tel: (1) 707 826 4115
Fax: (1) 707 826 3205

Native and colonial mapping in southern New England, 1630s to 1750s; colonization and local, large-scale mapping; North American indigenous cartographical history

'Native mapping in southern New England Indian deeds', in G. Malcolm Lewis (ed), *Cartographic Encounters* (Chicago: University of Chicago Press, 1998), 157-186.

PEDLEY, Mary Sponberg
Assistant Curator of Maps
William L. Clements Library
University of Michigan
ANN ARBOR, Michigan 48109
USA
Tel: (1) 313 764 2347 (office)
     (1) 313 761 1728 (home)
Fax: (1) 313 747 0716
E-mail: mpedley@umich.edu

Associate Editor, *Imago Mundi*; French cartography, 17th to 19th century; map trade; scientific links between France and Italy during the Enlightenment

'"Commode, complet, uniforme, et suivi"': Problems in atlas editing in Enlightenment France', in Joan Winearls (ed), *Editing Early and Historical Atlases* (Toronto: University of Toronto Press, 1995), 83-108. [Re-published in *The Journal of Scholarly Publishing*, January 1996.]

'Maps, war, and commerce: business correspondence with the London map firm of Thomas Jefferys and William Faden, *Imago Mundi* 48 (1996): 161-173.

'Map wars: the role of maps in the Nova Scotia/Acadia boundary disputes of 1750', *Imago Mundi*, 50 (1998): 96-104.

PELLETIER, Monique
Map Curator
Cartes et Plans
Bibliothèque Nationale de France
58, rue de Richelieu
75084 PARIS
France
Tel: (33) 1 47 03 83 69
Fax: (33) 1 47 03 83 61
E-mail: monique.pelletier@bnf.fr

Renaissance globes; Portuguese and Catalan illuminated portolans

(with C. Hofmann, D. Lecocq, E. Netchine), *Le globe et son image* (Paris: Bibliothèque national de France, 1995).

'Die herzförmigen Weltkarten von Oronce Fine', *Cartographica Helvetica* 12 (1995): 27-37.

(with H. Ozanne), *Portraits de la France: les cartes témoins de l'histoire* (Paris: Hachette, 1995).

(with P. Prost and G. Palsky), *La cartografia francesa: 5è curs, 21-25 de febrer de 1994* (Barcelona: Institut cartogràfic de Catalunya, 1996).

How to Identify a Mapmaker: An International Bibliographic Guide / Comment identifier un cartographe: guide bibliographique internationale (Tring, Herts: Map Collector Publ.; Paris: Comité français de cartographie, 1996).

'Espace et temps. Mississippi et Louisiane sous le règne de Louis XIV: les hésitations de la géographie et de l'histoire', *Revue française d'histoire du livre* 94-95 (1997): 13-40.

'Les géographes et l'histoire, de la Renaissance au siècle des Lumières', in R. Pitte (ed), *Apologie pour la géographie: mélanges offerts à Alice Saunier-Seïté* (Paris: Société de géographie, 1997), 145-156.

'Sciences et cartographie marine', in E. Taillemite and D. Lieppe (eds), *La percée de l'Europe sur les océans vers 1690-vers 1790* (Paris: Presses de l'Université de Paris-Sorbonne, 1997), 265-291.

PENNING, William Edward (Drs)
Leyden University
Breitnerlaan 6
2391 GC HAZERSWOUDE
Netherlands
Tel: (31) 0171 589 789

Historical town plans, specially in the Netherlands

'Balthasar Florisz. van Berckenrode en de plattegrondjes in het *Theatrum* van Boxhorn' [Balthasar Florisz. van Berckenrode and the town plans in Boxhorn's *Theatrum*], *Caert-Thresoor* **16**:4 (1997): 85-87.

(with S. Groenveld and R.J.C. van Mannen), 'Leiden', in *Historische stadsplattegronden van Nederlandse steden*, Vol. 7 (Alphen a/d Rijn: Canaletto, 1997).

PFLEDERER, Richard L.
1628 Founder's Hill North
WILLIAMSBURG, Virginia 23185
USA
Tel: (1) 201 807 3349
Fax: (1) 201 641 6708
E-mail: rwdw38a@prodigy.com

Portuguese and Dutch discoveries in East and South Asia; Portuguese manuscript cartographers; early European influences in Japan

'Early European adventures and the opening of Japan', *Mercator's World* 1:3 (1996): 14-20.

'The legacy of the Itinerario: four centuries of European adventure in the East', *Mercator's World* 1:5 (1996): 22-29.

'The Portuguese century: the magnificent colonial maps of Fernão Vaz Dourado', *Mercator's World* 2:4 (1997): 24-28.

POBANZ, Wolfram
Institut für Kartographie
Freie Universität Berlin
Arno-Holz-Str. 12
D-12165 BERLIN
Germany
Tel: (49) 030 838 3893
Fax: (49) 030 838 6739

Map projections; cartographical technology in Germany

POKORNÝ, Ota (Dr)
Cihlářova 9/655
142 00 PRAHA 4
Czech Republic
Tel: (420) 2 471 1173

History of cartography of Czech lands; town plans

POLITES, Kiky
60 East Eighth Street
NEW YORK, NY 10003
USA
Tel: (1) 212 254 4577
Fax: (1) 212 995 8295
panantiquaria@mindspring.com

Publishing and engraving history of 16th-century 'IATO' atlases and their maps

POLK, Dora Beale (Dr)
Department of English
California State University, Long Beach
1250 Bellflower Boulevard
LONG BEACH, California 90840
USA
Tel: (1) 310 985 4223

Myth of the island of California, Francis Drake's landfall on the west coast of North America; John Dee's works

POLLAK, Martha (Prof)
Department of Art History
University of Illinois
935 W Harrison St.
CHICAGO, IL 60680
USA
Tel: (1) 312 413 2465
Fax: (1) 312 413 2460
E-mail: mpollak@uic.edu

Military contributions to 17th-century city plans

'Military architecture and cartography in the design of the Baroque city', in David Buisseret (ed) *Envisioning the City: Six Studies in Urban Cartography* (Chicago: University of Chicago Press, 1998).

POPE, Peter Edward (Dr)
Archaeology Unit
Department of Anthropology
Memorial University of
    Newfoundland
ST. JOHN'S, NF A1C 5S7
Canada
Tel: (1) 709 737 8311 (office)
    (1) 709 437 6134 (home)
Fax: (1) 709 737 2374
E-mail: ppope@plato.ucs.mun.ca

Port of St. John's,
Newfoundland; settlement
of Newfoundland's English
shore, 1610-1713, particularly South Avalon; voyages
of John Cabot; the early
modern fish trade; the early
modern wine trade

'A true and faithful account: Newfoundland in 1680',
Newfoundland Studies 12:1&2 (1996): 32-49.

The Many Landfalls of John Cabot (Toronto: University of Toronto
Press, 1997).

'The 16th-century fishing voyage', in C. Corbin (ed), *How Deep Is
the Ocean? History of the Northwest Atlantic Fishery* (Louisbourg
Institute; Sidney: University College of Cape Breton Press, 1997).

POST, Jeremiah Benjamin
Free Library of Philadelphia
1901 Vine Street
PHILADELPHIA, Pennsylvania
    19103
USA
Tel: (1) 215 563 4633
E-mail: postj@flpsys.library.phila.gov

Cartographical curiosities
and the borderlands of cartography; maps of
Philadelphia; illustrations
in North American county
atlases; artifacts (maps as
design objects)

'Dateline Philadelphia: maps about town', *NEMO Newsletter:
Quarterly Newsletter of the North East Map Organization*, No 25 (April
1997), 1-2.

POSTNIKOV, Alexei
    Vladimirovich (Prof Dr)
Institute of the History of Natural
    Sciences and Technology
1/5, Staropanskii St.
MOSCOW 103012
Russia
Tel: (7095) 925 70 03 (office)
Fax: (7095) 925 99 11
E:mail: apostnik@history.ihst.ru

History of cartography, historical geography.

(7095) 978 25 57 (home)

'Contact and conflict: Russian mapping of Finland and the development of Russian cartography in the 18th and early 19th centuries', *Fennia* 171:2 (Helsinki: Geographical Society of Finland,
1993): 63-98.

(compiler), *Karpinskii Collection Checklist: Provisional List* (Chicago:
Newberry Library, 1994).

*Geograficheskiye issledovaniy i kartografirovanie Pol'shi v poczesse soz-
daniya 'Topograficheskoi karty Czarstva Pol'skogo' (1818-1843 gg.)*
[Geographical exploration and mapping of Poland in the process of
the compilation of the 'Topographical Map of Polish Kingdom'
(1818-1843)] (Moscow: VINITI, 1995).

(with Evgenii M. Pospelov), 'The history of Russian names for seas,
with special reference on the development of the Korean (Japanese)
Sea presentation on maps (seventeenth through nineteenth centuries)', *The International Seminar on the Geographical Name of {East
Sea}*, Session 1 (Seoul, 1995): 32-65.

*The Mapping of Russian America: A History of Russian-American
Contacts in Cartography* (American Geographical Society Collection,
Special Publication No. 4; Milwaukee, 1995).

'K istorii kartografirovaniya severnoy chasti Tikhogo okeana i
Alyaski (do 80-kh gg. XVIII v.)' [On the history of mapping the
North Pacific and Alaska (prior to 1780s)], *Voprosy istorii yestestvoz-
naniya* 3 (1996): 108-125.

*Russia in Maps: A History of the Geographical Study and Cartography of
the Country* (Moscow: Nash Dom–L'Age d'Homme, 1996).

'Geograficheskiye issledovaniya v Russkoy Amerike (1741-1867
gg.) (K 130-letiyu prodazhi kolonyi Rossii Severo-Amerikanskim
Soedinennym Shtatam)' [Geographical Explorations in Russian
America (1741-1867) (The 130th anniversary of Alaska's purchase)], *Izvestiya Rossiyskoy Akademii Nauk, Seriya geograficheskaya* 3
(1997): 134-142.

'Prodazha Alaski i mezhdunarodnaia telegrafnaia ekspediziya'
[Alaska's Purchase, and International Telegraph Expedition],
Voprosy istorii estestvoznaniya i tekhniki 1 (1997): 3-38.

'Rossiiskoe nasledie na Alyaske (K 130-letiu prodazhi Russkoi
Ameriki)' [Russian heritage in Alaska (The 130th anniversary of
Alaska's purchase)], *Izvestiya RGO* 129:5 (1997): 60-70.

(with Józef Babicz), 'Statistical Atlas of the Polish Kingdom (1840)
as the thematic atlas, the monument of cartography, and the

source on the history of science', *Proceedings, 18th ICA/ACI Cartographic Conference*, Stockholm, 23-27 June 1997, Vol. 4 (Gävle, 1997), 2187-2194.

POTTER, Jonathan
125 New Bond St.
LONDON W1Y 9AF
UK
Tel: (44) 0171 491 3520
Fax: (44) 0171 491 9754
E-mail: jpmaps@ibm.net

General history of cartography

POTTER, Simon R. (Dr)
Faculty of Liberal Arts
Saitama University
Shimo-Okubo 255
URAWA-SHI, Saitama-ken
338 Japan
Tel: (81) 048 858 3088
Fax: (81) 048 858 3685

Japanese cartography; the legend of Noah's ark, part of which relies on old maps; Russian cartography; cartographic illustrations (cartouches, vignettes)

PRAVDA, Jan
Geografiký ùsto Sav
Stefànikova 49
81473 BRATISLAVA
Slovakia
E-mail: pravda@savba.sk

Prehistoric maps

'Najstaršie známe mapy' [The oldest known maps], in *Historické mapy: zborník z vedeckej konferencie, Bratislava, 24.–25. Apríla 1997* [Historical maps: papers from the Scientific Conference, Bratislava, 24th.–25th. April 1997] (Bratislava: Slovenský narodný archív, 1997), 76-88.

'The oldest-known map', *Mercator's World* 3:2 (1998): 82.

PRESCOTT, Dorothy Francis
44 Lucas St.
EAST BRIGHTON, Victoria 3187
Australia
Tel: (61) 3 9592 5156
Fax: (61) 3 9593 1624
E-mail: prescott@geography.unimelb.edu.au

Arrowsmith maps of Australia; aboriginal maps; cartobibliography of Australian maps in 19th-century books

(with T.M. Perry), *Guide to Maps of Australia in Books Published 1780 to 1830: An Annotated Cartobibliography* (Canberra: National Library of Australia, 1996).

'Maps of Australia in books: a cartobibliography', *The Globe: Journal of the Australian Map Circle* 45 (1997): 19-31.

PRESCOTT, John Robert Victor
   (Prof. emeritus)
44 Lucas St.
EAST BRIGHTON, Victoria 3187
Australia
Tel: (61) 3 9592 5156
Fax: (61) 3 9593 1624
E-mail: prescott@geography.unimelb.edu.au

Charts of the South China Sea before 1940; maps accompanying boundary treaties before 1950

(with David Hancox), *Secret Hydrographic Surveys of the South China Sea* (Kuala Lumpur: Maritime Institute of Malaysia, 1997).

'Significant contributions of maps to the development of international boundary disputes before 1914', *The Globe: Journal of the Australian Map Circle* 45 (1997): 42-54.

PRIKRYL, L'ubomír Viliam
A. Bernoláka 27
01001 ŽILINA
Slovakia
Tel: (421) 89 34845

Cartography of Slovakia

'Katalogizovanie starých máp zo zbierok Čaplovičovej knižnice v Dolnom Kubíne' [Cataloguing old maps from the collection of Čaplovic Library in Dolný Kubín], in *Historické mapy: zborník z vedeckej konferencie, Bratislava, 24.–25. Apríla 1997* [Historical maps: papers from the Scientific Conference, Bratislava, 24th.–25th. April 1997] (Bratislava: Slovenský narodný archív, 1997), 21-24.

PUCHADES BATALLER,
Ramon Josep
Universitat de València
Facultat de Geografia i Història
Unitat Docent de Paleografia i
Diplomàtica
Av. Blasco Ibáñez, 28
46010 VALÈNCIA
Spain
Tel: (34) 96 386 4239 (office)
Fax: (34) 96 386 4249
E-mail: ramon.j.puchades@uv.es

Portolan charts (13th-15th centuries); paleographical analysis and documentary research about mapmakers, charts and owners

(34) 96 396 0339 (home)

PUTMAN, Robert (Drs)
P.O.Box 30074
1007 KB, AMSTERDAM
Netherlands
Tel: (31) 20 670 1700
Fax: (31) 20 670 0350
E-mail: putmap@wxs.nl

Dutch sea charts; sea charts of the Dutch East India Company

QUINN, David Beers
(Prof emeritus)
9 Knowsley Road
LIVERPOOL L19 0PF
UK
Tel: (44) 0151 427 2041

Martin Frobisher and the north-west voyages, 1577-1579

'The early cartography of Maine', in Emerson L.W. Baker et al, *American Beginning: Exploration, Culture, and Cartography in the Land of Norumbega* (Lincoln: University of Nebraska Press, 1994), 37-60.

'The Northwest Passage in theory and practice', in J.L. Allen (ed), *North American Exploration* (Lincoln: University of Nebraska Press, 1997), 292-343.

RAINVILLE, Alain
National Archives of Canada
Visual and Sound Archives Division
Cartographic and Architectural
    Section
395 Wellington Street
OTTAWA, Ontario K1A 0N3
Canada
Tel: (1) 613 996 7618
Fax: (10 613 995 6226
E-mail: arainville@archives.ca

Canadian fire insurance plans, 1850s-1950s: production, legal deposit in Canada and Britain, linkage of Canadian copyright submissions with plans in map archives and libraries; true sets Canadian fortification surveys in the 1860s

'Fire insurance plans in Canada' = 'Les plans d'assurance contre l'incendie au Canada', *The Archivist* = *L'Archiviste* (Ottawa: National Archives of Canada), 111 (1996): 25–31.

RAMASWAMY, Sumathi (Dr)
Department of History
University of Pennsylvania
352 B, 3401 Walnut St.
PHILADELPHIA, PA 19104
USA
Tel: (1) 215 898 8452
Fax: (1) 215 573 2089
E-mail: ramaswam@mail.sas.upenn.edu

Fantasy lands, especially maps of lost islands and contients such as Atlantis and Lemuria; gender and cartography: use of female bodies in nationalist maps of India

RANDLES, William Graham
    Lister (Prof)
Maison des Pays Iberiques
Université de Bordeaux
12 rue de Gaulle
MEZIN 47170
France
Tel: (33) 53 65 71 25

History of the cartography of the discoveries

'Pedro Nunes discovery of the loxodromic curve (1537): how Portuguese sailors in the early sixteenth century, navigating with globes, had failed to solve the difficulties encountered with the plane chart', *Journal of Navigation* 50:1 (1997): 85-96.

RATCLIFF, James E., Jr.
300 Montgomery St., Suite 700
SAN FRANCISCO,
California 94104
USA
Tel: (1) 415 981 1434 (office)
Fax: (1) 415 989 7319

United States Coast Survey history and charts to c.1866

(1) 510 654 3180 (home)

RAURALA, Nils-Erik
John Nurminen Foundation
Rudolfintie 15.l
FIN-00870 HELSINKI
Finland
Tel & fax: (358) 9 698 7082

Sea charts of the Baltic Sea; maritime surveys in Swedish waters by Sir John Norris (Foulweather Jack)

Adam Olearius ja hänen Itämeren karttansa 'Mare Balticum oder Ost See' [Adam Olearius and his map 'Mare Balticum oder Ost See'] (Helsinki: FOI-International, 1995).

(editor), *Mare Balticum: 2000 vuotta Itämeren historiaa (Rinnakkaispainokset: Mare Balticum: The Baltic: 2000 Years; Mare Balticum: 2000 år av Östersjöns historia; Mare Balticum: 2000 Jahre der Geschichte der Ostsee),* by Ulla Ehrensvärd, Juha Nurminen and Pellervo Kokkonen (Helsinki, Otava ja John Nurminen Säätiö, 1995, 1996).

'Laivanvanustajan kartat' [Shipowners' sea charts and maps], *Bibliophilos* 55:4 (Forssa, 1996): 12-19.

'Nurmisen kattakokoelman harvinaisuuksia' [Specialties of the map collection of the John Nurminen Foundation] (Helsinki: Rotary Club of Helsinki, 1997).

RAVENHILL, Mary Rose
Westnorth
Beech Avenue
EXETER EX4 6HE
UK
Tel: (44) 01392 277 728

Large-scale manuscript maps of Devon – descriptive catalogue

'Sir William Courten and Mark Pierces's map of Cullompton of 1613', in Todd Gray (ed), *Devon Documents in Honour of Mrs. Margery Rowe* (Tiverton: Devon & Cornwall Notes & Queries, 1996), xix-xxiii.

RAY, P. Andrew
Department of Geography
Mackintosh-Corry Hall, D 201
Queen's University
KINGSTON, Ontario
Canada
Tel: (1) 613 378 1493
Fax: (1) 613 378 1494
E-mail: par@adan.kingston.net

Sociological history of cartography; cadastral mapping in Upper and Lower Canada, 1783-1840; 18th century British military and topographic mapping

REBERT, Paula (Dr)
922 Grove Street
DeKALB, Illinois 60115-4260
USA
Tel: (1) 815 758 0456
E-mail: prebert@niu.edu

United States-Mexico boundary maps and surveys

'Mapping the United States-Mexico boundary: cooperation and controversy', *Terrae Incognitae* **28** (1996): 58-71.

'The United States-Mexico boundary: manuscript maps of 1857', *Bulletin*, Special Libraries Association Geography and Map Division, 186 (Summer 1997): 2-35.

RECKER, Gabriele
Seminar für Historische Geographie
Konviktstr 11
D-53113 BONN
Germany
Tel: (49) 0228 735871 (office)
Fax: (49) 0228 737650 (office)
E-mail: uzswiz@uni-bonn.de

Cartography of the Rhineland (15th-19th centuries); cartography of roads

(49) 0228 476507 (home)

'Altkarten und ihre Auswertung: Kartographiegeschichte contra Historische Geographie?' in Klaus-Dieter Kleefeld and Peter Burggraaff (eds), *Perspektiven der Historischen Geographie: Siedlung – Kulturlandschaft – Umwelt in Mitteleuropa* (Bonn: Selbstverlag, 1997), 151-159.

'Augenschein in Sachen Köln contra Köln: Zwei Exemplare einer Prozeßkarte', *Jahrbuch des Kölnischen Geschichtsvereins* **68** (1997): 143-152.

REDMOND, Edward
Library of Congress
Geography and Map Division
101 Independence Avenue
WASHINGTON, DC 20540-4650
USA
Tel: (1) 202 707 8548
Fax: (1) 202 707 8531
E-mail: ered@loc.gov

Cartographic career of
George Washington, colo-
nial American land surveys

REINHARTZ, Dennis (Prof)
Department of History
Box 19529
The University of Texas at Arlington
ARLINGTON, TX 76019-0529
USA
Tel: (1) 817 272 2907 (office)
(1) 817 274 7086 (home)
Fax: (1) 817 272 2852
E-mail: dprein@utarlg.uta.edu

Herman Moll; native
Balkan cartography from
17th century to present;
18th-century maps of
northern New Spain;
Russian cartography

'The cartography of the interior: the American Southwest', *IMCoS Journal* 63 (1995): 9-11.

'Cartography', in *Encyclopedia of Latin American History* (New York: Charles Scribner's Sons, 1996), 583-586.

'Drawing the line: Herman Moll and the Texas-Louisiana border', *Frontieras* (Fall 1996): 2-3.

'Two manuscript maps of Nueva Santandar in northern New Spain from the eighteenth century', *British Library Journal* 22:1 (1996): 66-87 (also in Karen Severud Cook (ed), *Images and Icons of the New World: Essays on American Cartography* (London: The British Library, 1996), 66-87).

The Cartographer and the Literati: Herman Moll and His Intellectual Circle (Lewiston/Queenston/Lampeter: The Edwin Mellen Press, 1997).

REITINGER, Franz (Dr)
Linzergasse 8
A-5020 SALZBURG
Austria
Tel: (43) 0662 884441
E-mail: fr-asb@salzburg.co.at

Cartographical curiosities
(religious, moral, political)
in Europe and the United
States, 16th to 19th cen-
turies

'"Kampf um Rom": Von der Befreiung sinnorientierten Denkens im kartographischen Raum am Beispiel einer Weltkarte des Papismus aus der Zeit der französischen Religionskriege', in Götz Pochat and Brigitte Wagner (eds), *Utopie: Gesellschaftsformen – Künstlerträume* (Graz: ADEVA 1996), 100-140.

'Die Konstruktion anderer Welten', in Brigitte Felderer (ed), *Wunschmaschine Welterfindung: Eine Geschichte der Technikvisionen seit dem 18. Jahrhundert* (Vienna: Springer, 1996), 145-166.

Schüsse, die ihn nicht erreichten. Eine Motivgeschichte des Gottesattentats (Paderborn: Verlag Ferdinand Schöningh, 1996).

RELAÑO, Francesc
Plaza Santa Maria Magdalena 2
25008 LLEIDA
Spain
E-mail: arelano@pie.xtec.es

Africa on medieval and
Renaissance maps; myths
and cartography; the diffusion of geographical knowledge from southern to
northern Europe in the
Renaissance

REN Jincheng
National Library of China
39 Bai Shi Qiao Road
BEIJING 10008
China
Tel: (86) 1 841 5566 ext 5054

Ancient Chinese cartogra-
phy; Chinese maps in for-
eign collections

REYES VAYSSADE, Martin
Ave. Toluca 1047 - A8
Col. Olivar de los Padres
DELEGACION ALVARO
OBREGÓN
01780 Mexico, D. F.
Tel: (52) 683 60 04
Fax: (52) 604 00 53

New Spain and Mexico
from 16th to 19th cen-
turies; pre-hispanic
Mesoamerican cartography

RICHARDSON, William Arthur Ridley
P.O. Box 33
MACCLESFIELD, South Australia 5153
Australia
Tel: (61) 8 8388 9078
Fax: (61) 8 8388 9522

Martellus's Dragon's Tail: a pre-Columbian map of South America? inscriptions on early maps; coastal place-name enigmas on early charts of England and Wales and in sailing directions; Ptolemy and the Miller Atlas

'The Smalls, Hats and Barrels: navigational and toponymic hazards', *Nomina* (Journal of the Society for Name Studies in Britain and Ireland), **17** (1994): 71-97.

'A cartographical nightmare: Manuel Godinho de Erédia's search for India Meridional', in Francis Dutra and João Camilo dos Santos (eds), *The Portuguese and the Pacific* (Santa Barbara: Center for Portuguese Studies, University of California, Santa Barbara, 1995), 314-348.

'A critique of Spanish and Portuguese claims to have discovered Australia', *Investigator* (Magazine of the Geelong Historical Society), **30**:3 (1995): 83-107; **30**:4 (1995): 131-147.

'Coastal place-name enigmas on early charts and in early sailing directions', *Journal of the English Place-Name Society* **29** (1996-1997): 5-61.

RICHEY, Michael W.
16 Lewes Crescent
BRIGHTON BN12 1GB
UK
Tel & fax: (44) 01273 680 835

Navigation in the great age of discovery (with D.W. Waters)

'A voyage of navigational discovery', *Journal of Navigation* **48** (1995).

RISTOW Walter W.
10450 Lottsford Road, No 4115
MITCHELLVILLE, Maryland 20721
USA
Tel: (1) 301 925 7362

History of United States road maps

'Early American atlases and their publishers', in John A. Wolter and Ronald E. Grim (eds), *Images of the World: The Atlas through History* (Washington, DC: Library of Congress, 1997), 301-329.

RITCHIE, George Stephen (Rear Admiral)
Sea View
Collieston
ELLON, Aberdeenshire AB41 8RS
UK
Tel: (44) 01358 751 216

Hydrographical personalities of various nationalities, their instruments and methods prior to 1950 and the computer age

No Day Too Long – A Hydrographic Tale (2nd ed; Edinburgh, Cambridge, Durham: Pentland Press, 1994).

The Admiralty Chart – British Naval Hydrography in the Nineteenth Century – A New Edition (Edinburgh, Cambridge, Durham: Pentland Press, 1995).

'The bicentenary of the British Hydrographic Office: the first hundred years', *IMCoS Journal* **62** (1995): 7-15.

'As it was' (a bi-monthly hydrographic-history column), in *Hydro International*, since February 1997.

RIZZO, Gerald J. (Dr)
1201 5th Avenue N, No. 302
ST PETERSBURG, Florida 33705
USA
Tel: (1) 813 821 2388
Fax: (1) 813 821 6887
E-mail: gjrizzo@ix.netcom.com

Early maps of African kingdoms and the salt trade

ROBERTS, Iolo
83 Whitmore Road
NEWCASTLE, Staffs. ST5 3LZ
UK
Tel: (44) 01782 616346

Cartography of Wales before c.1840; Welsh cartographers

(with Menai Roberts), 'William Owen (Pughe) y Mapiwr', *Journal of the National Library of Wales* (Summer 1998): 1-24.

ROBERTS, Menai
83 Whitmore Road
NEWCASTLE, Staffs. ST5 3LZ
UK
Tel: (44) 01782 616346

Cartography of Wales before c.1840; Welsh cartographers

(with Iolo Roberts), 'William Owen (Pughe) y Mapiwr', *Journal of the National Library of Wales* (Summer 1998): 1-24.

ROBERTSON, James
Craufurd (Dr)
History Department
University of the West Indies,
Mona
KINGSTON 7
Jamaica
Tel: (1) 876 927 1922 (office)
Fax: (1) 876 977 0622
E-mail: jrobrtsn@uwimona.edu.jm

Maps, surveyors and surveying: framing the initial English settlement of Jamaica

(1) 876 927 0622 (home)

ROBINSON, Arthur H. (Prof)
7802 Courtyard Drive
MADISON, Wisconsin 53719-3517
USA
Tel: (1) 608 833 5145
E-mail: ahrobins@facstaff.wisc.edu

18th and 19th century thematic cartography

'The president's globe', *Imago Mundi* 49 (1997): 143-152.

RODGER, Elizabeth Margaret
5 Rufus Close
LEWES BN7 1BG
UK
Tel: (44) 01273 471297

Cartobibliography of English county maps

'Large scale English county maps and plans of cities not printed in atlases. Part 17 Isle of Wight', *The Map Collector* 71 (1995): 24-27.

ROGERS, John Michael (Prof)
School of Oriental and African Studies
University of London
Thornhaugh Street
Russell Square
LONDON WC1H 0XG
UK
Tel: (44) 0171 637 2388
Fax: (44) 0171 436 3844

Role of Turkish and European maps in 16th-century Ottoman topographical illustration

ROHR, Hans Peter
Vordergasse 49
CH-8200 SCHAFFHAUSEN
Switzerland
Tel: (41) 52 624 82 48 (office)

History of the maps of Kanton Schaffhausen

(41) 52 624 11 79 (home)

'Die verschollen geglaubte Schaffhauserkarte von J.R. Frey, 1715', *Cartographica Helvetica* 18 (1998).

ROMBAI, Leonardo (Prof)
Istituto Interfacoltà di Geografia
dell'Università di Firenze
Via San Gallo, 10
50029 FIRENZE
Italy
Tel: (39) 055 2757932
Fax: (39) 055 283643

Tuscan cartography (15th-19th centuries); cartography of the states of central Italy before unification; Italian maps in archives and libraries of Paris and Vienna

ROMER, Frank (Dr)
Department of Classics–ML 371
University of Arizona
TUCSON, AZ 85721-0067
USA
Tel: (1) 520 621 3029 (office)
E-mail: feromer@u.arizona.edu

Ancient maps; Greek and Roman geographers; Pomponius Mela's *De Chorographia*

(1) 520 319 9524 (home)

Pomponius Mela's Description of the World (Ann Arbor: University of Michigan Press, 1998).

ROONEY, Dawn F. (Dr)
Nana PO Box 1238
BANGKOK 10112
Thailand
Tel: (662) 671 1064
Fax: (662) 671 1065
E-mail: drooney@msn.com

Maps of mainland Southeast Asia (Cambodia, Laos, Thailand, Burma, Vietnam)

'Terra Incognita', *Sawasdee* 27:2 (Hong Kong, 1997): 26-33.

ROPER, Peter William
Green Acres
Thelda Avenue
KEYWORTH, Nottingham
NG12 5HU
UK
Tel: (44) 0115 937 2064
E-mail: p.roper@btinternet.com

Surveyors of the Parliamentary enclosures of Nottinghamshire villages, 1750-1850

ROSS, Robert
P.O. Box 8362
CALABASAS, California 91372
USA
Tel & fax: (1) 818 348 7867
E-mail: rossmaps@earthlink.net

Antique maps, atlases and globes

'The lure of old maps: defining parameters of new collections', *Mercator's World* 1:1 (1996): 42-45.

ROSSI, Massimo
Istituto di Studi Rinascimentali
Via Boccaleone 19
FERRARA 44100
Italy
Tel: (39) 0532 760002
Fax: (39) 0532 761331

The Dukedom of Ferrara; land reclamation in the Po Valley; cartobibliography (16th-18th centuries); G.B. Aleotti (1546-1636); computerization of maps

RUBIN, Rehav (Dr)
Department of Geography
Hebrew University of Jerusalem
Mt Scopus
JERUSALEM 91905
Israel
Tel: (972) 2 588 1141 (office)
      (972) 2 534 5008 (home)
E-mail: msbuni@pluto.mscc.huji.ac.il

Early maps of Jerusalem and the Holy Land; models and 3-D maps (with H. Goren); maps as religious and cultural documents (especially in reference to pilgrimage)

'From pictorial to scientific maps of Jerusalem', *Cathedra* 75 (1995): 55-68 [in Hebrew].

(with Haim Goren), 'Conrad Schick's models of Jerusalem and its monuments', *Palestine Exploration Quarterly* 128 (1996): 103-124.

(with M. Levy-Rubin), 'The image of the Holy City: maps and mapping of Jerusalem', in N. Rosovsky (ed), *City of the Great King: Jerusalem from David to Present* (Cambridge, Mass.: Harvard University Press, 1996), 352-379.

'Jerusalem in Braun & Hogenberg's *Civitates*', *The Cartographic Journal* 2 (1996): 119-129.

RUNDSTROM, Robert A.
Department of Geography
University of Oklahoma
NORMAN, Oklahoma 73019
USA
Tel (1) 405 325 5325
Fax (1) 405 325 6090
E-mail: rrundstrom@ou.edu

Cultural and social cartography; cartography of indigenous North Americans

RUSHTON, Gillian Anne
Principal Archivist
Hampshire Record Office
Sussex Street
WINCHESTER, Hants SO23 8TH
UK
Tel: (44) 01962 846154
Fax: (44) 01962 878681
E-mail: sadegr@hants.gov.uk

Pre-1800 manuscript estate maps for Hampshire

RYAVEC, Karl E
Department of Geography
University of Hawaii
Porteus Hall 445
HONOLULU, Hawaii 96822
USA
Tel: (1) 808 956 8465
Fax: (1) 808 956 3512
E-mail: ryavec@uhunix.uhcc.hawaii.edu

Traditional Tibetan cartography; Chinese maps of Tibetan Plateau region; Western mapping of central and east Asia

RYCKAERT, Marc
Provincie West-Vlaanderen, Dienst
   voor Cultuur
Koning Leopold III laan 41
B-8200 BRUGGE
Belgium
Tel: (32) 50 403 418
Fax: (32) 50 403 100

Flemish towns plans, 16th to 20th centuries; Belgian coastal maps, 16th to 20th centuries

SAFIER, Neil
Department of History
The Johns Hopkins University
3400 N. Charles St.
BALTIMORE, Maryland 21218
USA
E-mail: neilsaf@jhu.edu

Cartography of French
explorers in the Americas,
18th century

SAJUTO, Heru
Jl. Ametis IV/16
Permata Hijau Estate
JAKARTA 12210
Indonesia
Tel: (62) 21 8759020 (office)
Fax: (62) 21 8759025 (office)

Maps of Indonesia, South-
east Asia, Asia, and the
world

(62) 21 5480687 (home)
(62) 21 5350904 (home)

SALES, Pierre Lucien
9907 Deerfield Pond Drive
GREAT FALLS, Virginia 22066
USA
Tel: (1) 703 759 2592
Fax: (1) 703 759 3507

History and cartography of
Africa

SALWAY, Richard William
    Benet (Dr)
Research Fellow
History Department
University College London
Gower Street
LONDON WC1E 6BT
UK
Tel: (44) 0171 380 7396 (office)
Fax: (44) 0171 413 8394 (office)
E-mail: ucrarws@ucl.ac.uk

Roman roads and itiner-
aries, including the Tabula
Peutingeriana

(44) 0171 249 1715 (home)
(44) 0171 503 9576 (home)

SANCHIS BALLESTER, Francisca
Biblioteca Nacional España
Servicio de Cartografía
Paseo de Recoletos 20
28071 MADRID
Spain
Tel: (34) 91 580 7813
Fax: (34) 91 577 5634

Spanish cartography of
16th to 19th century;
atlases in the National
Library of Spain

SANDER, Thomas F.
Washington Map Society
P.O. Box 10793
BURKE, Virginia 22009-0793
USA
Tel: (1) 703 426 2880
Fax: (1) 703 426 2881
E-mail: sanderva@erols.com

Editor, *The Portolan*;
European maps, 16th to
19th century; cartographical curiosities

SAUNDERS, Richard L.
Renne Library
Montana State University
BOZEMAN, Montana 59717
USA
Tel: (1) 406 994 4991
E-mail: saunders/lib@renne.lib.montana.edu

Geographical knowledge
and mapping of
Yellowstone National Park,
1800-1880

SAVAGE-SMITH, Emilie (Dr)
Senior Research Associate
Wellcome Unit for the History of
    Medicine
45-47 Banbury Road
OXFORD OX2 6PE
UK
Tel: (44) 01865 274600 (office)
Fax: (44) 01865 274605
E-mail: emilie.savage-smith@wuhmo.ox.ac.uk

Islamic celestial maps and
globes; Islamic cartographical conventions

(44) 01865 247787 (home)

(with Colin Wakefield), 'Jacobus Golius and celestial cartography',
in W.D. Hackman and A.J. Turner (eds), *Learning, Language and
Invention: Essays Presented to Francis Maddison* (London: Variorum,
1994), 238-260.

'Globes' and 'Maps and mapmaking: celestial Islamic maps', in
Helaine Selin (ed), *Encyclopedia of the History of Science, Technology and
Medicine in Non-Western Cultures* (Dordrecht: Kluwer, 1997).

'Mapping the universe', in Francis Maddison and Emilie Savage-
Smith, *Science, Tools and Magic, Part 1* [The Nassar D. Khalili
Collection of Islamic Art, XII] (London: Azimuth Editions, and
Oxford: Oxford University Press, 1997), 168-287.

SAVOURS, Ann Margaret
[Mrs A.M. Shirley]
Little Bridge Place
BRIDGE, Canterbury,
Kent CT4 5LG
UK
Tel: (44) 01227 831 810

Arctic voyages of Sir
Martin Frobisher, 1576-
1578; search for the Northwest Passage: from
Frobisher to Franklin and
beyond

(with H.G.R. King, ed), *Polar Pundit: Reminiscences about Brian
Birley Roberts* (Cambridge: Scott Polar Research Institute, Polar
Publ. 1995).

'Clements Markham: longest serving officer, most prolific editor',
in R.C. Bridges and P.E.H. Hair, *Compassing the Vaste Globe of the
Earth: Studies in the History of the Hakluyt Society, 1846-1996*
(London: Hakluyt Society, 1996), 164-188.

(with Anita McConnell), 'Return to Rossbank: magnetism and
meteorology at Hobart in theory and practice, 1840-54', in Joan
Kenworthy and J. Malcolm Walker (eds), *Colonial Observatories and
Observations: Meteorology and Geophysics* (University of Durham,
Geography Department, with the Royal Meteorological Society,
1997), 49-58.

SCAFI, Alessandro (Dr)
The Warburg Institute
Woburn Square
LONDON WC1H 0AB
UK
Tel: (44) 0171 580 9663 (office)
Fax: (44) 0171 436 2852
E-mail: a.scafi@sas.ac.uk
and
Via del Mascherone 63
ROMA 00186
Italy
Tel: (39) 6 6830 7801

Mapping of the earthly
paradise

SCHARFE, Wolfgang W.P.
   (Prof Dr)
Weimarische Str. 4
D-10715 BERLIN
Germany
Tel: (49) 30 838 4807 (office)
   (49) 30 853 3386 (home)
Fax: (49) 30 838 6739
E-mail: scharfe@geog.fu-berlin.de

Brandenburg, Prussia,
Germany; thematic cartog-
raphy; mass-media cartog-
raphy; theory of
cartography

'Vorlesungen zur Geschichte der Kartographie der deutschsprachigen Länder in Barcelona', *Cartographica Helvetica* 12 (1995): 50;
also in *Kartographische Nachrichten* 45 (1995): 150-151.

(editor), *Gerhard Mercator und seine Zeit. 7. Kartographiehistorisches
Colloquium Duisburg. 6.-8. Oktober 1994: Vorträge und Berichte*
(Duisburg: Braun, 1996).

'Das kartographische Bild von Berlin-Brandenburg auf
Deutschland- und Mitteleuropa-Karten im 15. und 16.
Jahrhundert', in Jürgen Wetzel (ed), *Berlin in Geschichte und
Gegewart. Jahrbuch des Landesarchivs Berlin 1996* (Berlin: Gebrüder
Mann, 1996), 7-46.

(with Ralf Bitter), 'Lückenfüller oder "Infotainment"? Landkarten
in Tageszeitungen', *Mitteilungen der DFG* 3 (1996): 9-11.

'Minimum standards for teaching the history of cartography to
librarians, archivists, and cartographers', in Ferjan Ormeling and
Barend Köbben (eds), *Proceedings of the Seminar on 'Teaching the
History of Cartographpy III': Teaching Concepts in the History of
Cartography...* (Enschede: International Cartographic Association,
1996), 9-14.

'Approaches to the history of cartography in German-speaking
countries', 19-41; 'Cartography in Germany between the
Renaissance and the 18th century: regional development and atlas
cartography', 45-66; 'Surveys of German territories from the late
18th to the early 20th centuries', 69-86; 'Thematic cartography
and atlas cartography in Germany in the 19th and early 20th centuries', 89-103; 'Map collections and map librarianship in
Germany', 107-118, in *La cartografia dels països de parla alemanya:
Alemanya, Àustria i Suïssa, 20-24 de febrer de 1995* (Barcelona:
Institut Cartogràfic de Catalunya, 1997).

'Arbeitsgruppe D-A-CH deutscher österreichischer und schweizerischer Kartographiehistoriker öffiziell begründet', *Kartographische Nachrichten* 47 (1997): 67-68.

'Cartographie et représentation du paysage au XVIIe et au XIXe siècle: géométrisation, inventarisation, codification', *Revue Germanique Internazionale* 7 (1997).

'German atlas development during the nineteenth century', in John A. Wolter and Ronald E. Grim (eds), *Images of the World: The Atlas through History* (New York: McGraw-Hill, 1997), 207-232.

(editor), *International Conference on Mass Media Maps: Approaches, Results, Social Impact: Proceedings* (Berlin: Selbstverlag Fachbereich Geowissenschaften – Freie Universität Berlin, 1997).

'Karten in Bibliotheken', *Bibliothek und Wissenschaft* 30 (1997): 71-87.

SCHAUP, Wilhelm (Prof Dr)
Strada di Gandria 39c
CH-6976 CASTAGNOLA
Switzerland
Tel: (41) 052 242 38 61

Printed maps of the (now Austrian) province of Salzburg; annotated carto-bibliography to 1866/67

SCHERTENLEIB, Urban (Dr)
Albanistrasse 9
CH-8400 WINTERTHUR
Switzerland
Tel & fax: (41) 052 213 98 67

Weather maps; European cartography in the 18th and 19th centuries; methods in private and public Swiss cartography; school atlases; wall maps; biographies

Kartographie in Winterthur: Beiträge der Winterthur Kartographie-Betriebe zur Methodengeschichte der Kartographie des 19. Jahrhunderts (Winterthur: Stadtbibliothek, 1994).

'Schulkartograph Johann Sebastian Gerster – ein Erinnerung', *Vermessung Photogrammetrie Kulturtechnik* 93:10 (1995): 626-629.

'Fridolin Becker (1854-1922): Topograph, Kartograph, Innovator', *Cartographica Helvetica* 15 (1997): 3-10.

SCHILDER, Günter (Prof Dr)
Faculty of Geographical Sciences
University of Utrecht
PO Box 80115
3508 TC UTRECHT
Netherlands
Tel: (31) 302 532051
Fax: (31) 302 540604
E-mail: g.schilder@frw.ruu.nl

Dutch cartography of the 16th to 18th centuries

'Los Blaeu, una familia de cartografos y editores de mapas en el Amsterdam del siglo d'oro', in *De Mercator a Blaeu. España y la eda de oro de la cartografía en las Diecisiete Provincias de los Paises Bajos* (Madrid: Fundación Carlos de Amberes, 1995), 73-92.

'Monumenta Cartographica Neerlandica. Ein Foschungsprojekt ar der Universität Utrecht zur Förderung der niederländischen Kartengeschichte', *Duisburger Forschungen* 42 (1996): 233-239.

Monumenta Cartographica Neerlandica. V. Tien wandkaarten van Blae en Visscher [Ten Wall Maps by Blaeu and Visscher] (Alphen aan den Rijn: Canaletto, 1996).

'Lucas Janszoon Waghenaer's nautical atlases and pilot books', in John A. Wolter and Ronald E. Grim (eds), *Images of the World: Th Atlas through History* (New York: McGraw-Hill, 1997), 135-159.

SCHLÖGL, Daniel
Institut für Bayerische Geschichte
Universität München
Ludwigstr. 14
D-80539 MÜNCHEN
Germany
Tel: (49) 089 546 9131 (home)
Fax: (49) 089 2863 8506 (office)
E-mail: d.schloegl@bg.fak09.uni-muenchen.de

Cartography and late absolutist reform policy in Bavaria in the second half of the 18th century

'Althegnenberg und die Straßenverbindung Augsburg-München vom späten Mittelalter bis ins 19. Jahrhudert', in Toni Drexler an Angelika Fox (eds), *Althegnenberg – Hörbach: Beiträge zur Geschichte der Gemeinde Althegnenberg* (St. Ottilien: EOS Verlag, 1996), 207-214.

'Cartography in the service of reform policy in late absolutist Bavaria, c.1750-1777', *Imago Mundi* 49 (1997): 116-128.

THE OBSERVATORY

RARE AND COMMON BOOKS, MAPS, PRINTS

Alaska and Other Polar Regions

Dee Longenbaugh, proprietor
235 Second Street, Juneau, Alaska 99801 USA
Phone: 907/586-9676
Fax: 907/586-9606
E-mail: deelong@alaska.net

SCHMIDT, Rudolf (Prof)
Internationale Coronelli-Gesellschaft
    für Globen-und Instrumentekunde
Dominikanerbastei 21/28
A-1010 WIEN
Austria
Tel: (43) 1 533 32 85
Fax: (43) 1 532 08 24

History of terrestrial and
celestial globes and their
makers

'Zur Arbeitsweise Vincenzo Coronellis', *Der Globusfreund* 43/44
(1995).

'Der gedruckte Horizontring am Gestell alter Globen', *Information*
(Wien: Internationale Coronelli-Gesellschaft für Globen- und
Instrumentenkunde), 23 (1996): 3-9.

'Globen in Klöstern und Stiften', 174-197; (with Heide
Wohlschläger), 'Globen in Österreich', 320-379; 'Globenforschung
in Österreich', 224-229; (with Heide Wohlschläger),
'Globenhersteller aus aller Welt', 236-319; 'Die Herstellung und
Verwendung von Globen', 30-47; 'Karte, Globus, Weltmodell',
10-29; and (with Franz Wawrik), Über das Sammeln von Globen
Privatsammlungen in Österreich', 144-173; in Peter E. Allmayer-
Beck (ed), *Modelle der Welt. Erd- und Himmelsgloben. Kulturerbe aus
österreichen Sammlungen* (Wien: Brandstätter, 1997).

'Johann Friedrich Gottlob Haug, ein bisher wenig bekannter
Globushersteller', *Information* (Wien: Internationale Coronelli-
Gesellschaft für Globen- und Instrumentenkunde), 24 (1997): 2–3.

SCHNALL, Uwe (Dr)
Deutsches Schiffahrtsmuseum
Hans-Scharoun-Platz 1
D-27568 BREMERHAVEN
Germany
Tel: (49) 0471 482 0728
Fax: (49) 0471 482 0755

Sea charts, especially those
of northern and western
European waters, 16th to
18th century; charts of the
coastal waters of Germany;
medieval maps; sea atlases

'Seekarten als Mittel im Konkurrenzkampf zwischen Hamburg
und Bremen?' in Joachim Neumann (ed), *Karten hüten und
bewahren: Festgabe für Lothar Zögner* (*Kartensammlung und
Kartendokumentation* 11; Gotha: Perthes, 1995), 175-183.

'Probleme der praktischen Navigation auf den neuen Seewegen um
die Erde im 16. Jahrhundert', *Deutsches Schiffahrtsarchiv* 20 (1997):
329-346.

SCHNAYDER, Edward Franciszek
Retired Map Curator
Jagiellonian University Library
KRAKÓW
(Home): Krowoderska 37/8
31-141 KRAKÓW
Poland
Tel: (48) 012 6 325 448

Cartographical curiosities,
in particular from the 19th
and 20th centuries, espe-
cially in the Jagiellonian
University Library

'Niemieckie wojskowe mapy tematyczne rejonu bitwy pod
Kurskiem (ze zbiorów Biblioteki Jagiellońskiej w Krakowie)'
[German military thematic maps of the zone around Kursk, Russia
(in the collection of the Jagiellonian University Library)], *Polski
Przegląd Kartograficzny* 27:4 (1995): 203-208.

'Polska kartografia wojskowa w czasie II wojny światowej.
Przypomni nie w 50-lecie zakończenia wojny' [Polish military cartography during the Second World War. Reminder on the occasion of the 50th anniversary of the war's end], *Polski Przegląd
Kartograficzny* 27:4 (1995): 191-200.

'Rękopiśmienna późnośredniowieczna mapa wojskowogeograficzna
wschod niej części Półwyspu Bałkańskiego (w 550-lecie bitwy pod
Warną)' [Manuscript late-medieval military-geographical map of
the eastern part of the Balkan Peninsula (on the occasion of the
550 anniversary of the battle of Varna), *Polski Przegląd
Kartograficzny* 27:3 (1995): 140-142.

'O jednej śląskiej mapie powstańczej (w 75-lecie wybuchu III, ostat
niego Powstania Śląskiego w nocy 2-3.V.1921). W hołdzie
Powstańcom Śląskim' [On one Silesian insurgent map (on the
occasion of the 75th anniversary of the outbreak of the 3rd, last
Silesian anti-German uprising in the night of the 2/3 May 1921).
In tribute to the Silesian insurgents], *Biuletyn Biblioteki
Jagiellońskiej* 46:1/2 (1996): 277-283.

(with J. Bzinkowska) 'Poland', in Monique Pelletier (ed), *How to
Identify a Mapmaker. An International Bibliographic Guide* (Paris,
International Cartographic Association, 1996), 57-60.

'Dwie nieznane mapy związane z dawnymi Prusami Wschodnimi z
Archizum Wojennego w Sztokholmie' [Two unknown maps con-
nected with the former East Prussia in the Military Archives in
Stockholm], in *Z dziejów kartografii*, vol. 8: *Ziemie dawnych Prus
Wschodnich w kartografii* (Olsztyn, 1997), 93-102.

SCHULTE, Karl-Werner
Am Schwarzenstein 28
D 65366 GEISENHEIM
Germany
Tel: (49) 6722 71412
Fax: (49) 6722 64874

Maps of Iceland

SCHULTEN, Susan (Dr)
Department of History
University of Denver
2199 South University Blvd.
DENVER, Colorado 80208
USA
Tel: (1) 303 871 2970 (office)   (1) 303 780 0420 (home)
Fax: (1) 303 871 2957
E-mail: sschulte@du.edu

World atlases in American
culture, 1870-1950; war
maps in American popular
culture

'Richard Edes Harrison and the challenge to American cartography', *Imago Mundi*, **50** (1998): 174-188.

SCHULZ, Günther Ernst
      Richard (Dr)
Johannisburger Allee 3
D-14055 BERLIN
Germany
Tel: (49) 030 304 8771

Maps and plans of the city
of Berlin

Stadtpläne von Berlin, 1650-1920 (Berlin: Mann, 1998).

SCHWARTZBERG,
      Joseph E. (Prof)
Department of Geography
University of Minnesota
MINNEAPOLIS, MN 55455
USA
Tel: (1) 612 625 4577 (office)   (1) 612 926 7118 (home)
Fax: (1) 612 624 1044
E-mail: schwa004@tc.umn.edu

Indigenous cartography of
South and Southeast Asia

'Maps and mapping in India', 'Maps and mapping in Southeast Asia', 'Maps and mapmaking in Tibet', *Encyclopaedia of the History of Science, Technology and Medicine in Non-Western Cultures* (Dordrecht: Kluwer Academic Publishers, 1997), 48-50, 67-69, 69-70.

SCHWARZ, Uwe
Kölnisches Stadtmuseum
Zeughausstr. 1-3
D-50667 KÖLN
Germany
Tel: (49) 0221 221 4320 (office)
      (49) 0222 323 228 (home)
Fax: (49) 0221 221 4154

Cartobibliography of
Cologne and Rhinish maps;
Wiebeking and his role in
cartography; cartobibliography of Wiebeking's map
sheets

'Quo vadis? Anmerkungen zu Kölner Stadtplänen', in Werner Schäfke and Peter Ditgen (eds), *Köln auf alten Ansichtskarten, Band II – Kölner Stadtbild* (Köln: Kölnisches Stadtmuseum, 1996), 29-35.

SCKOLNICK, Lewis Barnard
The Library of the Boston Athenaeum
130 Rattlesnake
LEVERETT, Massachusetts 01054
USA
Tel: (1) 413 548 9708
Fax: (1) 413 367 2853

Life and work of Rufus
Putnam

SCOTT, James Murray (Prof)
Trinity Western University
7600 Glover Road
LANGLEY, British Columbia
      V2Y 1Y1
Canada
Tel: (1) 604 888 7511 (office)   (1) 604 855 0242 (home)
Fax: (1) 604 513 2018
E-mail: scott@twu.ca

Jewish geographical lore;
the Christian reception of
Jubilees 8-9 to the medieval
mappaemundi

'The division of the earth in *Jubilees* 8:11–9:15 and early Christian chronography', in M. Albani et al (eds), *Studies in the Book of Jubilees* (Texte und Studien zum antiken Judentum 65; Tübingen: Mohr-Siebeck, 1997).

SCOTT, Valerie Gillian
Map Collector Publications Ltd
48 High Street
TRING, Herts HP23 5BH
UK
Tel: (44) 01442 824977
Fax: (44) 01442 827712
E-mail: gp86@dial.pipex.com

Research for the revised edition of Tooley's Dictionary of Mapmakers

'One of my favourite maps: Cruchley's road and railway map of the county of Hertford', *IMCoS Journal* 69 (1997): 17-21.

'Where have all the old maps gone', *Mercator's World* 2:3 (1997): 11.

SCURFIELD, Judith Mary
State Library of Victoria
328 Swanston Street
MELBOURNE, Victoria 3000
Australia
Tel: (61) 3 9669 9954
Fax: (61) 3 9669 9012
E-mail: judiths@slv.vic.gov.au

Mapping and charting of Victoria, Australia

(with Gordon Scurfield), *The Hoddle Years: Surveying in Victoria, 1836-1853* (Canberra: Institution of Surveyors Australia, Inc, 1995).

(with Gordon Scurfield), 'Introduction', *Plan of the Township of Hamilton 1853* (Hamilton, Vic.: Bellcourt Books, 1995).

(with Gordon Scurfield), 'Creating a landlord's landscape: special surveys in Victoria', *The Globe* 44 (1996): 24-40.

SEAVER, Kirsten A.
3638 Bryant St.
PALO ALTO, California 94306
USA
Tel: (1) 650 493 2651
Fax: (1) 650 493 5291
E-mail: seaver@leland.stanford.edu

Early exploration and cartography in the North Sea and the North Atlantic

'The "Vinland Map": who made it, and why? New light on an old controversy', *The Map Collector* 70 (1995): 32-40.

The Frozen Echo: Greenland and the Exploration of North America ca. 1000-1500 A.D. (Palo Alto: Stanford University Press, 1996; paperback 1997).

'The mystery of the "Vinland Map" manuscript volume', *The Map Collector* 74 (1996): 24-29.

'"A very common and usuall trade": the relationship between cartographic perceptions and fishing in the Davis Strait ca. 1500-1550', in Karen S. Cook (ed), *Images & Icons of the New World: Essays on American Cartography* (London: British Library Publications, 1996 = *British Library Journal* 22:1, 1996): 1-26.

'Albertin de Virga and the Far North', *Mercator's World* 2:6 (1997): 58-62.

'The many faces of the great captain', *The Medal* (London: British Art Medal Society) 30 (1997): 10-18.

'The Vinland map: a $3,500 duckling that became a $25,000,000 swan', *Mercator's World* 2:2 (1997): 42-47.

'Norumbega and *harmonia mundi* in sixteenth-century cartography', *Imago Mundi*, 50 (1998): 34-58.

SEGAL, Daniel
Pitzer College
CLAREMONT, California 91711
USA
Tel: (1) 909 607 3645
Fax: (1) 909 607 5470
E-mail: dan_segal@pitzer.edu

The history the idea of continents and the relationship of that history to the formation of racial categories and identities; graphic design of maps for textbooks, and how they encode allegories of racial and national identities

SELIGMANN, Matthew S. (Dr)
Department of History
Nene University College
    Northampton
Boughton Green Road
NORTHAMPTON NN2 7AL
UK
Tel: (44) 01604 735500
Fax: (44) 01604 720636
E-mail: matthew.seligmann@nene.ac.uk

Role of maps in colonial diplomacy of the late 19th century

'Maps as the progenitors of territorial disputes: two examples from nineteenth century southern Africa, *Imago Mundi* 47 (1995): 173-183.

SEMOTANOVÁ, Eva (Dr)
Historický ústav AVČR
Prosecká 76
190 00 PRAHA 9
Czech Republic
Tel & fax: (420) 2 88 75 13
E-mail: semotanova@hiu.cas.cz

History of geodesy and cartography in Czech Lands: theory, methods, cartographical sources; atlas of historical towns of the Czech Republic

(with J. Dvořák et al), *Historický atlas měst České republicky sv. 1, Litoměřice; 2, Pardubice; 3, České Budějovice* (Praha: Historický ústav, 1996).

'Mapy v kulturních dějinách nebo kulturní dějiny na mapách? [Maps in culture history or culture history on maps?], in L. Slezák (ed), *K poctě Jaroslava Marka* (Praha: Historický ústav, 1996), 119-133.

'Thematische Kartographie in den Böhmischen Ländern im 19. Jahrundert', in Z. Jindra (ed), *Prager Wirtschafts- und sozialhistorische Mitteilungen* 3 (Praha: Univerzita Karlova, 1996), 37-49.

'Cestovní a turistické mapy v českých zemích v 19. století' [Travel and touristic maps in Czech lands in the 19th century], in L. Bobková (ed), *Cesty a cestovánt v životě společnosti. Reisen im Leben der Gesellschaft* (Ústí nad Labem: Universitas Purkinianae, 1997), 483-488.

'Katalog Mapové sbírky Historického ústavu AVČR, I. Plány měst' [Catalogue of the map collection of the Institute of History of the Academy of Sciences of the Czech Republic, I. city maps], in E. Semotanová (ed), *Historická geografie* 29 (Praha: Historický ústav, 1997), 275-312.

SHEFRIN, Jill A.
34 Marchmount Rd.
TORONTO, Ontario, M6G 2A9
Canada
Tel & fax: (1) 416 654 2595
E-mail: jshefrin@sympatico.ca

English map table games, map card games, dissected map puzzles and map samplers as educational aids, in printing history, and in children's literature and pastimes

"Ingenious Contrivances": Table Games and Puzzles for Children (Toronto: Friends of the Osborne & Lillian H. Smith Collections/ Toronto Public Library, 1996). [Based on an exhibition at The Osborne Collection of Early Children's Books, Toronto Public Library. November 7, 1996-February 8, 1997.]

SHIELDS, E. Thomson, Jr.
Director, Roanoke Colonies Research Office
c/o Department of English
East Carolina University
GREENVILLE, N. C. 27858-4353
USA
Tel: (1) 252 328 6715
Fax: (1) 252 328 4889
E-mail: shieldse@mail.ecu.edu

World maps as representations of beliefs about the Americas, 1500-1800; North America in maps representing territorial claims as opposed to actual European settlements, 1500-1800; maps in connection with Richard Hakluyt's works

SHIRLEY, Rodney W.
The Manor House
Church Street
BUCKINGHAM MK18 1BY
UK
Tel: (44) 01280 812158
E-mail: rws@dial.pipex.com

Collation of all maps in pre-1800 atlases in the British Library; decorative titlepages and frontispieces from atlases and related works; 16th century Italian maps

'Early Italian atlas maps in the Mercator Museum, Sint-Niklaas, Belgium', *IMCoS Journal* 60 (1995): 15-17.

'The maritime maps and atlases of Seller, Thornton, and Mount & Page', *The Map Collector* 73 (1995): 2-9.

'A rare early Italian map of Japan by Giacomo Piccaglia', *IMCoS Journal* 60 (1995): 21-24.

'The face of the maker: portraits of cartographers concealed in maps and titlepages', *Mercator's World* 1:4 (1996): 14-19.

'De Nederlandse bijdrage aan de decoratieve kartografische titel-pagina' *Caert-Thresoor* 2 (1996): 29-35.

'Something old, something new from Paris and Nancy: yet more early and rare Italiana, including 14 maps by Pagano or Vavassore' *IMCoS Journal* 67 (1996): 32-36.

'The wall map of the world by Pieter van den Keere in the Sutro Library, San Francisco', *California State Library Foundation Bulletin* 56 (July 1996): 1-6.

'Matteo Pagano's map of the British Isles, 1555', *IMCoS Journal* 68 (1997): 29-31.

'Old atlases in the library of Vilnius University: a postscript', *IMCoS Journal* 68 (1997): 51-52.

'Unusual Cromwellian map of the British Isles', *IMCoS Journal* 69 (1997): 31-33.

'Language and nationhood: two ethnographic maps of Germany', *Mercator's World* 3:1 (1998): 11.

'Scarce map of Cyprus in National Széchényi Library, Budapest', *IMCoS Journal* 73 (1998): 42-43.

'Three sixteenth-century Italian atlases from the former Austro-Hungarian Empire', *IMCoS Journal* 72 (1998): 39-43.

SHKURKIN, Vladimir Vladimirovich
6025 Rose Arbor
SAN PABLO, California 94806-4147
USA
Tel: (1) 510 232 7742
Fax: (1) 510 236 7050
E-mail: shkurkin@ix.netcom.com
Web: http://www.dvgu.ru/rus/fesu/info/graduate/shkurkin.htm

Sanborn Company fire insurance maps; historic Russian maps of Manchuria and the Far East

Olga Mikhailovna Bakich, *The Shkurkin Far East Archive: An Initial Annotated Sampler*, ed. Vlad Shkurkin (2nd ed; San Pablo, CA: Shkurkin, 1997) [mostly in Russian].

SIDER, Sandra (Dr)
The Pierpont Morgan Library
29 East 36 Street
NEW YORK, NY 10016-3490
USA
Tel: (1) 212 685 0008 (ext. 370)
Fax: (1) 212 685 4740

Iconographical aspects of compass rose and wind systems in portolan charts; manuscript cartographical and cosmographical drawings in 15th- and 16th-century copies of Dati's *La sfera*

SIHORSCH, P. Daniel (Mag)
Stift Kremsmünster
A-4550 KREMSMÜNSTER
Austria
Tel: (43) 75 83 5275
E-mail: sternwarte.kremsmuenster@telecom.at

Globes

'Die Globen der Sternwarte Kremsmünster', *Anselm Desing Verein Berichte* 36 (1997).

SILVERMAN, Eric Kline
Department of Sociology/ Anthropology
DePauw University
GREENCASTLE, Indiana 46135
USA
Tel: (1) 317 658 4889
Fax: (1) 317 658 4177
E-mail: erics@depauw.edu

Indigenous form of maps and representations of space (cosmology, ritual, religion, morality, gender) in Papua New Guinea, Melanesia, Pacific Islands

SILVESTER, Robert John
Clwyd-Powys Archaeological Trust
7A Church St.
WELSHPOOL, Powys
UK
Tel: (44) 01938 553670 (office)   (44) 01938 500641 (home)
Fax: (44) 01938 552179
E-mail: bobsilvester@cpat.demon.co.uk

Maps of William Haiwarde; maps of the East Anglian fens

SILVESTRE, Marguerite
Scientific Associate
Section des Cartes et Plans
Bibliothèque Royale de Belgique
Boulevard de l'Empereur 4
1000 BRUXELLES
Belgium
Tel: (32) 02 519 57 40
E-mail: savants.belges@kbr.be

19th-century cartography; Philippe Vandermaelen (with Michel-Benoit Fincoeur)

'Le démantèlement de l'Etablissement géographique de Bruxelles à l'origine des collections Vandermaelen de la Bibliothèque Royale', *Bulletin d'information*, Bibliothèque royale Albert Ier (Bruxelles), 41:1 (1997): 9-15.

SIMS, Douglas
211 Brighton 15 Street, 3G
BROOKLYN, New York 11735
USA
Tel & fax: (1) 718 891 6684
E-mail: gastaldi@ix.netcom.com

Giacomo Gastaldi and 16th century Italian cartography; bio-bibliography of historians of cartography; bibliography of history of cartography

ICHC: The International Conferences on the History of Cartography: A Short Historical Survey and a Bibliography of Papers (Brooklyn, New York, 1995).

SMITH, David Anthony
Bexley College
Tower Road
BELVEDERE, Kent DA17 6JA
UK
Tel: (44) 01322 404252 (office)
    (44) 01322 556710 (home)

British town maps; 19th-century British map publishers and the London map trade; cartobibliography of atlases of the British Isles; business organization of mapmaking

'The mapping of British urban conditions, characteristics and social provision', *Bulletin of the Society of Cartographers* 29:2 (1995): 3-15.

'The preparation of the town maps for Lysons' *Magna Britannia*', *The Cartographic Journal* 32:1 (1995): 11-17.

'The mapping of British urban roads and road transport', *Bulletin of the Society of Cartographers* 30:1 (1996): 17-28.

'William Blackwood & Sons: map publishers of the nineteenth century', *Mercator's World* 1:5 (1996): 56-61.

'A. & C. Black 1807-c.1900', *IMCoS Journal* 71 (1997): 15-21.

'Cassell and Company, 1848-c.1890', *IMCoS Journal* 70 (1997): 7-17.

'The interpretation of cartographic publishing imprints: the case of the Wylds', *IMCoS Journal* 68 (1997): 37-43.

'John Heywood and others' *IMCoS Journal* 69 (1997): 23-30.

'Gall & Inglis, c.1810-c.1900', *IMCoS Journal* 73 (1998): 7-12.

'The leisure mapping of British towns', *Bulletin of the Society of Cartographers* 31:1 (1998): 1-13.

SPATA, Manfred
Landesvermessungamt Nordrhein-
    Westfalen
Muffendorfer Strasse 19-21
D-53177 BONN
Germany
Tel: (49) 0228 846 2200
Fax: (49) 0228 846 2002
E-mail: spata.bonn@t-online.de

Maps of Silesia and Glatz

(with B. Ruf), 'Lichtenbergs astronomische Ortsbestimmungen 1772/73 für die Kurhannoversche Landesaufnahme', *Der Vermessungsingenieur (VI)* 46 (1995): 71-77.

'Das Luftbildplanwerk 1:25000 des Deutschen Reiches – Eine Quelle für landes- und heimatkundliche Studien', *Schlesischer Kulturspiegel* 30 (1995): 17-18.

(with L. Hyss), *Die Grafschaft Glatz zwischen Böhmen und Schlesien: eine ausstellung historischer Landkarten* (Ausstellungskatalog des Museums für Landeskunde Haus Schlesien; Königswinter, 1996).

'Die Schlesienkarte von Martin Helwig aus dem Jahre 1561', in K. Brunner and H. Musall (eds), *Martin Helwigs Karte von Schlesien 1561* (Karlsruher Geowissenschaftliche Schriften, Reihe C: Alte Karten, Band 9; Karlsruhe, 1996), 5-18 (with facsimile).

SPERLING, Walter
  (Prof emeritus Dr)
Kreuzflus 11
D-54296 TRIER
Germany
Tel: (49) 0651 16448

Topographical mapping in 18th and 19th centuries; history of school atlases and wall maps

Comenius Karte von Mähren 1627 (Karlsruhe: Fachhochschule Karlsruhe, Fachbereich Geoinformationswesen, 1994).

'Geographische Namen, politisch instrumentalisiert: Das Beispiel Schlesien', in Joachim Neumann (ed), *Karten hüten und bewahren: Festgabe für Lothar Zögner* (Kartensammlung und Kartendokumentation 11; Gotha: Verlag Justus Perthes, 1995), 185-203.

(with H.P. Brogiato and others), 'Paul Langhals und seine Wandkarte der deutschen Kolonien in Afrika (1908)', in Harald Leisch (ed), *Perspektiven der Entwicklungsländerforschung: Festschrift für Hans Hecklau* (Trier Geographische Studien 11; Trier: SV der Geographischen Gesellschaft Trier, 1995), 81-102.

'Schlesische Landschaftsnamen: Bemerkungen zu einem Forschungsvorhaben', *Jahrbuch der schlesischen Friedrich-Wilhelms-Universität zu Breslau* 36-37 (1996): 385-421.

'Geographische Namen politisch instrumentalisiert: Das Beispiel Lothringen', in Rainer Graafen and Wolf Tietze (eds), *Raumwirksame Staatstätigkeit: Festschrift für Klaus-Achim Boesler zum 65. Geburtstag* (Colloquium Geographicum 23; Bonn: Dümmler, 1997), 233-246.

SPERO, Frederick H.
14 Earl Road
EAST SANDWICH, Massachusetts
    02537
USA
Tel: (1) 508 833 1701
Fax: (1) 800 763 9343
E-mail: sperof@ma.ultranet.com   sperof@mail.dnb.com

Nautical cartography of the United States; US Coast & Geodetic Survey pilot books/sailing directions; independent American hydrographers

The American Coast Pilot: A New Bibliography (Providence, RI: John Carter Brown Library, 1998).

STAMS, Werner (Dr)
An der Jägermühle 26
D-01445 RADEBEUL
Germany

Historical atlases

(editor), *Deutsche in Amerika: die Entwanderung im Kartenbild: Kolloquiumsbeiträge und Texte zur Austellung der Library of Congress, Washington DC an der Technischen Universität Dresden* (Dresden: Sächsisch Landesbibliothek, 1994).

'Sächsen, Meissen und die Lausitzen bei Gerard Mercator', in W. Scharfe (ed), *Gerhard Mercator und seine Zeit. 7. Kartographiehistorisches Colloquium Duisburg 1994* (Duisburg: Braun, 1996), 73-87.

STANDER, Richard R.
746 Clifton Blvd
MANSFIELD, Ohio 44907
USA
Tel: (1) 419 756 6010

Influence of transport on the settlement and economic development of the 'Territory Northwest of the River Ohio'

STEENGE, Albert E. (Prof Dr)
University of Twente
Faculty of Public Administration
    and Public Policy
P.O. Box 217
7500 AE ENSCHEDE
Netherlands
Tel: (31) 53 489 3260 (office)   (31) 53 434 0411 (home)
Fax: (31) 53 489 4682 (office)   (31) 53 434 2144 (home)
E-mail: a.e.steenge@bsk.utwente.nl

Maps of the polar regions, Arctic Ocean and Antarctica

STEINHARDT, Nancy
    Shatzman (Prof)
Department of Asian and Middle
    Eastern Studies
University of Pennsylvania
PHILADELPHIA, PA 19104-6305
USA
Tel: (1) 215 898 7466
Fax: (1) 215 573 9617
E-mail: nssteinh@sas.upenn.edu

East Asian urban planning, architecture and cartography

'Chinese cartography and calligraphy', *Oriental Art* **43**:1 (1997): 10-20.

'Mapping the Chinese city: the image and the reality', in David Buisseret (ed), *Envisioning the City: Six Studies in Urban Cartography* (Chicago: University of Chicago Press, 1998), 1-33.

STELMACH, Mieczysław (Prof)
Instytut Historii
Uniwersytet Szczeciński
ul. Wojska Polskiego 65
70-478 SZCZECIN
Poland
Tel: (48) 091 4343 818 (office)   (48) 091 4393 683 (home)
Fax: (48) 091 4334 466

Propaganda maps in 16th to 18th century Pomerania

[*Catalogue of Town Plans in Polish Archives*] (Warsaw, 1996).

['Cartographic recording and the team issue', *Computerisation of Archives*] **3** (Torun, 1997): 75-78.

['Maps of the southern Baltic Sea', in *An Outline of History of Pomerian Cartography*] (Szczecin, 1997), 69-83.

(editor), *Mapy południowego Bałtyku* [Maps of the Southern Baltic Sea] (Szczecin, Uniwersytet, 1997).

['Report on the 17th National Conference of Historians of Cartography "Maps of the southern Baltic Sea", Szczecin 6-7 September 1996'], *Przegląd Zachodniopomorski* [West Pomeranian Newsletter] **12**:1-2 (1997): 219-257.

STEPHENSON, Francis
Richard (Prof)
Department of Physics
Rochester Building
University of Durham
South Road
DURHAM DH1 3LE
UK
Tel: (44) 0191 374 2153 (office)   (44) 0191 274 5402 (home)
Fax: (44) 0191 374 3749
E-mail: f.r.stephenson@durham.ac.uk

East Asian celestial cartography from ancient times to the Jesuit period; historical eclipse maps

'Astronomia coreana', *L'Astronomia* **174** (1997): 24-32.

'Celestial East Asian maps', in H. Selin (ed), *Encyclopaedia of the History of Science, Technology and Medicine in Non-Western Cultures* (Dordrecht: Kluwer, 1997), 562-565.

'Oriental star maps and their applications', *Yearbook of Science and the Future* (Chicago: Encyclopedia Britannica, 1998).

STEPHENSON, Richard W.
238 Greenbriar Circle
CROSS JUNCTION, Virginia 22625
USA
Tel: (1) 540 888 3508
E-mail: rstephen@mnsinc.com

Virginia in maps (with Marianne McKee)

STEUR, Albert Gerard van der
17 Nieuwe Gracht
2011 NB HAARLEM
Netherlands
Tel: (31) 023 32 42 37
Fax: (31) 023 42 06 70

Maps of the town of Haarlem and environs; maps of the region around Leiden

STEVENSON, William George
Map/Research Librarian
Aalborg University Library
Postbox 8200
Langagervej 2
DK 9000 AALBORG
Denmark
Tel: (45) 9635 9384 (office)
     (45) 9811 3996 (home)
Fax: (45) 9815 3844 (office)
     (45) 9811 3996 (home)
E-mail: bste@aub.auc.dk

National mapping in Europe, its use in education and politics to develop national identities (17th-19th centuries); information contained in these maps, e.g., geomorphology, land use, settlement patterns, public works, architecture, etc.

STEWARD, Henry J (Prof)
Graduate School of Geography
Clark University
WORCESTER,
     Massachusetts 01610-1477
USA
Tel: (1) 508 793 7383
Fax: (1) 508 793 8881

Life and work of William Mayo (1684-1744) and the working context of the 18th-century British colonial surveyor; map projection and geosophical interests of Bernard Cahill (1866-1943)

STOKSIK, Janina Mirosława (Dr)
Archiwum Pa´nstwowe w Krakowie
     (State Archive)
ul. Sienna 16
30-960 KRAKÓW
Poland
Tel: (48) 12 422 4094 (office)   (48) 12 421 0730 (home)
Fax: (48) 12 421 3544

History of the geodetic staff in Little Poland from the 16th to the 18th century

'Galicyjski kataster gruntowy – jego gromadzenie i opracowywanie w Archiwum Pańatwowym w Krakowie' [Galician property cadaster – its cumulation and elaboration in the State Archive in Kraków], *Krakowski Rocznik Archiwalny* **1** (1995): 46-57.

'Siewierz i księstwo siewierskie w XVII i XVIII-wiecznych przekazach kartograficznych' [Siewierz Dukedom in 17th and 18th century cartographic monographs], in F. Kiryk (ed), *Siewierz-Czeladź-Koziegłowy. Studia i materiały z dziejów księstwa siewierskiego* [Studies and materials from the history of the Siewierz Dukedom] (Katowice: Silesian Museum, 1994 [1995]), 597-613.

'Udział Akademii Krakowskiej w kaztałceniu geodetów w XVII i

XVIII stuleciu' [Participation of the Kraków Academy in the education of geodesists in the 17th and 18th centuries], *Krakowski Rocznik Archiwalny* **3** (1997): 35-53.

'Zbiory Kartografików w Archiwum Potockich z Krzeszowic' [Collection of maps in the Potocki historical archives from Krzeszowice], *Miscelanea Historico-Archivistica* **8** (Warsaw, 1997): 74-85.

STONE, Jeffrey C. (Dr)
20 Springfield Road
ABERDEEN AB15 7RR
UK
Tel: (44) 01224 315210
E-mail: j.stone@abdn.ac.uk

Index to the place-names on the Pont, Gordon and Blaeu maps of Scotland; maps of the African explorers

'The cartography of colonialism and decolonisation: the case of Swaziland', in M. Bell, R. Butlin and M. Heffernan (eds), *Geography and Imperialism 1820-1940* (Manchester University Press, 1995), 298-324.

A Short History of the Cartography of Africa (African Studies 39; New York: The Edwin Mellen Press, 1995).

'The early years of official topographic mapping in Northern Rhodesia', *South African Journal of Surveying and Mapping* **23**:4 (1996): 217-231.

'The 1933 maps of "Bechuanaland Protectorate" at 1:500,000: a milestone in the mapping of Botswana', *Botswana Notes and Records* **27** (1996): 71-84.

STOOKE, Philip J. (Prof)
Department of Geography
University of Western Ontario
LONDON, Ontario N6A 5C2
Canada
Tel: (1) 519 679 2111, ext. 5022
E-mail: pjstooke@julian.uwo.ca
Web: www.geog.uwo.ca/stooke.html

History of lunar and planetary cartography

'Neolithic lunar maps at Knowth and Baltinglass, Ireland', *Journal for the History of Astronomy* **25** (1994), 39-55.

'The mirror in the moon', *Sky & Telescope* **91**:3 (1996): 96-98.

STOPP, Klaus D. (Prof Dr)
Draiser Str. 108
D-55128 MAINZ
Germany
Tel: (49) 6131 34466
Fax: (49) 6131 338705

Maps with marginal views by Dutch engravers; German cartographers: Nicolaus Person, Gottfried Haupt, David Funck, Johann Michael Probst

STRAUCHMANIS, Janis (Prof Dr)
Department of Human Geography
University of Latvia
Tallinas Street 83-40
LV-1009 RIGA
Latvia
Tel: (371) 7 334 765 (office)   (371) 7 290 572 (home)
Fax: (371) 7 820 113

Latvia; the Baltic region; thematic and atlas cartography; cartobibliogrphy of maps and atlases of the Baltic region (pre-1900)

Latvijas kartogrāfijas vêsture. Bibliogrāfisks rādītājs (Riga, Mācību grāmata, 1994).

Matiss Silins, the First Latvian Cartographer (Riga, University of Latvia, 1994).

Symbols on Old Maps (Riga, University of Latvia, 1994).

'History of cartography of the Baltic States', *IMCoS Journal* **67** (1996): 6-11.

STRONGILOS, Themis
19 Rigillis Street
GR-106 74 ATHENS
Greece
Tel: (30) 1 722 4796 (office)   (30) 1 721 4582 (home)
Fax: (30) 1 723 8379
E-mail: strong@otenet.gr

Portolan charts

STROUP, Alice (Prof)
Department of History
Bard College
ANNANDALE-ON-HUDSON,
New York 12504
USA
Tel: (1) 914 758 7234 (office)   (1) 914 758 5912 (home)
Fax: (1) 914 758 7544
E-mail: stroup@bard.edu

French cartography, 1650-1715

and 11 bis rue Coysevox
75018 PARIS
France
Tel: (33) 1 42 28 75 29

SUAREZ, Thomas
225 Warren Avenue
HAWTHORNE, New York 10532
USA
Tel: (1) 914 741 6155
Fax: (1) 914 741 6156
E-mail: siam@ibm.net

Early mapping of Southeast Asia

(with Richard Casten), 'A revised chronology for the mapping of America in the late sixteenth century: Hogenberg, Mazza, Ortelius', *The Map Collector* **70** (1995): 26-30.

'A 2,000-year premonition: maps of the great southern continent before its discovery', *Mercator's World* **1**:2 (1996): 10-17.

'The mapping of Terra Australis: an Australian collector shares his passion', *Mercator's World* **2**:1 (1997): 60-63.

SULLIVAN, Garrett A., Jr. (Dr)
Department of English
103 Burrowes Building
Pennsylvania State University
UNIVERSITY PARK, PA 16802
USA
Tel: (1) 814 863 9585 (office)   (1) 814 235 9624 (home)
Fax: (1) 814 863 7285
E-mail: gas11@psu.edu

Renaissance cartography in England; surveying; road atlases

'"Arden lay murdered in that plot of ground": surveying, land and *Arden of Faversham*', *ELH* [English Literary History] **61** (1994): 231-252.

The Drama of Landscape: Land, Property and Social Relations on the Early Modern Stage (Stanford: Stanford University Press, 1998).

SUN Guoqing
National Library of China
39 Bai Shi Qiao Road
100081 BEIJING
China
Tel: (86) 1 841 5566, ext. 5054

Ancient Chinese cartography; descriptive catalogue of the pre-1949 Chinese maps in the National Library; administration and use of ancient maps in China

SUZUKI, Junko
Special Materials Department
National Diet Library
1-10-1 Nagata-cho, Chiyoda-ku
TOKYO 100
Japan
Tel: (81) 03 3581 2331
Fax: (81) 03 3581 2290

Maps as historical documents; infrastructure of official map making during the Tokugawa Shogunate

SZANIAWSKA, Lucyna
Biblioteka Narodowa
Zakiad Zbiorów Kartograficznych
skr. poczt. 36
al. Niepodległóśu 213
OO-973 WARZAWA 22
Poland
Tel: (48) 022 831 3241 (office)   (48) 022 39 0531 (home)
Fax: (48) 022 635 4498

'Wystewa "Z Bristolu do Warszewy. Mapy i atlasy – dar Barbary i Jerzego Czarny-Karaslów" w Bibliotece Narodowej w Warszwie' [The Exhibition "from Bristol to Warsaw. Maps and atlases – the gift of Mrs Barbara and Mr Jerzy Czarny-Karaś" in the National Library in Warsaw], *Polski Przegląd Kartograficzny* **27**:1 (1995): 55-57.

'Ewolucja reymannowskiej mapy topograficznej Europy Środkowej wydawanej w latach 1844-1874 w Głogowie przez Zaklad kartograficzny Karola Flemminga' [Evolution of Reymann's topographic map of central Europe and its editions by Carl Flemming 1844-1874], *Czasopismo Zakładu Narodowego Imineia Ossolińskich* **7** (Wrocław, 1996): 89-110.

'Mapy topograficzne Wojskowego Istytutu Geograficznego w zbiorach Biblioteki Narodowej' [Topographic maps of the Wojskowy Instytut Geograficzny in collections of the National Library in

Warsaw], *Rocznik Biblioteki Narodowej* 30-31 (Warszawa: Biblioteka Narodowa, 1997): 271-296.

'X Konferencja Grupy Bibliotekaizy Kartografów LIBER w Berlinie' [10th Conference of the Groupe des Cartothécaires de LIBER], *Polski Przegląd Kartograficzny* 29:1 (1997): 76-77.

'Wystawa "Cartographia Rappersviliana Polonorum. Mapy Rzeczpospolitej XV-XVIII w. w zbiorach rapperswilskich" na Zamku Krolewskim w Warszawie' [The exhibition "Cartographia Rappersviliana Polonorum. Maps of the Commonwealth of Poland and Lithuania in the 15th to 18th centuries in Rappersviliana's collections" at the Kingdom Castle in Warsaw], *Polski Przegląd Kartograficzny* 29:3 (1997): 204-205.

SZÁNTAI, Lajos
55 rue Richaume G.2
F-78360 MONTESSON
France
Tel & fax: (33) 01 39 52 06 46

Maps of Hungary to 1850; Hungarian cartographers; engravings of Hungarian towns, fortifications and battles

Atlas Hungaricus (vols 1-2; Budapest: Akadémiai Kaidó, 1996) [in Hungarian and English].

'Magyaroszág városképes térképmetszetei' [Maps of Hungary with engraved town views], *Cartographica Hungarica* 5 (1996): 30-40.

SZATHMÁRY, Tibor
Rudolf utca 1
H-2800 TATABÁNYA II
Hungary
Tel & fax: (36) 34 333 010

Maps of Hungary to 1850; Hungarian cartographers; editor of *Cartographica Hungarica*

'Reilly térképei' [The maps of Reilly], *Cartographica Hungarica* 5 (1996): 2-7.

SZELIGA, Jan (Prof)
38-709 Polana 61
BIESZCZADY
Poland

Maps of East Prussia made by Samuel Suchodolec and Jan Wł. Suchodolec, 1679-1750

(with Jerzy Ostrowski), 'Działalność profesora Stanisława Pietkiewicza w zakresie historii kartografii w setną rocznicę urodzin' [The work of professor Stanisław Pietkiewicz in the history of cartography on his 100th birthday], in *Z Dziejów Kartografii*, vol. 7: *Dwudziestolecie Zespołu Historii Kartografii*

(Warsaw: Polska Akademia Nauk Instytut Historii Nauki, 1995), 59-71.

'Mapy batymetryczne rejonu ujścia Wisly z konca XVII wieku' [Bathymetric charts of the Vistula river mouth from the late 17th century], *Polski przegląd kartograficzny* 29:3 (1997): 169-171.

'Mapy Prus Ksiazech Józefa Naronowicza-Narońskiego z lat 1660-1678' [Maps of ducal Prussia by Józef Naronowicz-Naroński from the years 1660-1678], in *Z Dziejów Kartografii*, vol. 8: *Ziemie dawnych Prus wschodnich w Kartografii* (Olsztyn: Polska Akademia Nauk Instytut Historii Nauki, 1997), 49-66.

'Rękopismienne mapy Prus Książęcych Józefa Naronowicza-Narońskiego z drugiej połowy XVII wieku' [Manuscript maps of ducal Prussia by Jósef Naronowicz-Naroński from the second half of the 17th century], *Studia i materiały z historii kartografii* 15 (Warsaw, Biblioteka Narodowa, 1997).

'Zarys rozwoju kartografii południowego Bałtyku' [An outline history of the cartography of the southern Baltic], in *Z Dziejów Kartografii*, vol. 9: *Mapy południowego Bałtyku* (Szczecin: Polska Akademia Nauk Instytut Historii Nauki, 1997), 13-34.

SZYKUŁA, Krystyna Anna
Map Curator
Oddzial Zbiorow Kartograficznych
Biblioteka Uniwersytecka
ul. Św. Jadwigi 3/4
50-266 WROCŁAW
Poland
Tel: (48) 71 402 422 (office)   (48) 3 482 696 (home)
Fax: (48) 71 443 432

Jenkinson's 1562 map of Russia; history of the University Library's cartographical collection

'Odnaleziona mapa Rosji Jenkinsona z 1562 r. Pierwsza próba analizy mapy' [Jenkinson's map of Russia dated 1562. The first author's attitude to the analysis of the map], *Acta Universitatis Wratislaviensis* 2 (1995): 7-31.

(with Jan Kozák), *Das Prager Stadtpanorama aus dem Jahre 1562 von Jan Kozel und Michael Peterle nach dem Exemplar der Universitätsbibliothek Wrocław/Breslau* (Weissenhorn: Konrad Verlag, 1995).

(with Mariola Strygewska), 'Zbiory kartograficzne: Polonika zagraniczne w Bibliotece Uniwersyteckiej we Wrocławiu' [Cartographical Collection: the case study of foreign Polonicas in the Wrocław University Library], in *Wydawnictwo Uniwersytetu Wrocławskiego* (Wrocław, 1998).

TALBERT, Richard J.A. (Prof)
History Department
University of North Carolina
CHAPEL HILL, NC 27599-3195
USA
Tel: (1) 919 962 3942
Fax: (1) 919 962 1403
E-mail: talbert@email.unc.edu
Web: http://www.unc.edu/depts/cl_atlas

Director of American
Philological Association
classsical atlas project

'Maps of the classical world: where do we go from here?' *American Journal of Philology* 11 (1997): 323-327.

TANG, Eve
National Library of Estonia
Fine Arts Department
Cartographic Section
Tonismagi 2
EE0106 TALLINN
Estonia
Tel: (372) 6 307 156; (372) 6 307 140
Fax: (372) 6 311 410
E-mail: eve@nlib.ee *or* evetang@hotmail.com

Bibliography of Estonian
maps, 1918-1945, highly
classified during Soviet
occupation

(editor), *Eesti kaardid 1918–1944: bibliograafia* [Estonian maps 1918-1944: bibliography] (Tallinn: Eesti Rahvusraamatukogu, 1996).

(editor), *The maps: The Estonian national bibliography* (Tallinn: Eesti Rahvusraamatukogu, 1998).

TANTOULOS, Antonios (Dr)
NEAPOLIS LACONIA 23053
Greece
Tel: (30) 0734 22368
Fax: (30) 0734 22956

Maps of Morea and of the
Cyclades islands; portolan
charts of Greek waters

TAUB, Liba (Dr)
Curator
Whipple Museum of the History of Science
University of Cambridge
Free School Lane
CAMBRIDGE CB2 3RH
UK
Tel: (44) 01223 334 545 (office)   (44) 01223 329 753 (home)
Fax: (44) 01223 534 554
E-mail: lct1001@hermes.cam.ac.uk

Celestial maps; ancient
Greek and Roman cartog-
raphy

TAUCHÉ, W.E. Bruno (Dr)
Die Kartensammlung
Institut für Geographie
H.-u-Th.-Mann-Strasse 26
D-06108 HALLE/SAALE
Germany
Tel: (49) 0345 55 26010 (office)   (49) 0344 41 23739 (home)
Fax: (49) 0345 55 27142
E-mail: tauche@geographie.uni-halle.de

Heinrich August Riedel;
cartography of planning
and of melioration

TAYLOR, Anne
Head, Map Room
Cambridge University Library
West Road
CAMBRIDGE CB3 9DR
UK
Tel: (44) 01223 333041
Fax: (44) 01223 333160
E-mail: aemt@ula.cam.ac.uk

Map collections at
Cambridge University

TAYLOR, Iain C. (Dr)
Research Associate
Dalhousie University,
5830 Chain Rock Drive
HALIFAX, NS B3H 1A1
Canada
Tel: (1) 902 425 0668
Fax:(1) 902 425 1338
E-mail: mapman@hfx.andara.com

Commercial mapping of
western Canada before
1922; government map-
ping programmes and state
creation in Canada; cartobibliography of printed
maps of British Columbia
to 1869; topographical
mapping of the Rockies to
1920

TAYLOR, Kenneth L.
Professor of History of Science
Physical Sciences Building 622
University of Oklahoma
NORMAN, OK 73019-0315
USA
Tel: (1) 405 325 5416 (office)
      (1) 405 329 8906 (home)
Fax: (1) 405 325 2363
E-mail: ktaylor@ou.edu

Geological maps and mapping in France to 1830; cartographical (and other visual) representations of geological regularities in the 18th century

'Nicolas Desmarest and Italian geology', in Gaetano Giglia, Carlo Maccagni and Nicoletta Morello (eds), *Rocks, Fossils and History* (Florence: Edizioni Festina Lente, 1995), 95-109.

'La genèse d'un naturaliste: Desmarest, la lecture et la nature', in Théodore Monod, Gabriel Gohau, and Goulven Laurent (eds), *De la géologie à son histoire: Essais présentés à François Ellenberger pour son 80ème anniversaire* (Paris: Comité des Travaux Historiques et Scientifiques, 1997), 61-74.

TEN, Antonio E. (Prof)
Instituto de estudios documentales e
      históricos sobre la ciencia
Facultad de Medicina
Univ. de Valencia
Av. Blasco Ibañez 17
E-46010 VALENCIA
Spain
Tel: (34) 6 386 4164 (office)
Fax: (34) 6 361 3975 (office)
E-mail: antonio.e.ten@uv.es

History of geodesy (18th-19th centuries); history of the metric system and its related Earth-measurements; the origins and early works of the map of Spain (19th century)

(34) 6 372 2367 (home)
(34) 6 372 2367 (home)

(with J. Castro Soler), 'El proyecto del mapa de España: los primeros trabajos (1853-1857), *Estudios geográficos* **54**:213 (1993): 543-574.

Catálogo de las revistas científicas y técnicas publicadas en España durante el siglo XIX (Valencia: IEDHC, 1996).

Medir el Metro. La historia de la prolongación del arco de meridiano Dunkerque-Barcelona, base del Sistema Métrico Decimal (Valencia: IEDHC, 1996).

THEUNISSEN, Yolanda
Curator and Head of Cartographic
      Collections
Osher Map Library and Smith
      Center for Cartographic Education
University of Southern Maine
P.O. Box 9301
314 Forest Avenue
PORTLAND, ME 04104-9301
Tel: (1) 207 780 4516
Fax: (1) 207 780 5310
yolanda@usm.maine.edu

Maps in the collections at the Osher Map Library

THOMAS, Garth (Dr)
Map and Picture Department
Public Record Office
KEW, Surrey TW9 4DU
UK
Tel: (44) 0181 876 3444
Fax: (44) 0181 878 8905

Maps of 19th century imperial wars

THROWER, Norman Joseph
      William (Prof Dr)
Department of Geography
University of California (UCLA)
LOS ANGELES, CA 90095-1524
USA
Tel: (1) 310 825 3727 (office)
Fax: (1) 310 206 5976

Maps and civilization; mapping the American West; maps and longitude

(1) 310 454 5949 (home)

'Longitude in the context of cartography', in William J.H. Andrewes (ed), *The Quest for Longitude* (Cambridge, Mass.: Collection of Historical Scientific Instruments, Harvard University, 1996), 48-62.

Maps and Civilization: Cartography in Culture and Society (Chicago: University of Chicago Press, 1996).

TIBBETTS, Gerald Randall (Dr)
Chatterholt, Cassington Road
EYNSHAM, Oxon. OX8 1LF
UK
Tel: (44) 01865 881291

Classical Arabic geographers; Arabic cartography

TIGGESBÄUMKER, Günter (Dr)
Princely Library of Corvey
Corvey Castle
D-37671 HOEXTER
[private: Hochstiftsgrasse 16
D-33100 PADERBORN]
Germany
Tel: (49) 05271 6810
Fax: (49) 05271 68140

History of maps; maps in libraries; map librarianship and library history; history of travel

'Franken: eine "Kartenlandschaft"', in *Mitteilungen, Freundeskreis für Cartographica in der Stiftung Preussischer Kulturbesitz e. V.* 11 (1997): 34-39.

TOBLER, Waldo (Prof emeritus)
Geography Department
University of California Santa
    Barbara
SANTA BARBARA, CA 93106
USA
Tel: (1) 805 964 0116
Fax: (1) 805 893 3146
E-mail: tobler@geog.ucsb.edu

Map-projection mathematics; mathematical analysis of old maps; portolan charts

TOLMACHEVA, Marina A.
    (Prof Dr)
Department of History
Washington State University
PULLMAN, WA 99164-4030
USA
Tel: (1) 509 335 3267 & 335 5139
Fax: (1) 509 335 4171
E-mail: tolmache@wsu.edu

Islamic geography; cartography of Africa; trade routes to 1800

'The medieval Arabic geographers and the beginnings of modern orientalism', *International Journal of Middle East Studies* 27:2 (1995): 143-158.

'Essays in Swahili geographical thought', *Swahili Forum* 2 (Afrikanistische Arbeitspapier 42) (Cologne 1995): 1-40; *Swahili Forum* 3 (Afrikanistische Arbeitspapier 47) (1996): 173-196.

'Bertius and al-Idrisi: an experiment in orientalist cartography, *Terrae Incognitae* 28 (1996): 36-45.

TOMASCH, Sylvia (Prof)
English Department
Hunter College (CUNY)
695 Park Avenue
NEW YORK, New York 10021
U.S.A.
Tel: (1) 212 772 5079
Fax: (1) 212 772 5138
E-mail:
stomasch@shiva.hunter.cuny.edu

Medieval European literary/geographical relations; mappaemundi, particularly T-O maps; politics and ideology of medieval maps in Europe; Andreas Walsperger's world map; map-images in Lambert of St. Omer's *Liber floridus*

(with Sealy Gilles, ed), *Text and Territory: Geographical Imagination and the European Middle Ages* (University of Pennsylvania Press, 1997).

TÖRÖK, Zsolt (Dr)
Department of Cartography
Eötvös University
Ludovika 2
H-1083 BUDAPEST
Hungary
Tel: (36) 1 1342785
E-mail: zoltorok@ludens.elte.hu

Map reproduction techniques; facsimile printing using original reproduction methods; thematic cartography in 19th-century America and Germany

'A Lázár-térkép és a modern europai térképeszet' [The Lazarus map and the modern map of Europe], *Cartographica Hungarica* 5 (1996): 44-45.

'Desert love: László Almásy the real "English Patient"' , *Mercator's World* 2:5 (1997): 42-47.

'The map of Lazarus and the beginnings of modern cartography', *IMCoS Journal* 71 (1997): 5-9.

TORRESANI, Stefano (Prof)
Dpt. di Discipline Storiche
University of Bologna
Piazza S. Giovanni in Monte N.2
40124 BOLOGNA
Italy
Tel: (39) 51 645 7644
Fax: (39) 51 645 7620
E-mail: torresani@biblio.cib.unibo.it

Adriatic Sea coastal maps (16th-18th century); Italian cartography (16th-19th century)

(with A. Bonazzi et al.), *Giacomo Cantelli Geografo del Serenissimo* (Bologna: Grafis Edizione, 1995), 63-74.

'Spazio e tempo nei Sistemi informativi geografici: un'analisi preliminare', in 'Momenti e Problemi della Geografia contemporanea', *Atti del Convegno Internazionale in onore di Giuseppe Caraci* (Genova: Centro Italiano per gli Studi Storico-Geografici, 1995), 241-261.

(with A. Lodovisi), 'Evaluating historical cartography as a tool for the study of coastal areas', in P.S. Jones et al. (eds), *Studies in European Coastal Management* (Tresaith: Samara Publishing, 1996), 111-120.

(with A. Lodovisi), *Storia della cartografia* (Bologna: Patron, 1996).

'Figurazione e invenzione de realtà nella rappresentazione cartografica', in C. Tugnoli (ed), *I contorni della terra e del mare. La geografia tra rappresentazione e invenzione della realtà* (Bologna: Pitagora Editrice, 1997), 119-172.

'L'indagine geografica "giudiziale" sullo spazio costiero dell'Emilia-Romagna tra XVI e XVII secolo', in C. Cerreti and A. Taberini (eds), *Ambiente geografico, storia, cultura e società in Italia* (Roma: Centro italiano per gli studi storico-cartografici, 1997), 65-76.

TOULOUSE, Sarah
Bibliothèque municipale de Rennes
1 rue de La Borderie
35 042 RENNES
France
Tel: (33) 2 99 87 98 98
Fax: (33) 2 99 87 98 99

Charts in Normandy of the 16th to 18th centuries (Dieppe School)

TOUS MELIÁ, Juan (Colonel)
Coronel Director
Museo Militar Regional de Canarias
Calle San Isidro, n° 2
38001 SANTA CRUZ DE TENERIFE
Islas Canarias
Spain
Tel & fax: (34) 22 27 42 24 (office)
Tel: (34) 22 25 86 83 (home)
Fax: (34) 22 25 39 86

Description of the Canary Islands by Dr Antonio Riviere (1740-1743)

Plano de las islas Canarias by Francisco Machado y Fiesco, 1792 (Santa Cruz de Tenerife: Museo Militar, 1994).

Santa Cruz de Tenerife a través de la cartografía (1588-1899) (Santa Cruz de Tenerife: Museo Militar, 1994).

El primer mapa impreso en las islas Canarias, 1768 (Santa Cruz de Tenerife: Museo Militar, 1995).

Las Palmas de Gran Canaria a través de la cartografía (1588-1899) (Santa Cruz de Tenerife: Museo Militar, 1995).

edited and prepared maps for: José María Pinto de la Rosa, *Apuntes para la historia de las antiguas fortificaciones de Canarias* (Madrid: Tabapress, 1996).

El plan de las Afortunadas Islas del Reyno de Canarias y la Isla de San Borondón (Madrid: Tabapress, 1996).

Tenerife a través de la Cartografía (1588-1899) (Madrid: Tabapress, 1996).

TURNBULL, David (Dr)
Arts Faculty
Deakin University
GEELONG 3217
Australia
Tel: (61) 03 52 272593
Fax: (61) 03 52 272018
E-mail: turnbull@deakin.edu.au

Ethnocartography; indigenous mapping; maps and power; science, cartography and the state

'Comparing knowledge systems: Pacific navigation and Western science', in John Morrison et al. (eds), *Science of the Pacific Island Peoples*. Vol. 1, *Ocean and Coastal Studies* (Suva: Institute of Pacific Studies, 1994), 129-144.

'Local knowledge and comparative scientific traditions', *Knowledge and Policy* 6:3-4 (1994): 29-54.

'Rendering turbulence orderly', *Social Studies of Science* 25:1 (1995): 9-33.

(with Helen Verran), 'Science and other indigenous knowledge production systems', in S. Jasanoff et al. (eds), *Handbook of Science and Technology Studies* (Thousand Oaks: Sage Publications, 1995), 115-139.

'Cartography and science: mapping the construction of knowledge spaces', *Imago Mundi* 48 (1996): 5-24.

'Constructing knowledge spaces and locating sites of resistance in the modern cartographic transformation', in Rolland Paulston (ed), *Social Cartography: Mapping Ways of Seeing Social and Educational Change* (New York and London: Garland Publishing, 1996), 53-79.

'Bamboo', p. 150; 'Knowledge systems: local knowledge', pp. 485-490; 'Maps and mapmaking of the Australian Aboriginal People', pp. 560-562; 'Rationality, objectivity, and method', pp. 845-850, in Helaine Selin (ed), *Encyclopedia of the History of Science, Technology and Medicine in Non-Western Cultures* (Dordrecht: Kluwer Academic Publishers, 1997).

TURNER, Anthony John
24 rue du Buisson Richard
78600 LE MESNIL-LE-ROI
France
Tel: (33) 01 39 12 11 91
Fax: (33) 01 39 62 07 22

Astrolabes, globes and spheres; maps of Oxfordshire and Staffordshire by Robert Plot; 18th-century French hydrography; Jacques de Vaux

'Destombian discovery and doubt: the problem of the oldest Latin astrolabe', in Guy B. Wesley et al. (eds), *The Oldest Latin Astrolabe* (*Physis*, n.s. 32 (1995)), 191-207.

'The vitreous globe: an 18th century novelty', *Bulletin of the Scientific Instrument Society* 47 (1995): 8-11.

'Les globes célestes en verre', *Musée des Arts et Métiers: La Revue* 11 (1996): 51-57.

'In the wake of the Act, but mainly before', in William J.H. Andrewes (ed), *The Quest for Longitude* (Cambridge, Mass, 1996), 115-132.

'Robert Plot, first Keeper of the Ashmolean Museum, 1640-1696', *Sphaera, The Newsletter of the Museum of the History of Science, Oxford* 4 (1996): 4-5.

TYACKE, Sarah J. (Dr)
Public Record Office
Ruskin Avenue
KEW, Surrey TW9 4DU
UK
Tel: (44) 0181 878 1250
Fax: (44) 0181 878 8905
E-mail: 100114.3155@compuserve.com

English overseas chart-making, c.1500-1650s: chart fragments; Helen Wallis papers (1951-1995)

TYNER, Judith Ann (Prof)
Department of Geography
California State University
LONG BEACH, CA
USA
Tel: (1) 562 985 5332 (office)
    (1) 562 424 2850 (home)
Fax: (1) 562 985 8993
E-mail: jztyner@csulb.edu

Embroidered maps and globes; 19th century American cartography; women in cartography; cartographical curiosities

'The origins of American atlas cartography: Mathew Carey and the Philadelphia mapmakers', *Mercator's World* 1:6 (1996): 36-41.

'The world in silk: embroidered globes of Westtown School', *The Map Collector* 74 (1996): 11-14.

'The hidden cartographers: women in mapmaking', *Mercator's World* 2:6 (1997): 46-51.

UNNO, Kazutaka (Prof)
Higashi 1-135
Suzurandai
NABARI, Mie, 518-0401
Japan
Tel: (81) 0595 68 2781

East Asian cartography; early cartographical communication between Asia and Europe

'Cartography in Japan', in J.B. Harley and D. Woodward (eds), *The History of Cartography*, Vol. 2, Book 2: *Cartography in the Traditional East and Southeast Asian Societies* (Chicago: University of Chicago Press, 1994), 346-477.

'Shūgaishō koshahon ni okeru chizu: Tembun-jūshichi-nen bon o chūshin to shite' [Maps and plans illustrating the early manuscripts of the Shūgaishō: focusing on the codex of 1548]. *Biblia: Bulletin of Tenri Central Library* **101, 102** (1994): 2-23, 2-21.

'Sekaichizu no nakano Ajia: Seiyō kara no shisen' [Asia on world maps: a glance from the West], *Gekkan Shinika {Monthly Sinica}* 6:2 (1995): 8-21.

'A surveying instrument designed by Hōjō Ujinaga, 1609-1670', in K. Hashimoto et al (eds), *East Asian Science: Tradition and Beyond* (Osaka: Kansai University Press, 1995), 411-417.

Chuzu No Bunkashi: Sekai to Nippon [A Cultural History of Maps and Charts in the World and Japan] (Tokyo: Yasaka Shobō, 1996).

'"Kansei Rekisho" shosai tenchiryōkyūgi zu' [The celestial and terrestrial globes illustrated in the Kansei Rekisho, an expository book on the Kansei calendar compiled in 1893], *Yogaku: Yōgakushigakkai Kenkyūnempō* [Western Learning: Annual Report of Research of the Society for the History of Western Learning in Japan] 4 (1996): 13-43.

'Fukada Seishitsu no Bankokuzenzu, Juntengi, Jimeishō' [The world map, an armillary sphere, and a clock of Fukada Seishitsu, ?-1663], *Tsuchiura-shiritsu Hakubutsukan Kiyō* [Bulletin of the Tsuchiura City Museum] 8 (1997): 11-30.

UNVERHAU, Dagmar (Dr)
Neue Kulmer Strasse 2
10827 BERLIN
Germany
Tel: (49) 030 784 49 95

Schleswig-Holstein and Danewerk, north Europe

URNESS, Carol L. (Prof)
Curator, James Ford Bell Library
472 Wilson Library
University of Minnesota
309 19th Avenue South
MINNEAPOLIS, MN 55455
USA
Tel: (1) 612 624 6895 (office)   (1) 612 781 3921 (home)
Fax: (1) 612 626 9353
E-mail: c-urne@tc.umn.edu

Mapping the North Pacific prior to 1800; maps of first and second Kamchatka expeditions of Vitus Bering; European maps, 1400-1800

'Russian mapping of the North Pacific to 1792', in Stephen Haycox et al (eds), *Enlightenment and Exploration in the North Pacific, 1741-1805* (Seattle: University of Washington Press, 1997), 132-146.

VALERIO, Vladimiro
via Tito Angelini 21/C
80129 NAPOLI
Italy
Tel & fax: (39) 081 556 9536
E-mail: vladimir@cds.unina.it

Cartobibliography of atlases printed in Italy; biographies of Italian mapmakers; lithography; Ptolemaic projections and projective geometry

Ferdinando Visconti. Carteggio (1818-1847) (Firenze: Leo S. Olschki, 1995).

'Il Vesuvio. Immagini e misurazioni', *L'Universo* 75:2 (1995): 238-252.

'All'origine ella rappresentazione scientifica del Vesuvio', *Notiziario del Centro Italiano per gli Studi Storico-Geografici* 4:2 & 3 (1996): 3-13.

'Cartografia militare e technologie indotte nel Regno di Napoli tra Settecento e Ottocento', in *La politica della Scienza. Toscana e stati italiani nel tardo Settecento* (Firenze: Leo S. Olschki, 1996), 551-567.

(with Maria Teresa Penta), *Napoli in Prospettiva. Vedute della città dal XV al XIX secolo nelle stampe della Raccolta d'Arte Pagliara* (Napoli: Istituto Suor Orsola Benincasa, 1996).

'Carta per le Carte. Filigrane dall'Archivio dell'Istituto Geografico Militare', *L'Universo* 77:1 (1997): 119-132.

'Late eighteenth- and early nineteenth-century Italian atlases', in John A. Wolter and Ronald E. Grim (eds), *Images of the World* (Washington: Library of Congress, 1997), 257-300.

VAN EE, Patricia Molen
Specialist in Cartographic History
Geography and Map Division
Library of Congress
101 Independence Ave. S.E.
WASHINGTON, D.C. 20540-4650
USA
Tel: (1) 202 707 8534 (office)   (1) 410 997 7790 (home)
Fax: (1) 202 707 8531
E-mail: pvanee@loc.gov

Colonial period, early American history; cartographical sources for the study of American women's history

VARANKA, Dalia
U S Department of the Interior
Bureau of Land Management
ste 225, 310 W. Wisconsin Ave.
MILWAUKEE, Wisconsin 53203
USA
Tel: (1) 414 297 4436
Fax: (1) 414 297 4409

Early English world atlases, 1600-1730

VARGAS MARTÍNEZ, Gustavo (Prof Dr)
Escuela Nacional de Antropología e Historia
Periférico Sur y Zapote
MÉXICO 22 DF
México
Tel: (52) 665 9228 (office)   (52) 655 2225 (home)
Fax: (52) 665 9228

Image of the world in the 16th century; old Chinese maps

Atlas antiquo de América, siglos XV y XVI (Colección La Linterna Mágica No 22; México: Editorial Trillas, 1995).

América en un mapa de 1489, Prólogode Germán Arciniegas (México: Ediciones Taller Abierto, 1996).

VOGELER, Albert R. (Dr)
Curator
Roy V. Boswell Collection for the History of Cartography
California State University, Fullerton
FULLERTON, CA 92834
USA
Tel: (1) 714 278 3444 (office)   (1) 714 871 2192 (home)
E-mail: avogeler@fullerton.edu

Non-existent Lake Chia May; Southeast Asia (16th-18th centuries); Western Hemisphere and world maps (16th-18th centuries)

WAHLL, Andrew
National Geographic Society
1145 17th Street NW
WASHINGTON DC 20036-4688
USA
Tel: (1) 202 775 7874
Fax: (1) 202 429 5704
E-mail: awahll@ngs.org

World exploration and discovery; Popham Colony (Maine), 1607; Braddock Expedition (western Pennsylvania), 1755; Santa Fe Trail

WAJNTRAUB, Eva and Gimpel (Dr)
4 Brenner St
JERUSALEM 92103
Israel
Tel: (972) 2 569 6811 (office)
     (972) 2 561 1687 (home)
Fax: (972) 2 563 3356 (office)
     (972) 2 563 6972 (home)

Italian maps of the Holy Land; crusader maps of Jerusalem; physicians as mapmakers; editor, Israeli Map Collectors Society Journal

'Gerard Mercator's map of Palestine, 1537', *Journal, Israeli Map Collectors Society* 11 (1994): 1-6.

'Holy Land maps and views by German cartographers, IV', *Journal, Israeli Map Collectors Society* 11 (1994): 24-36.

'Hebrew maps of the Land of Israel', *Proceedings of the International Conference on Geography in Jewish Studies*, 1995.

'The holy city of Jerusalem' *Journal, Israeli Map Collectors Society* 11 (1995): special issue.

'Ancient maps of Jerusalem', *JUF News* 26:5 (Chicago, 1996): 32-33.

'Holy Land maps and views by German cartographers, V', *Journal, Israeli Map Collectors Society* 13 (1996): 48-55.

'An illustrated history of the Holy City', *Mercator's World* 1:4 (1996): 26-33.

'Holy Land maps and views by German cartographers, VI', *Journal, Israeli Map Collectors Society* 14 (1997): 23-47.

'19th-century evolution of Jerusalem outside the walls', *Journal, Israeli Map Collectors Society* 15 (1997): 18-51.

WALSMIT, Erik
St Rijksmuseum het Zuiderzeemuseum
Postbus 42
1600 AA ENKHUIZEN
Netherlands
Tel: (31) 2280 10122
Fax: (31) 2280 10230

Maps and prints of the editions of Lodovico Guicciardini's 'Descrittione di tutti i Paesi Bassi' (1567-1660)

WALTER, Lutz
German East-Asiatic Society (OAG)
7-5-56 Akasaka
Minato-ku
TOKYO 107-0052
Japan
Tel: (81) 3 3589 0410
Fax: (81) 3 3751 7970

Cartobibliography of Western printed maps of Japan (with Jason C. Hubbard)

WANG Qianjin
Institute of the History of
    Natural Science
Chinese Academy of Science
137 Chaoyangmen neidajie
100010 BEIJING
China

Chinese cartography; geography in ancient China

WARDINGTON, Christopher (Lord)
Wardington Manor
BANBURY, Oxfordshire
    0X17 1SW
UK
Tel: (44) 01295 750 202
Fax: (44) 01295 750 805

Sir Robert Dudley's *Arcano del Mare*

WARHUS, Mark
4071 North Stowell Avenue
MILWAUKEE, Wisconsin 53211
USA
Tel: (1) 414 963 0821
E-mail: markw@csd.uwm.edu

Native American cartography; non-Western cartography

WATELET, Marcel (Dr)
Attaché scientifique and Map Curator
    (Bruxelles)
Ministère wallon de l'Équipement et
    des Transports
Rue Abbesse 74
B-1457 NIL-SAINT-VINCENT
Belgium
Tel: (32) 02 208 33 30 (office)
    (32) 010 65 86 53 (home)
Fax: (32) 02 208 33 36 (office)
    (32) 010 65 09 44 (home)

Military mapping of France and Belgium by the Allies (1815-1818); thematic cartography of southern Belgium (16th-20th centuries); Franco-Belgian boundaries (17th-19th centuries); Duchy of Luxembourg; cartography and engineering; historiography of history of cartography in Belgium (19th century); Gérard Mercator (1512-1594)

(general editor), *Gerardi Mercatoris. Atlas Europae. Facsimilé des cartes de Gérard Mercator contenues dans l'atlas de l'Europe, vers 1570-1572* (Anvers: Bibliothèque des Amis du Fonds Mercator, 1994). [Published in English as *The Mercator Atlas of Europe: Facsimile of the Maps by Gerardus Mercator Contained in the Atlas of Europe, circa 1570-1572* (Pleasant Hill: Oregon: Walking Tree Press, 1997).]

'Le patrimoine cartographique de Wallonie: un horizon de recherche', in L. Courtois and J. Pirotte (eds), *L'Imaginaire wallon. Jalons pour une identité qui se construit* (Série Recherches, Vol. 1, 1994; Louvain-la-Neuve: Publications de la Fondation wallonne P.-M. et J.-F. Humblet), 217-222.

'Le nord de la France au coeur des enjeux européens: contribution à la cartographie des Alliés (russes et prussiens) dans le département des Ardennes', in P. Salmon and J. Rousseau (eds), *Sedan. De l'Europe des Principautés à l'Europe des Nations* (Nancy: Presses Universitaires de Nancy, 1995), 106-121.

(with B. Neefs et al.), *Le terrain des ingénieurs: la cartographie routière en Wallonie au XVIIe siècle* ([*Patrimoine cartographique de Wallonie. Monumenta Cartographica Walloniae II*] Namur: Ministère wallon de l'Equipement et des Transports, and Bruxelles, Editions Racine, 1995).

'Gerardo Mercatore e l'Italia', in G. Mangani and Feliciano Paoli (eds), *Gerardo Mercatore. Sulle tracce di geografi e viaggiatori nelle Marche* (Urbania: Edizioni Biblioteca e Civico Museo di Urbania, 1996), 17-23.

'Mercator (Gérard) (1512–1595)', in *Centuriae Latinae: cent une figures humanistes de la Renaissance aux Lumières offertes à Jacques Chomaut* (Genève: Droz, 1997), 551-557.

'Production cartographique et enjeux diplomatiques: le problème des routes et de la frontière entre les Pays-Bas Autrichiens et la France (1769–1779)', *Imago Mundi*, **50** (1998): 84-95.

WATERS, David Watkin
    (Lt Cmdr, RN)
6 Brewery Row
Little Compton
MORETON-IN-THE MARSH,
Glos, GL56 0RY
UK
Tel & fax: (44) 01608 674 495

Medieval and Renaissance sea charts and sailing directions: European, Indian and Pacific oceans

WAWRIK, Franz (Dr)
Österreichische Nationalbibliothek
Kartensammlung und
    Globenmuseum
Josefsplatz 1
A-1015 WIEN
Austria
Tel: (43) 1 53 410 292
Fax: (43) 1 53 410 319
E-mail: wawrik@onb.ac.at

History of cartography of the 15th to 17th centuries; old globes

'Die Ansicht Neu-Amsterdams der Österreichischen Nationalbibliothek', in *Flores litterarum Ioanni Marte sexagenario oblati. Wissenschaft in der Bibliothek* (Wien, Köln, Weimar: Böhlau, 1995), 171-191.

(with Helga Hühnel, Jan Mokre, Elisabeth Zeilinger, ed), *Kartographische Zimelien. Die 50 schönsten Karten und Globen der Österreichischen Nationalbibliothek* (Wien: Holzhausen, 1995).

'Die berühmtesten Globenhersteller', 47-69; 'Öffentliche Globensammlungen in Österreich', 132-143; and (with Rudolf Schmidt), 'Über das Sammeln von Globen, Privatsammlungen in Österreich', 144-173; in Peter E. Allmayer-Beck (ed), *Modelle der Welt. Erd- und Himmelsgloben* (Kulturerbe aus österreichen Sammlungen; Wien: Brandstätter, 1997).

'Kartensammlung – quo vadis', in Edith Stumpf-Fischer (ed), *Der wohlinformierte Mensch. Eine Utopie. Festschrift für Magda Strebl zum 65. Geburtstag* (Graz: Akad. Druck- u. Verlagsanstalt, 1997), 71-90.

WEBB, David Francis
Kestenen
48d Bath Road
ATWORTH, Nr Melksham
Wiltshire SN12 8JX
UK
Tel: (44) 01225 702351

Road/strip maps and itineraries

WEBSTER, Diana C.F.
Map Library
National Library of Scotland
33 Salisbury Place
EDINBURGH EH9 1SL
UK
Tel: (44) 0131 226 4531 ext 3418
Fax: (44) 0131 466 3812
E-mail: d.webster@nls.uk

Scottish sea charts; Murdoch Mackenzie Senior; surveying instruments and methods; cartouches; failed Scottish mapping proposals (with M. Wilkes)

WERNER, Jan W.H. (Drs)
Map Curator
Universiteitsbibliotheek
Kaartenzaal
Singel 425
1012 WP AMSTERDAM
postal address: P.O. Box 19185
1000 GD AMSTERDAM
Netherlands
Tel: (31) 020 5252354 (office)   (31) 0299 652999 (home)
Fax: (31) 020 5252311
E-mail: werner@uba.uva.nl
Web: http://www.uba.uva.nl/nl/collecties/kaarten/

Muller Collection (in Amsterdam University Library); Frederick de Wit (1630-1706); Abraham Ortelius (1527-1598)

'A Hebrew map in a work by Hugh Broughton', in *Bibliotheca Rosenthaliana, Treasures of Jewish Booklore* (Amsterdam: Amsterdam University Press, 1994), 22-23.

Inde Witte Pascaert: kaarten en atlassen van Frederick de Wit, uitgever te Amsterdam (ca. 1630-1706); catalogus bij de gelijknamige tentoonstelling in de Universiteitsbibliotheek Amsterdam, gehouden naar aanleiding van de voltooide restauratie van vijf monumentale wandkaarten 23 september - 4 november 1994 (Amsterdam: Universiteitsbibliotheek, 1994).

'De nieuwe Kaartenzaal van de Universiteitsbibliotheek Amsterdam officieel geopend', *Kartografisch Tijdschrift* 22: 1 (1996): 23-28.

'De uitdaging van de kaarten en atlassen, conservering in de Kaartenzaal', in *In de rij voor behoud: een kijk op het conserveren en restaureren van bibliotheek-collecties* (Amsterdam: Universiteitsbibliotheek Amsterdam, 1996), 24-40.

(with Coen L. Temminck Groll), 'Cornelius Groll (1781-1896),

Ingenieur-Verificateur bij het Kadaster van Noord-Holland, een biografische schets', in *Caert-Thresoor* 16:2 (1997): 45-50.

'De kaarten- en atlassencollectie van het Koninklijk Nederlands Aardrijkskundig Genootschap in de Universiteitsbibliotheek Amsterdam', in *NVK publikatiereeks* 22 (1997): 63-82. (Also published in *Kartografisch Tijdschrift* 22:3 (1997): 21-33.)

'Pasletters: passende letters op de paskaart van Europa door Adriaen Gerritsen (1587)', in *Scripta manent, drukletters over schoonschrift ...* (Amsterdam: Universiteitsbibliotheek, 1997), 19-26.

Abraham Ortelius (1527-1598), aartsvader van onze atlas: catalogus bij de gelijknamige tentoonstelling in de Universiteitsbibliotheek Amsterdam, ter gelegenheid van het 400ste sterfjaar van Abraham Ortelius 1598-1998, 12 juni-21 augustus 1998 (Amsterdam: Universiteitsbibliotheek Amsterdam, 1998).

WERNEROWA, Wiesława (Mgr)
Bulwar Ikara 10 M. 21
PL-54-130 WROCŁAW
Poland
Tel: (48) 71 348 2248 (office)   (48) 71 510 693 (home)

Polish history of geography and cartography

'Dorobek ogólnopolskich konferencji historyków kartografii 1975-1995' [Achievements of the conferences of historians of geography and cartography 1975-1995], and 'Ze studiów nad opisami parafii diecezji wileńskiej z 1784 r. w relacji ze szkicami K. de Perthecsa' [From studis on descriptions of parishes of Wilno Diocese from 1784 in relation to sketches by K. de Perthees], in J. Ostrowski and W. Wernerowa (eds), *Z Dziejów Kartografii*. Vol 7: *Dwudziestolecie Zespołu Historii Kartografii* (Warsaw: Polska Akademia Nauk Instytut Historii Nauki, 1995), 28-48, 125-140.

Rękopiśmienne oplsy parafii litewskich z 1784 roku. Dekanat Knyszyński i Dekanat Augustowski [Manuscript descriptions of parishes in Lithuania] (Warsaw: IHN PAN, 1996).

(with Jerzy Ostrowski), 'Nieznana wersja wielkiego rękopiśmiennego planu Warszawy z 1771 roku w zbiorach Biblioteki Narodowej w Kijowie: Wiadomość wstępna' [The unknown version of a manuscript map of Warsaw issued 1771 from the collection of the National Library in Kiev], *Polski Przegląd Kartograficzny* 29:1 (1997): 32-35.

WESTRA, Frans (Dr)
Rijkstraatweg 281
9752 CD HAREN
Netherlands
Tel: (31) 5031 36897 (office)   (31) 5053 47939 (home)
Fax: (31) 5031 30406

Dutch fortification maps around 1600

WHISTANCE-SMITH, Ronald
14520 84th Ave. NW
EDMONTON, Alberta T5R 3X2
Canada
Tel & fax: (1) 403 483 5858
E-mail: rwhistan@compusmart.ab.ca

Land-ownership mapping in Alberta prior to 1950; mapping of western Canada; mapmakers in western Canada before 1950

'The rural map directory company: a locally based early attempt to produce a land ownership map series of Alberta', *Bulletin, Association of Canadian Map Libraries and Archives* 100 (Fall 1997): 17-22.

WHITEHEAD, Neil Lancelot (Prof)
Department of Anthropology
University of Wisconsin-Madison
1180 Observatory Drive
MADISON, WI 53706
USA
Tel: (1) 608 262 2866 (office)   (1) 608 233 1946 (home)
Fax: (1) 608 265 4216
E-mail: nlwhiteh@facstaff.wisc.edu

Indigenous mapping in South America; Renaissance cartography

WIKANDER, Johann Anton
Kong Inges gt 41
N-7017 TRONDHEIM
Norway
Tel: (47) 7 257 2555
Fax: (47) 7 257 2600

Mapping and history of the outer ports on the south coast of Norway, rock-engraved compass roses in ports

'Britisk kartlegging på Agdesiden 1570-1814' [British charting around Agder 1570-1814], *Agder Historielag* (Kristiansand) 72 (1996): 37-69.

WILKES, Margaret
Map Library
National Library of Scotland
33 Salisbury Place
EDINBURGH EH9 1SL
UK
Tel: (44) 0131 226 4531
Fax: (44) 0131 668 3472
E-mail: m.wilkes@nls.uk

Little-known maps of Scotland in the National Library of Scotland; failed early Scottish mapping proposals (with Diana Webster)

WILLIAMS, Glyndwr (Prof)
Department of History
Queen Mary & Westfield College
Mile End Road
LONDON E1 4NS
UK
Tel: (44) 0171 975 5016 (office)
Fax: (44) 01732 521463 (home)
Fax: (44) 0181 980 8400

Speculative cartography: Pacific and North America, 1600-1800

'Buccaneers, castaways, and satirists: the South Sea in the English consciousness before 1750', *Eighteenth-Century Life* **18**:3 (1995): 114-128.

'"To make discoveries of countries hitherto unknown": the Admiralty and Pacific exploration in the eighteenth century', *Mariner's Mirror* **82**:1 (1996): 14-27.

(with Alan Frost), 'The beginnings of Britain's exploration of the Pacific Ocean in the eighteenth century', *Mariner's Mirror* **83**:4 (1997): 410-418.

'George Vancouver, the Admiralty, and Exploration', in Stephen Haycox et al (eds), *Enlightenment and Exploration in the North Pacific 1741-1805* (Seattle and London: University of Washington Press, 1997), 38-48.

The Great South Sea: English Voyages and Encounters 1570-1750 (New Haven and London: Yale University Press, 1997).

'The second age of discovery: the opening of the Pacific', in John B. Hattendorf (ed), *Maritime History*, Vol. II, *The Eighteenth Century* (Malabar, Florida: Krieger Publishing, 1977), 3-43.

(editor), *The Voyages of Captain Cook* (London: Folio Society, 1997).

WILLIAMS, John W. (Prof)
Department of the History of Art
    & Architecture
University of Pittsburgh
PITTSBURGH, Pennsylvania 15260
USA
Tel: (1) 412 648 2404 (office)
Fax: (1) 412 648 2792
E-mail: jww23+@pitt.edu

Spanish maps of medieval period

(1) 412 363 5059 (home)

The Illustrated Beatus: A Corpus of the Illustrations of the Commentary on the Apocalypse (5 vols; London: Harvey Miller, 1994ff).

'Isidore, Orosius and the Beatus map', *Imago Mundi* **49** (1997): 7-32.

WINEARLS, Joan
Map Librarian, University of
    Toronto [retired]
273 Erskine Ave.
TORONTO, Ontario M4P 1Z6
Canada
Tel: (1) 416 978 5205
E-mail: winearls@library.utoronto.ca

Mapping western North America in the 18th century, with particular reference to the De Fonte fantasy; the Canada Company map of Upper Canada, 1825-1826, and its antecedents

(editor), *Editing of Early Historical Atlases: Papers Given at the Twenty-Ninth Annual Conference on Editorial Problems* (Toronto: Toronto University Press, 1995).

'Thomas Jefferys's "Map of Canada" and the mapping of the western part of North America, 1750-1768', in Karen S. Cook (ed), *Images & Icons of the New World: Essays on American Cartography* (London: The British Library, 1996), 27-54. (Also issued in *The British Library Journal* **22**:1 (Spring 1996).

WINTLE, Michael Joseph (Dr)
Department of European Studies
University of Hull
HULL HU6 7RX
UK
Tel: (44) 01482 465043 (office)
Fax: (44) 01482 465020
E-mail: m.j.wintle@hull.ac.uk

Portrayal of Europe in maps and iconography

(44) 01482 447578 (home)

'Europe's image: visual representations of Europe from the earliest times to the twentieth century', in M.J. Wintle (ed), *Culture and Identity in Europe: Perceptions of Divergence and Unity in Past and Present* (Aldershot: Avebury Press, 1996), 52-97.

WITHERS, Charles W.J. (Prof)
Department of Geography
University of Edinburgh
Drummond Street
EDINBURGH EH8 9XP
UK
Tel: (44) 0131 650 2559
Fax: (44) 0131 650 2524
E-mail: cwjw@geo.ed.ac.uk

History of mapping in Scotland; geography, science and national identity

'Geography, science and national identity in early modern Britain: the case of Scotland and the role of Sir Robert Sibbald (1641-1722)' *Annals of Science* 53:1 (1996): 29-73.

'Linguistic changes before 1707', in *Atlas of Scottish History to 1707* (Edinburgh: Scottish Cultural Press, 1996).

'Sir Robert Sibbald (1641-1722)', *Geographers' Bibliographic Studies* 17 (1996): 82-91.

WOHLSCHLÄGER, Heide
Internationale Coronelli-Gesellschaft
für Globen-und Instrumentenkunde
Dominikanerbastei 21/28
A-1010 WEIN
Austria
Tel: (43) 1 533 32 85
Fax: (43) 1 532 08 24

Central European terrestrial and celestial globes of the 19th and 20th centuries

'Globen der neueren Zeit', 198-223; (with Rudolf Schmidt), 'Globen in Österreich', 320-379; (with Rudolf Schmidt), 'Globenhersteller aus aller Welt', 236-319; in Peter E. Allmayer-Beck (ed), *Modelle der Welt. Erd- und Himmelsgloben* (Kulturerbe aus österreichen Sammlungen; Wien: Brandstätter, 1997).

WOLF, Armin (Prof Dr)
Max-Planck-Institut für Europäische
Rechtsgeschichte
Hausener Weg 120
D-60457 FRANKFURT AM MAIN
Germany
Tel: (49) 069 789 78151
Fax: (49) 069 789 78169

Ebstorf world map; historical atlases; school history atlases; Putzger; Homeric geography

'Das Einzugsgebiet der Elbe auf der Ebstorfer Weltkarte (um 1239)', in *Die Elbe im Kartenbild Kartographische Bausteine 9* (Dresden, Technische Universität, Institut für Kartographie, 1994), pp. 3-10.

'Gervasius von Tilbury und die Welfen: zugleich Bemerkungen zum Ebstorfer Weltkarte', in Bernd Schneidmüller (ed), *Die Welfen und ihr Braunschweiger Hof im hohen Mittelalter: Vorträge gehalten anlässlich des 33. Wolfenbütteler Symposions vom 16. bis 19. Februar 1993* (Wiesbaden: Harrassowitz, 1995), 407-438.

'Hatte Homer eine Karte? Beobachtungen zu den Anfängen der europäischen Kartographie', *Karlsruher Geowissenschaftliche Schriften, Reihe 1: Kartographhie und Geographie*, Band 8 (Karlsruhe: Fachhochschule, 1997).

WOLF, Eric W.
6300 Waterway Drive
FALLS CHURCH, Virginia 22044-1316
USA
Tel: (1) 703 256 9217
E-mail: ewwolf@capaccess.org

Cartobibliography; cartographic curiosities

'Acta Cartographica: a series of monographs and studies on the history of cartography, reprinted from periodicals since 1800. Integrated table of contents and index to the 27 volumes published Amsterdam: Theatrum Orbis Terrarum, 1967-1981', *The Portolan*, 30 (Special Issue), Summer 1994.

'A bibliographic excursion: a cartographic reference list for the beginning collector', *Mercator's World* 2:5 (1997): 48-53.

'The "Evil Genius" and other cartographic-political satires', *The Portolan* 38 (Spring 1997): 23-31.

WOLFF, Fritz (Dr)
Director
Hessisches Staatsarchiv
Postfach 540
D-35017 MARBURG
Germany
Tel: (49) 06421 92500 (office)
    (49) 06421 25028 (home)
Fax: (49) 06421 161125

Manuscript maps of the Rhine-Maine area (16th century); 15th-century regional maps in German archives; cartographical scripts and typography

'Ein Dokument zu Arnold Mercators Tod', *Freundeskreis für Cartographica Mitteilungsblatt* **8** (1994): 14-17.

'Karten und Atlanten in fürstlichen Bibliotheken des 16. und 17. Jahrhunderts', in Joachim Neumann (ed), *Karten hüten und bewahren, Festgabe für Lothar Zögner* (Gotha, 1995), 221-232.

'Kartographische Raritäten in einer Ausstellung über das Reichskammergericht', *Freundeskreis für Cartographica Mitteilungsblatt* **10** (1996): 19-22.

WOLFF, Hans (Dr)
Bayerische Staatsbibliothek
Ludwigstr. 16
D-80328 MÜNCHEN
Germany
Tel: (49) 089 2863 8346
Fax: (49) 089 2863 8293

Bavaria; history of cartography and atlases; geological maps and their history

(editor), *400 Jahre Mercator, 400 Jahre Atlas* (Bayerische Staatsbibliothek München, Aussfellungskatalog 65; Weissenhorn: Konrad, 1995

WOLODTSCHENKO
    [Volodchenko], Alexander (Dr)
Technische Universitat Dresden
Institut für Kartographie
01062 DRESDEN
Germany
Tel: (49) 351 463 4809
Fax: (49) 315 463 7028

Prehistoric maps; cartosemiotical aspects of prehistoric maps

(with M Stenzel), 'Zur Frage der Untersuchung von prähistorischen Karten', in *Aktiviti v kartografii '94* (Bratislava 1994): 69-73.

'Erste kartenähnliche Darstellungen', in *Kartographie im Umbruch – neue Herausforderungen, neue Technologien, Beiträge zum Kartographiekongress Interlaken 96* (1996): 353-354.

Kartosemiotika i doistoričeskiye karty (Barnaul & Dresden: Izd. Altaiuniversitet, 1997).

'Syntactical peculiarities of signs of hydrographic objects in prehistoric and early historic maps', in *Proceedings of the 18th International Cartographic Conference*, Vol. 1 (Gävle: Swedish Cartographic Society, 1997): 602-608.

WOLTER, John A. (Dr)
5430 Ring Dove Lane
COLUMBIA, Maryland 21044
USA
Tel:
(Apr 15–Oct 15): (1) 410 730 6692
(Oct 16–Apr 14): (1) 520 295 1116

Great Lakes charting 1815-1970; Northern Transcontinental Survey 1881-1884; Socotra: annotated bibliography

(with H.A. Koch and M.B. Krewson, ed), *Progress of Discovery: Johann George Kohl. Auf Den Spuren Der Entdecker* (Graz: Akademische Druck- und Verlaganstalt, 1993).

(with R.E. Grim, ed), *Images of the World: The Atlas through History* (Washington, DC: Library of Congress; New York: McGraw Hill, 1997).

WOODFIN, Thomas M.
Department of Landscape
    Architecture & Urban Planning
Mailstop 3137
Texas A & M University
COLLEGE STATION, TX 77843
USA
Tel: (1) 409 845 1079 (office)
    (1) 409-775-5031 (home)
Fax: (1) 409 862 1784
E-mail: woodfin@taz.tamu.edu

World-systems theory and cartographical knowledge applied to agricultural capitalism; Texas-Mexico border studies; history of geographical information systems in economic mapping

WOODWARD, David (Prof)
Department of Geography
University of Wisconsin-Madison
550 North Park Street
MADISON, WI 53706-1491
USA
Tel: (1) 608 262 0505 (office)   (1) 608 251 1074 (home)
Fax: (1) 608 263 0762
E-mail: dawoodw@facstaff.wisc.edu
Web: http://feature.geography.wisc.edu/histcart/

Medieval and Renaissance cartography; map printing and publishing

'Mapping map history: the history of cartography project at the University of Wisconsin-Madison', *Wisconsin Academy Review* 42 (1995-1996): 4-10.

Catalogue of Watermarks in Italian Printed Maps, ca. 1540-1600 (Biblioteca di Bibliografia Italiana 141; Florence: Leo S. Olschki, 1996; Chicago: University of Chicago Press, 1996).

Maps as Prints in the Italian Renaissance: Makers, Distributors & Consumers (The 1995 Panizzi Lectures; London: British Library, 1996).

'History of maps', in UK edition of *Microsoft Encarta Encyclopedia* (1997).

'Italian composite atlases of the sixteenth century', in John A. Wolter and Ronald E. Grim (eds), *Images of the World: The Atlas through History* (Washington, DC: Library of Congress, 1997).

'A map for getting lost: the cultural map of Wisconsin', *Mercator's World* 2:2 (March/April 1997): 32-35.

(with Herbert M. Howe), 'Roger Bacon on geography and cartography', in Jeremiah Hackett (ed), *Roger Bacon and the Sciences: Commemorative Essays* (Leiden: E.J. Brill, 1997), 199-222.

'The Description of the Four Parts of the World:' Camocio's Wall Maps in the Bell Library and Their Place in the Italian Tradition (James Ford Bell Lecture No. 34; Minneapolis: James Ford Bell Library, 1998).

(with G. Malcolm Lewis, ed.), *History of Cartography*. Volume 2, Book 3: *Cartography in the Traditional African, American, Arctic, Australian, and Pacific Societies* (Chicago: University of Chicago Press, 1998).

'Maps as popular prints', *Mercator's World* 3:3 (1998): 22-29.

WOODWARD, Frances Mary
Historical Maps and Cartographic
  Archives
Special Collections and University
  Archives Division
Main Library
University of British Columbia
1956 Main Mall
VANCOUVER, BC V6T 1Z1
Canada
Tel: (1) 604 822 2819 (office)   (1) 604 224 7961 (home)
Fax: (1) 604 822 9587 (office)
E-mail: franwood@interchange.ubc.ca

Mapping in British Columbia; mapping the Canadian Rockies; maps and map producers of Vancouver; bird's-eye views and fire insurance plans of British Columbia munici-palities; Japanese maps of the Edo period, 1615-1867

WOOLWAY, Joanne (Dr)
Westcote House
Jesus Lane
CAMBRIDGE CB5 8BP
UK

Renaissance literature, geography and religion; editor (with Richard Helgerson) of on-line jour-nal *Early Modern Literary Studies: Literature and Geography*:
http://purl.oclc.org/emls/emlshome.html

WORMS, Laurence John
Ash Rare Books
25 Royal Exchange
LONDON EC3V 3LP
UK
Tel: (44) 0171 626 2665 (office)   (44) 0181 672 7721 (home)
Fax: (44) 0171 623 9052

British map engravers to 1850; London map trade in the 18th century

'The book trade at the Royal Exchange', in Ann Saunders (ed), *The Royal Exchange* (London: London Topographical Society, 1997), 209-226.

WYTYCZAK, Roman (Dr)
Map Curator
Zakład Narodowy im. Ossolińskich
we Wrocławiu
ul. Szewska 37
50-139 WROCŁAW
Poland
Tel: (48) 71 444471 (office)   (48) 71 573149 (home)
Fax: (48) 71 448561

Silesian cartography, 15th to 18th centuries; catalogue of Silesian maps

'The history and work of Carl Flemming's Cartographical Institute (1833-1931) in Glogau (Lower Saxony)', in *Czasopismo Zakładu Narodowego Imienia Ossoliński* 7 (1996), 11-55 (in Polish).

YEE, Cordell D.K. (Dr)
St. John's College
P.O. Box 2800
ANNAPOLIS, Maryland 21404-2800
USA
Tel: (1) 410 263-9355
E-mail: c-yee@sjca.edu

History of Chinese cartography

(assistant editor and author of essays on Chinese cartography), *The History of Cartography*, Vol. 2, Book 2: *Cartography in the Traditional East and Southeast Asian Societies*, ed. J.B. Harley and David Woodward (Chicago: University of Chicago Press, 1995).

Space and Place: Mapmaking East and West (Annapolis: St. John's College Press, 1996).

YIN Junke (Prof)
Institute of History
Academy of Social Science of Beijing
1 Bei Chen Xi Lu
100101 BEIJING
China
Tel: (86) 1 255 9461, ext. 2410

History of cartography of ancient China

ZAISBERGER, Friederike (Dr)
Schwarzstr. 33
A-5020 SALZBURG
Austria
Tel: (43) 0662 870550

Archbishopric of Salzburg

'Eine Landkarten-Zimelie im Kloster Michaelbeuern von Joseph

Fürstaller', in *Michaeli-Brief, Michael-beuern* (1994), 18-19.

ZANDVLIET, Kees (Cornelis Johannes) (Dr)
Rijksmuseum
Department of Dutch History
Hobbemastraat 21
P.O. Box 74888
1070 DN AMSTERDAM
Netherlands
Tel: (31) 020 673 2121 (office)   (31) 071 517 1126 (home)
Fax: (31) 020 679 8146
E-mail: collecties@rijskmuseum.nl

Dutch history and maps before 1800; maps in relation to Dutch overseas expansion; Dutch cartography and art

'Vermeer and the significance of cartography in his time', in T. Brandenbarg et al., *The Scholarly World of Vermeer* (The Hague: Museum van het Boek/Meermanno-Westreenianum, 1996). [Exhibition catalogue.]

Shigi shiji Helanjen Te Taiwan lau Ditu [The Seventeenth-Century Maps of Taiwan Drawn by the Dutch] (2 vols.; Taipei: Echo Publishing, 1997).

ZEILINGER, Elisabeth (Mag)
Österreichische Nationalbibliothek
Kartensammlung und
   Globenmuseum
Josefsplatz 1
A-1015 WIEN
Austria
Tel: (43) 1 53 410 297
Fax: (43) 1 53 410 319

Central European and Austrian mapping; history of the Globe Museum of the Austrian National Library; history of exploration and discovery

'Das India orientalis–Konvolut aus dem Atlas Stosch der Österreichischen Nationalbibliothek', in Joachim Neuman (ed), *Karten hüten und bewahren. Festgabe für Lothar Zögner* (Kartensammlung und Kartendokumentation 11; Gotha: Justes Perthes, 1995): 233-254.

(with Franz Wawrik, Helga Hühnel and Jan Mokre, ed), *Kartographische Zimelien. Die 50 schönsten Karten und Globen der Österreichischen Nationalbibliothek* (Wien: Holzhausen, 1995).

(with Markus Heinz), 'Ordnung auf der Kugel? Die Abfolge von Karten in Atlanten (16.-18. Jahrhundert)', in W. Scharfe (ed), *Gerhard Mercator und seine Zeit. 7. Kartographiehistorisches Colloquium*

Duisburg 1994 (Duisburg: Braun, 1996), 217-223.

'Die Welt vor Augen: ein Rundgang durch Geschichte und Bestände des Globenmeuseums der Österreichischen Nationalbibliothek', in Peter E. Allmayer-Beck (ed), *Modelle der Welt. Erd- und Himmelsgloben: Kulturerbe aus österreichen Sammlungen* (Wien: Brandstätter, 1997), 106-131.

ZHENG Xihuang
Institute for History of Natural
    Sciences
Chinese Academy of Sciences
Chao Nei Da Jie 137
BEIJING 100010
China
Tel: (86) 10 640 43989 (office)
Fax: (86) 10 640 17637

History of geographical development in China; history of cartography in China

(86) 10 684 37346 (home)

(with Cao Wanru et al, ed), *An Atlas of Ancient Maps of China: the Ming Dynasty (1368-1644)* (Beijing: Cultural Relics Publishing House, 1994).

(with Cao Wanru et al, ed), *An Atlas of Ancient Maps of China: the Qing Dynasty (1644-1910)* (Beijing: Cultural Relics Publishing House, 1997).

ZIMMERMANN, Georg (Dr)
Kartensammlung
Sächsische Landesbibliothek
Marienallee 12
D-01099 DRESDEN
Germany
Tel: (49) 351 5630138

Saxony

ZÖGNER, Gudrun K.
Burgherrenstr. 7
D-12101 BERLIN
Germany
Tel: (49) 030 785 5213

Heinrich Kiepert; dictionary of German mapmakers (with Lothar Zögner); German wall maps

ZÖGNER, Lothar (Dr)
Map Curator
Staatsbibliothek zu Berlin
Potsdamer Str. 33
D-10772 BERLIN
Germany
Tel: (49) 030 266 2419 (office)
    (49) 030 785 5213 (home)
Fax: (49) 030 266 2726
E-mail: lothar.zoegner@sbb.spk-berlin.de

Map collections in Berlin; dictionary of German mapmakers (with G.K. Zögner); J.G. Schleenstein; maps in the Staatsbibliothek zu Berlin

'Arnold Mercators Aufnahme des Landes zwischen Mosel und Blies', *Mitteilungsblatt des Freundeskreis für Cartographica* 8 (1994): 9-13.

'Deutsche Atlanten im 19. Jahrhundert: Von Ritter und Humboldt bis Andree und Debes', in Hans Wolff (ed), *400 Jahre Mercator, 400 Jahre Atlas* (Bayerische Staatsbibliothek München, Aussfellungskatalog 65; Weissenhorn: Konrad, 1995), 117-135.

'Das Griechenland-Skizzenbuch des Geographen Carl Ritter', *Jarhbuch Preußischer Kulturbesitz* 33 (1996): 404-414.

Imago Germaniae. Das Deutschlandbild der Kartenmacher in fünf Jahrhunderten (Weissenhorn: Anton H. Konrad, 1996). [Exhibition catalogue.]

'Kartographische Sammlungen in Deutschland: Süd- und Südwestdeutschland', *Kartographisches Taschenbuch 1996/97*, 99-121.

'Ferdinand von Richthofen – neue Sicht auf ein altes Land', in H.-M. Hinz and Chr. Lind (eds), *Tsingtau: ein Kapitel deutscher Kolonialgeschichte in China, 1897-1914* (Berlin: Deutsches Historisches Museum, 1998), 72-75.

(with Egon Klemp and Gudrun Maurer), *Verzeichnis der Kartensammlungen in Deutschland* (Wiesbaden: Harrassowitz, 1998).

12.1 INDEX: PEOPLE

Rennell, James BRAVO
Reymann, D G SZANIAWSKA
Ribeiro, Diogo ABEYDEERA
Ricci, Matteo DAY
Richthofen, Ferdinand von ZÖGNER, L
Riedel, Heinrich August TAUCHÉ
Ripa, Matteo LI
Ritter, Karl ZÖGNER, L
Riviere, Antonio TOUS MELIÁ
Robe, Frederick H. GOREN
Rosenfelt, Werner von EHRENSVÄRD
Rosselli, Francesco KREUER
Roy, William ADAMS, KINNIBURGH
Sacrobosco AUJAC
Santa Cruz, Alonso de CUESTA DOMINGO, MEURER
Schick, Conrad GOREN, RUBIN
Schilde, Jan van MEURER
Schleenstein, J.G. ZÖGNER, L
Schleuen, Johann David LINDNER
Schmid, Sebastian DÜRST
Scull family MYERS
 Nicholas and William Scull DOCKTOR
Seller, John HUDSON, SHIRLEY
Seltzlin, David BRUNNER
Sixtus V, Pope BURROUGHS
Sgrothen, Christian MEURER
Sibbald, Sir Robert WITHERS
Silins, Matiss STRAUCHMANIS
Simony, Friedrich KRETSCHMER
Sohon, Gustavus GRIM
Solís, Juan Díaz de LAGUARDA TRIAS
Stamp, Dudley COSGROVE
Stanford (Edward and William) HERBERT
Stella, Tilemann MEURER, PÁPAY
Stempel, Gerhard MEURER
Suchodolec, Jan Wł. SZELIGA
Suchodolec, Samuel SZELIGA
Sulzberger, Johann Jakob FRÖMELT
Surhon, Jacques de MEURER
Suttinger, Daniel FISCHER, K
Techts, A. Th. DAHL, B W
Tempesta, Antonio ÅKERSTRÖM-HOUGEN

Théodose II GAUTIER DALCHÉ
Théodulf d'Orleans GAUTIER DALCHÉ
Thornton, John SHIRLEY
Tobler, Titus GOREN
Towerson, William ALSOP
Vancouver, George DAVID, WILLIAMS, G
Vandermaelen, Philippe FINCOEUR, SILVESTRE
Vaux, Jacques de TURNER
Vavassore, Giovanni Andrea SHIRLEY
Vaz Dourado, Fernão PFLEDERER
Verrazano, Gerolamo ABEYDEERA
Vespucci, Amerigo LAGUARDA TRIAS
Virga, Albertin de DÜRST, SEAVER
Vischer, G.M. KÖNIG
Visconti, Ferdinando VALERIO
Waghenaer, Lucas Janszoon SCHILDER
Walker, Josef FELDMANN
Walsperger, Andreas TOMASCH
Washington, George REDMOND
Watt family LAING
 James Watt HILLS, R L
 John Watt HILLS, R L, MOORE
Whitwell, Charles DEKKER
Wiebeking, Karl von SCHWARZ
Wijngaerde, Antoon van den GALERA MONEGAL
Willer, Georg MEURER
Wit, Frederick de WERNER
Wolff, Zacharias LAFRENZ
Wood, John HYDE
Wyld family SMITH
 James Wyld HOOKER
Zaddiq, Yaakov ben Abraham NEBENZAHL
Zellweger, Johann Kaspar KLÖTI

12.2 INDEX: PLACE

Arrangement is by continents (with separate sections for the British Isles), oceans, polar regions and world. The Americas and Asia are further broken down into subregions.

JAPAN. KAWAMURA, H, MICHEL-ZAITSU, MIYOSHI, POTTER, S R, UNNO
charts of East Indies showing Japan HUBBARD
communication with Europe MIYOSHI
early European influences in PFLEDERER
Edo period WOODWARD, F M
European printed maps in KIMURA
Italian map of, by Giacomo Piccaglia SHIRLEY
Jesuit Mission DEBERGH
map-making during the Tokugawa Shogunate MICHEL-ZAITSU, SUZUKI
papier-mâché relief map KAWAMURA, H
place-names, romanization of, on Western maps MICHEL-ZAITSU
Portuguese cartography in MARQUES
Western maps of HUBBARD, WALTER

KOREA. KAWAMURA, K
Jesuit Mission DEBERGH

PHILIPPINES, nautical and toponymic work CUESTA DOMINGO

TAIWAN, Dutch maps of ZANDVLIET

THAILAND. FREITAG, ROONEY

TIBET. RYAVEC, SCHWARTZBERG

INDIAN SUBCONTINENT. BHATTASALI
geographic construction of EDNEY
Himalayas NEBENZAHL

INDIA. SCHWARTZBERG
Bombay EDNEY, GOLE
colonial cartography COOK, A S, EDNEY
indigenous cartography ARUNACHALAM, GOGATE, GOLE
Maratha area maps ARUNACHALAM, GOGATE
Topographical Map Series COOK, A S
use of female bodies in nationalist maps of RAMASWAMY

SRI LANKA. Taprobane [Ceylon] ABEYDEERA

WESTERN ASIA
Babylonian world map DELANO SMITH
geographical sciences, Muslim d'HOLLANDER
Islamic maps KARAMUSTAFA, KING
Middle East COLLIER, NEBENZAHL
and biblical texts, maps in GRUBER

ARABIAN PENINSULA. HUIDEKOPER
Bahrain, Arabia and the Persian/Arabian Gulf JARMAN

ARMENIA. LICINI

CASPIAN SEA. ALA'I

GEORGIA. LICINI

HOLY LAND. GALLIANO, INGRAM, LECOQ, NEBENZAHL, RUBIN
German cartographers of WAJNTRAUB, E & G
Heinrich Kiepert in GOREN
international co-operation in GOREN
Italian maps of WAJNTRAUB, E & G
Jerusalem RUBIN
crusader maps of WAJNTRAUB, E & G
European concept of GOREN

ISRAEL AND PALESTINE
aerial photography GAVISH
Hebrew maps of WAJNTRAUB, E & G
Israel, seashores and lakes GOREN
military, cadastral and topographical mapping GAVISH
Palestine HODSON, A Y, KARK
Mamluk and Ottoman cadastral surveys KARK
medieval local and regional maps HARVEY
Mercator's map of WAJNTRAUB, E & G
PEF surveyors HODSON, A Y

OTTOMAN EMPIRE. GOODRICH
and Turkish military maps NOLAN
conquest of Armenia LICINI
Mamluk and Ottoman cadastral surveys of Palestine KARK
military surveys of COLLIER
topographical illustration ROGERS

Silesia, *see* SILESIA
south-western BERGS
  surveying FISCHER

GREECE
Morea and the Cyclades islands TANTOULOS
portolan charts STRONGILOS, TANTOULOS

HUNGARY. GRÓF, HRENKÓ, SZÁNTAI, SZATHMÁRY
Atlas Hungaricus SZÁNTAI
biography HRENKÓ
cartographers GRÓF, SZÁNTAI, SZATHMÁRY
globes, manuscript BARTHA
surveying BARTHA, HRENKÓ
surveyors GRÓF
views of towns, fortifications and battles SZÁNTAI

ITALY. GALLIANO, MARINO, MILANESI, SHIRLEY, SIMS,
  TORRESANI
ancient and medieval image GALLIANO
atlases, 18th-19th centuries VALERIO
  Agnese FALCHETTA
  Buondelmonte manuscript NEBENZAHL
  cartobibliography LAURETI, VALERIO
  composite WOODWARD, D
  from Austro-Hungarian Empire SHIRLEY
Camocio's wall maps WOODWARD, D
cosmography, 15th-17th centuries MILANESI
fascist political mapping ATKINSON
geology TAYLOR, K L
Istituto Geografico Militare VALERIO
Italian maps
  as prints in Renaissance WOODWARD, D
  conserved in archives and libraries of Paris and Vienna ROMBAI
  of the Holy Land WAJNTRAUB, E & G
Japan by Giacomo Piccaglia SHIRLEY
links with France during Enlightenment PEDLEY
map murals BOURNE, FIORANI, MILANESI
mapmakers HELLWIG, VALERIO
nautical cartography CONTI
  manuscript charts ASTENGO
Paduan Greek maps AUJAC

urban cartography BEVILACQUA, HILLS, H, NUTI
  images of the city in southern HILLS, H
  maps and views
    medieval FRIEDMAN, D H
    Renaissance FRIEDMAN, D H, HOOK
  urbanism (especially Rome) BURROUGHS
watermarks in Italian printed maps WOODWARD, D
world maps, monumental, in medieval northern FOX-FRIEDMAN

regions:
central, before unification ROMBAI
Ecclesiastical state and Marche region MANGANI
Emilia-Romagna TORRESANI
Ferrara ROSSI
Lecce (southern Italy) FAGIOLO
Naples HILLS, H, VALERIO
  Kingdom of, military maps, VALERIO
  Po Valley, land reclamation in the ROSSI
Rome BURROUGHS, FAGIOLO
  ancient ÅKERSTRÖM-HOUGEN
  Carolingian town plan BRODERSEN
  Vatican mural maps FIORANI, MILANESI
Sicily BREMNER
  Palermo HILLS, H
Tuscany ROMBAI
Venetian Republic CASTI MORESCHI
  nautical charts FALCHETTA
  Venetian-Turkish war maps FALCHETTA
Vesuvius VALERIO

LATVIA. STRAUCHMANIS

LITHUANIA. SZANIAWSKA, WERNEROWA
Grand Duchy of BELY

LUXEMBOURG. WATELET

MALTA. GANADO
16th-century plans of Valetta GANADO

MEDITERRANEAN SEA. GAUTIER DALCHÉ
British Parliamentary Papers, maps in GOLE

12.3 INDEX: SUBJECT

Summary of Subject Headings

12.3 SUBJECT INDEX

economic organization CASE, JONES, D C
ephemera NICHOLSON
Germany
Bibliographisches Institut AG HANLE
Geographie-Verlag DREYER-EIMBCKE
J.B. Homann, Homann Heirs and Fembo HEINZ
Justus Perthes DÖRFLINGER
New Zealand maps MARSHALL, B
IATO atlases, 16th-century POLITES
Low Countries KROGT
map printing and WOODWARD, D
map trade PEDLEY
London SMITH, WORMS
Netherlands DE VRIES, EDMOND, KROGT
Amsterdam, atlas production, 1630s KROGT
Hondius's shop GOLE
Covens & Mortier EGMOND
United States BRUN
atlases, early RISTOW
commercial and tourist maps CASE
urban map trades CONZEN
Victoria, Australia DARRAGH
see also COMMERCIAL CARTOGRAPHY; TECHNIQUES OF
MAP PRODUCTION, printing

RAILWAY MAPS. LIERZ
British BALDWIN
Cruchley's SCOTT, V G
revision on Ordnance Survey maps OLIVER
United States BRAKE, GOODWIN

RELIEF MAPS. CAVELTI, CAVELTI HAMMER, FELDMANN,
LIERZ, OEHRLI
Alps CAVELTI HAMMER
hypsometric ESPENHORST
levelling of maps, perspective uses BRESSOLIER-BOUSQUET
papier-mâché KAWAMURA, H
three-dimensional models CAVELTI, CAVELTI HAMMER,
RUBIN

RELIGIOUS CARTOGRAPHY. FIORANI, GALLIANO
Beatus maps WILLIAMS, J W

Bible
apocalyptic tradition GOW
biblical exegesis DELANO SMITH, GRUBER, INGRAM,
O'LOUGHLIN
legend of Noah's ark POTTER, S R
Bünting's *Itinerarium Sacrae Scripturae* HEIJDEN
cartographical curiosities REITINGER
church cartography in Olsztyn (Poland) GRABOWSKI
Hebrew maps WAJNTRAUB, E & G
in work by Hugh Broughton WERNER
hermetic meaning of cordiform projection MANGANI
image of creation HOFMANN
Jesuit cartography DAY, GODLEWSKA
Asia (China, Japan, Korea) DEBERGH
Central America BUISSERET
China DAY
Jewish geographical lore SCOTT, J M
Last Judgment and the Hereford mappamundi GLOVER
maps as documents RUBIN
meaning and identity KIVELSON
messianic visions, middle ages FOX-FRIEDMAN
paradise SCAFI
pilgrimage maps HILL, RUBIN
European KUPČÍK
Renaissance WOOLWAY
see also HOLY LAND (in Place index)

RENAISSANCE. CEREZO MARTÍNEZ, FIORANI, WHITE
HEAD, WOODWARD, D
Africa on maps RELAÑO
and newly discovered lands CATTANEO
classical tradition and CATTANEO, RELAÑO
cosmography CATTANEO, COSGROVE
diffusion of European knowledge from south to north RELAÑO
Egerton MS 1513 CAMPBELL
England SULLIVAN
maps in English drama BROTTON
globes PELLETIER
historical maps FIORANI
Italy
city maps and views FRIEDMAN, D H, HOOK
map murals BOURNE, FIORANI, MILANESI
maps as prints WOODWARD, D
Rome ÅKERSTRÖM-HOUGEN, BURROUGHS

literature, geography, religion WOOLWAY
map-making, map users, map display FIORANI
map-projection systems BENNETT, J A, GAMBIN
myths and cartography RELAÑO
North Atlantic, Arctic and America McINTOSH
Ptolemy
  and the Italian AUJAC
  impact of Ptolemy's maps on GAMBIN
regional cartography MASON, R
sea charts and sailing directions WATERS
urban cartography FRIEDMAN, D H, HOOK
Vienna-Klosterneuberg school GOW

RIVER PORTS. HUGHES

ROAD AND ROUTE MAPS. DELANO SMITH, LIERZ,
  RECKER
atlases SULLIVAN
British AKERMAN, BALDWIN
  Devon, cartobibliography BENNETT, F
  Hertfordshire, by Cruchley SCOTT, V G
  Lincolnshire, road-books CARROLL
  rights of way on HINDLE
  road-books and itineraries HODSON, D
  urban SMITH
cycling maps LIERZ
Roman, including Tabula Peutingeriana SALWAY
routes on old maps HOLZER
strip maps and itineraries WEBB
trade routes to 1800 TOLMACHEVA
United States AKERMAN, HERTERICK, RISTOW
  geographical literacy via American highway maps AKERMAN,
  DANZER

ROMAN CARTOGRAPHY, *see* ANTIQUITY

SALT TRADE, West African RIZZO

SCALE, *see* MATHEMATICS

SCHOOL CARTOGRAPHY, *see* EDUCATION

SETTLEMENT
Bulgarian BEŠELIEV
German rural, to Middle Ages ESPENHORST
immigrant and ethnic patterns in Virginia GRIM

SIGNS
cartographical language CASTI MORESCHI
Islamic cartographical conventions SAVAGE-SMITH
of glaciers and sea ice, early depiction of BRUNNER
of hydrographical objects WOLODTSCHENKO
on early printed maps DELANO SMITH
symbolization techniques GILMARTIN, STRAUCHMANIS
topographical information GOŁASKI
  in connection with written documents JANKOWSKA
visualization and representation of geo-data MESENBURG

SPACE
in 6th-12th century EDSON, GAUTIER DALCHÉ
construction of knowledge spaces TURNBULL
representation of BRESSOLIER-BOUSQUET
  by indigenous peoples EISENSTEIN, KRYGIER
  conceptualizaion, measurement and BURROUGHS
spatial accuracy of old maps FORSTNER
spatial perception HATANO
theory of BLANSETT, EDNEY

STAMPS, maps on BATTEN, KROGT

SURVEYING AND SURVEYS. SULLIVAN
instruments and methods BARTHA, DOLZ, WEBSTER
  Japanese instruments UNNO
nautical BARTON, CHAPUIS, FISHER, LAING
problems of, since 16th century FRÖMELT
  South China Sea PRESCOTT, J R V
  Swedish waters RAURALA
uses, techniques and content, interdependence of BIANCHIN

regions and countries:
British Isles
  early 17th century GUNASENA
  biographical memoirs BAIGENT
  British colonial STEWARD

WOMEN. CAMINO
cartographical sources for American women's history VAN EE
gender issues BLANSETT, RAMASWAMY
mapmakers HUDSON

WORLD MAPS, *see* MAPPAEMUNDI; WORLD (in Place index)

ZOOLOGICAL MAPPING, *see* THEMATIC MAPS

12.4 INDEX OF CONTRIBUTORS BY COUNTRY OF RESIDENCE

Argentina (5)

ARNAU Vicente Guillermo; CHARALAMBOUS Demetrio Antonio; DESTEFANI Laurio; GALLEZ Paul; IBARRA GRASSO Dick Edgar

Australia (9)

DARRAGH Thomas Alwynne; DEWEZ Simon James; HOOK Colin M; McKENZIE Stephen J L; PRESCOTT Dorothy Francis; PRESCOTT John R V; RICHARDSON William A R; SCURFIELD Judith Mary; TURNBULL David

Austria (19)

DAMMERER Franz Peter; DÖRFLINGER Johannes; EISENSTEIN Herbert; FISCHER Karl; FORSTNER Gustav G; GOEBL Hans; HOLZER Gerhard; HÜHNEL Helga; JAVORSKY Irene; KÖNIG Gebhard; KRETSCHMER Ingrid; MOKRE Jan; REITINGER Franz; SCHMIDT Rudolf; SIHORSCH P Daniel; WAWRIK Franz; WOHLSCHLÄGER Heide; ZAISBERGER Friederike; ZEILINGER Elisabeth

Belarus

BELY Alexander V

Belgium (9)

CHANTRENNE Claire; DEPUYDT Frans; DEPUYDT Joost F F; ELKHADEM Hossam; FINCOEUR Michel Benoit; LEMOINE-ISABEAU Claire; RYCKAERT Marc; SILVESTRE Marguerite; WATELET Marcel

Bulgaria

BEŠEVLIEV Bojan

Canada (27)

ALSOP James D.; AURINGER WOOD Alberta Gjertine; BELYEA Barbara; BOUDREAU Claude; CARDINAL Louis; DAHL Edward H; DUBREUIL Lorraine; FREEMAN Gordon Russel; GODLEWSKA Anne M C; GOFFART Walter A; GOW Andrew Colin; HEIDENREICH Conrad E; KERSHAW Kenneth Andrew; KOKS Frans E; LAYLAND Michael Franklin; MURRAY Jeffrey S; O'DEA Fabian; POPE Peter Edward; RAINVILLE Alain; RAY P Andrew; SCOTT James Murray; SHEFRIN Jill A; STOOKE Philip J.; TAYLOR Iain C; WHISTANCE-SMITH Ronald; WINEARLS Joan; WOODWARD Frances Mary

Chile

MARTINIC BEROS Mateo

China (8)

CHEN Jian; HOU Renzhi; LI Xiaocong; REN Jincheng; SUN Guoqing; WANG Qianjin; YIN Junke; ZHENG Xihuang

Cyprus

IACOVOU Maria

Czech Republic (9)

DRÁPELA Milan V; KOZÁK Jan; KREJČÍ Zdeněk; KUDRNOVSKA Olga; KUPČÍK Ivan; MUCHA Ludvík; NOVAK Václav; POKORNÝ Ota; SEMOTANOVÁ Eva

Denmark

CRIBB Robert Bridson; DAHL Bjørn Westerbeek; DUPONT Henrik; STEVENSON William George

Estonia

TANG Eve

Finland (8)

ALANEN Timo; FREDRIKSON Erkki O V; JAATINEN Stig; KEPSU Saulo Juhani; KOKKONEN Pellervo; KOSTET Juhani; MIEKKAVAARA Leena Kyllikki; RAURALA Nils-Erik

France (28)

ABEYDEERA Ananda; d'ABOVILLE Christian; AUJAC Germaine J J; BELLEC François-Paul; BRESSOLIER-BOUSQUET Catherine; CHAPUIS Olivier; DEBERGH Minako; DESBRIERE Michel; FILLIOZAT Manonmani Dominique; GAMBIN Marie-Thérèse; GAUTIER DALCHÉ Patrick; HOFMANN Catherine; d'HOLLANDER Raymond; JACOB Christian; KONVITZ Josef W; LAGARDE Lucie; LECOQ Danielle; LOISEAUX Olivier; MICHEA Hubert; PALSKY Gilles Stéphane; PASTOUREAU Mireille; PAVIOT Jacques; PELLETIER Monique; RANDLES William G L; STROUP Alice; SZÁNTAI Lajos; TOULOUSE Sarah; TURNER Anthony John

Germany (60)

BATTEN Kit; BERGS Irene-Annette; BLISS Winfried; BLUNCK Jürgen; BRICHZIN Hans; BRINCKEN Anna-Dorothee von den; BRODERSEN Kai; BRUNNER Kurt; CSAPLOVICS Elmar; DOLZ Wolfram; DREYER-EIMBCKE Oswald; DUKEN Albert John; ESPENHORST Jürgen; FISCHER Hanspeter; FLEISCHMANN Peter; FREITAG Ulrich Max; HABEL Rudolf; HANLE Adolf; HEINZ Markus; HELLWIG Fritz; JAEGER Eckhard; KALLENBACH Helga; KING David Anthony; KLEMP Egon; KRAACK Detlev; KRAACK Gerhard; KREUER Johannes Werner; KUPČÍK Ivan; LAFRENZ Jürgen H R; LINDGREN Uta; LINDNER Klaus; LORCH Richard P; MESENBURG Peter; MÜLLER Theo; MUSALL Heinz; NEUMANN Joachim; NIEWODNICZANSKI Thomas; PÁPAY Gyula; POBANZ Wolfram; RECKER Gabriele; SCHARFE Wolfgang W P; SCHLÖGL Daniel; SCHNALL Uwe; SCHULTE Karl-Werner; SCHULZ Günther E R; SCHWARZ Uwe; SPATA Manfred; SPERLING Walter; STAMS Werner; STOPP Klaus D; TAUCHÉ W E Bruno; TIGGESBÄUMKER Günter; UNVERHAU Dagmar; WOLF Armin; WOLFF Fritz; WOLFF Hans; WOLODTSCHENKO Alexander; ZIMMERMANN Georg; ZÖGNER Gudrun K; ZÖGNER Lothar

Greece

STRONGILOS Themis; TANTOULOS Antonios

Hungary

BARTHA Lajos J M; HOLLÓ Szilvia Andrea; HRENKÓ Pál; SZATHMÁRY Tibor; TÖRÖK Zsolt

India

ARUNACHALAM B; GOGATE Prasad

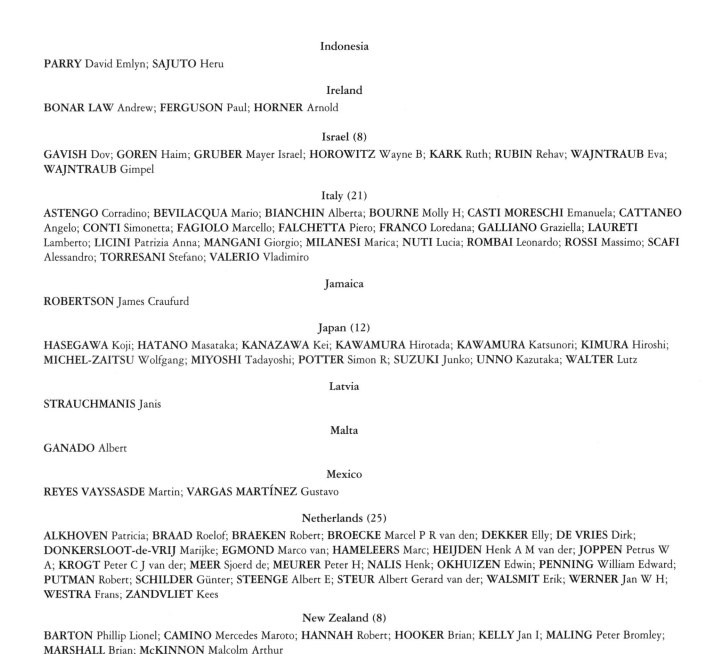

Indonesia

PARRY David Emlyn; **SAJUTO** Heru

Ireland

BONAR LAW Andrew; **FERGUSON** Paul; **HORNER** Arnold

Israel (8)

GAVISH Dov; **GOREN** Haim; **GRUBER** Mayer Israel; **HOROWITZ** Wayne B; **KARK** Ruth; **RUBIN** Rehav; **WAJNTRAUB** Eva; **WAJNTRAUB** Gimpel

Italy (21)

ASTENGO Corradino; **BEVILACQUA** Mario; **BIANCHIN** Alberta; **BOURNE** Molly H; **CASTI MORESCHI** Emanuela; **CATTANEO** Angelo; **CONTI** Simonetta; **FAGIOLO** Marcello; **FALCHETTA** Piero; **FRANCO** Loredana; **GALLIANO** Graziella; **LAURETI** Lamberto; **LICINI** Patrizia Anna; **MANGANI** Giorgio; **MILANESI** Marica; **NUTI** Lucia; **ROMBAI** Leonardo; **ROSSI** Massimo; **SCAFI** Alessandro; **TORRESANI** Stefano; **VALERIO** Vladimiro

Jamaica

ROBERTSON James Craufurd

Japan (12)

HASEGAWA Koji; **HATANO** Masataka; **KANAZAWA** Kei; **KAWAMURA** Hirotada; **KAWAMURA** Katsunori; **KIMURA** Hiroshi; **MICHEL-ZAITSU** Wolfgang; **MIYOSHI** Tadayoshi; **POTTER** Simon R; **SUZUKI** Junko; **UNNO** Kazutaka; **WALTER** Lutz

Latvia

STRAUCHMANIS Janis

Malta

GANADO Albert

Mexico

REYES VAYSSASDE Martin; **VARGAS MARTÍNEZ** Gustavo

Netherlands (25)

ALKHOVEN Patricia; **BRAAD** Roelof; **BRAEKEN** Robert; **BROECKE** Marcel P R van den; **DEKKER** Elly; **DE VRIES** Dirk; **DONKERSLOOT-de-VRIJ** Marijke; **EGMOND** Marco van; **HAMELEERS** Marc; **HEIJDEN** Henk A M van der; **JOPPEN** Petrus W A; **KROGT** Peter C J van der; **MEER** Sjoerd de; **MEURER** Peter H; **NALIS** Henk; **OKHUIZEN** Edwin; **PENNING** William Edward; **PUTMAN** Robert; **SCHILDER** Günter; **STEENGE** Albert E; **STEUR** Albert Gerard van der; **WALSMIT** Erik; **WERNER** Jan W H; **WESTRA** Frans; **ZANDVLIET** Kees

New Zealand (8)

BARTON Phillip Lionel; **CAMINO** Mercedes Maroto; **HANNAH** Robert; **HOOKER** Brian; **KELLY** Jan I; **MALING** Peter Bromley; **MARSHALL** Brian; **McKINNON** Malcolm Arthur

Norway

WIKANDER Johan Anton

Poland (17)

BABICZ Józef; BIAŁAS Zbigniew; BZINKOWSKA Jadwiga Teresa; GOŁASKI Janusz; GRABOWSKI Piotr; GREINER Piotr; JANKOWSKA Maria; KONOPSKA Beata; OSTROWSKI Jerzy; SCHNAYDER Edward Franciszek; STELMACH Mieczyław; STOKSIK Janina Mirosława; SZANIAWSKA Lucyna; SZELIGA Jan; SZYKUŁA Krystyna Anna; WERNEROWA Wiesława; WYTYCZAK Roman

Portugal

AMARAL Joaquim Ferreira do; CARVALHO DIAS José António; MARQUES Alfredo Pinheiro

Russia

CHEKIN Leonid S; KUSOV Vladimir S; POSTNIKOV Alexei

Saudi Arabia

HUIDEKOPER Fay

Slovakia

PRAVDA Jan; PRIKRYL L'ubomír Viliam

Slovenia

MIŠKOVIĆ Veselin

South Africa

LIEBENBERG Elizabeth Catharina

Spain (18)

CEREZO MARTÍNEZ Ricardo; CUESTA DOMINGO Mariano; FOGUET Rafael; GALERA MONEGAL Montserrat; GASSET ARGEMÍ Josep; GÓMEZ GÓMEZ Antonio Agustín; HERNANDO Agustín; LITER MAYAYO Carmen; MAGALLANES Luis; MARTIN-MERÁS Luisa; MONTANER GARCIA Carme; NADAL PIQUE Francesc; PALADINI Angel; PUCHADES BATALLER Ramon Josep; RELAÑO Francesc; SANCHIS BALLESTER Francisca; TEN Antonio E; TOUS MELIÁ Juan

Sweden

ÅKERSTRÖM-HOUGEN Gunilla; BÄÄRNHIELM Göran; EHRENSVÄRD Ulla

Switzerland (15)

BIRCHMEIER Christian; CAVELTI Alfons; CAVELTI HAMMER Madlena; DÜRST Arthur; FELDMANN Hans-Uli; FRÖMELT Hubert; GERMANN Thomas; HÖHENER Hans-Peter; KLÖTI Thomas; LIERZ Wolfgang; MOJSKI Piotr Maria; OEHRLI Markus; ROHR Hans Peter; SCHAUP Wilhelm; SCHERTENLEIB Urban

Thailand

ROONEY Dawn F

United Kingdom (123)

ADAMS Brian W; ALA'I Cyrus; ANDREWS John Harwood; ARMITAGE Geoffrey; ATKINSON David A; BAIGENT Elizabeth; BALDWIN Robert C D; BANNISTER David; BARBER Peter Michael; BARKHAM Selma Huxley; BARRON Roderick Michael; BEECH Geraldine; BENDALL Sarah; BENNETT Francis; BENNETT James Arthur; BERESINER Yasha; BLACK Jeremy Martin; BOARD Christopher; BOUD Roy C; BRAVO Michael T; BREMNER Robert Weyman; BROTTON Jerry; BURDEN Eugene Henry; BURDEN Philip D; BURGESS Robert Anthony; CAMPBELL Tony; CARROLL Raymond Albert; CHANG Stephen Tseng-Hsin; CLARKE Richard S J; COLLIER Peter; COOK Andrew S; COSGROVE Denis; DAVID Andrew C F; DAVIES Robert; DELANO SMITH Catherine; DRYBURG Paula S; DUNBABIN John P D; FISHER Susanna; FLEET Christopher James; FLETCHER David; FLINT Valerie I J; FRENCH Josephine Ruth; FROSTICK Raymond C; GOLE Susan; GOSS Josephus J S; GREEN David Richard; GRIFFITHS Ieuan; GRÓF László; GUNASENA Diana P H; HARVEY Paul D A; HERBERT Francis; HILLS Helen; HILLS Richard Leslie; HINDLE Brian Paul; HODSON Arundel Yolande; HODSON Donald; HOWSE Humphrey Derek; HUGHES Paul; HYDE Ralph; JARMAN Robert; JOHNSTON Stephen Andrew; JONES Ieuan Evans; KAIN Roger J P; KINNIBURGH Ian A G; KITCHEN Frank; LAING William; LAXTON Paul; LEISERACH Michael; LEWIS G Malcolm; LIVINGSTONE David N; MARTINS Luciana de Lima; MASON Adair Stuart; MASON Roger; MERCIER Raymond Paul; MERRIMAN Marcus H; MILLEA Nick; MITCHELL Rose; MOORE John Nicholas; MORRIS R J; MUMFORD Ian; NICHOLSON Timothy Robin; NOLAN Michael A; OLIVER Richard Ross; O'LOUGHLIN Thomas; PARRY David Emlyn; PAYNE Anthony; POTTER Jonathan; QUINN David Beers; RAVENHILL Mary Rose; RICHEY Michael W; RITCHIE George Stephen; ROBERTS Iolo; ROBERTS Menai; RODGER Elizabeth Margaret; ROGERS John Michael; ROPER Peter William; RUSHTON Gillian Anne; SALWAY Richard W B; SAVAGE-SMITH Emilie; SAVOURS Ann Margaret; SCAFI Alessandro; SCOTT Valerie Gillian; SELIGMANN Matthew S; SHIRLEY Rodney W; SILVESTER Robert John; SMITH David Anthony; STEPHENSON Francis Richard; STONE Jeffrey C; TAUB Liba; TAYLOR Anne; THOMAS Garth; TIBBETTS Gerald Randall; TYACKE Sarah J; WARDINGTON Christopher; WATERS David Watkin; WEBB David F; WEBSTER Diana C F; WILKES Margaret; WILLIAMS Glyndwr; WINTLE Michael Joseph; WITHERS Charles W J; WOOLWAY Joanne; WORMS Laurence John

United States (158)

AKERMAN James R; ALLEN David Yehling; ASHWORTH William B; BARROW William C; BARUTH Christopher; BASKES Roger S; BASSETT Thomas Joseph; BEDERMAN Sanford H; BHATTASALI Deepak; BLAKE Erin C; BLANSETT Lisa A; BOSSE David; BRAKE Scott; BRUN Christian F; BUISSERET David; BURNETT D Graham; BURNETTE Rand; BURROUGHS Charles; CAIN Mead Taylor; CASE Nathaniel; COBB David; CONLEY Tom Clark; CONZEN Michael P; COOK Karen Severud; CRAMPTON Jeremy; DANFORTH Susan; DANZER Gerald A; DAY John D; DeMERS Michael N; DeROGATIS Amy; DE VORSEY Louis; DOCKTOR John W; DRIEVER Steven Leiby; DUNNIGAN Brian Leigh; EDNEY Matthew H; EDSON Evelyn; EHRENBERG Ralph; ENGSTROM Kathryn L; ENTERLINE James; FERN William H; FIORANI Francesca; FITCH Richard; FITZGERALD Joseph H; FITZPATRICK Gary; FLATNESS James A; FOX-FRIEDMAN Jeanne; FRIEDMAN Anna Felicity; FRIEDMAN David Hodes; GARVER John B; GILMARTIN Patricia; GLOVER Sarah Rose; GOODRICH Thomas D; GOODWIN Katherine R; GRIM Ronald E; GUTHORN Peter Jay; HADSEL Fred Latimer; HAFT Adele J; HÉBERT John R; HELGERSON Richard; HERTERICK E J; HILL Sharon L; HOLZHEIMER Arthur; HOPKINS Daniel P; HSU Mei-Ling; HU Bangbo; HUBBARD Jason Clyde; HUDSON Alice; INGRAM Elizabeth Morley; JONES Derek Charles; KARAMUSTAFA Ahmet Targon; KARROW Robert W; KIVELSON Valerie A; KOEPP Donna P; KRYGIER John; KUPFER Marcia; LANE Christopher W; LANNON John; LONGENBAUGH Dee; MANASEK Francis John; MARINO John A; MARSHALL James A; McCORKLE Barbara B; McELFRESH Earl Bentley; McINTOSH Gregory C; McKEE Marianne M; McLAUGHLIN Glen; MOFFAT Riley Moore; MONMONIER Mark; MUKERJI Chandra; MUNDY Barbara E; MYERS James Phares, Jr; NEBENZAHL Kenneth; NEWMAN Alfred Willaim; ORLIN Lena Cowen; OSWALD Diane L; PADRÓN Ricardo A.; PATTON Jeffrey; PEARCE Margaret Wickens; PEDLEY Mary Sponberg; PFLEDERER Richard L; POLITES Kiky; POLK Dora Beale; POLLAK Martha; POST Jeremiah Benjamin; RAMASWAMY Sumathi; RATCLIFF James E, Jr; REBERT Paula; REDMOND Edward;

REINHARTZ Dennis; RISTOW Walter W; RIZZO Gerald J; ROBINSON Arthur H; ROMER Frank; ROSS Robert; RUNDSTROM, Robert A; RYAVEC Karl E; SAFIER Neil; SALES Pierre Lucien; SANDER Thomas F; SAUNDERS Richard L; SCHULTEN Susan; SCHWARTZBERG Joseph E; SCKOLNICK Lewis Bernard; SEAVER Kirsten A; SEGAL Daniel; SHIELDS E Thomson, Jr; SHKURKIN Vladimir; SIDER Sandra; SILVERMAN Eric Kline; SIMS Douglas; SPERO Frederick H; STANDER Richard R; STEINHARDT Nancy Shatzman; STEPHENSON Richard W; STEWARD Henry J; STROUP Alice; SUAREZ Thomas; SULLIVAN Garrett A, Jr; TALBERT Richard J A; TAYLOR Kenneth L; THEUNISSEN Yolanda; THROWER Norman J W; TOBLER Waldo; TOLMACHEVA Marina A; TOMASCH Sylvia; TYNER Judith Ann; URNESS Carol L; VAN EE Patricia Molen; VARANKA Dalia; VOGELER Albert R; WAHLL Andrew; WARHUS Mark; WHITEHEAD Neil Lancelot; WILLIAMS John W; WOLF Eric W; WOLTER John A; WOODFIN Thomas M; WOODWARD David; YEE Cordell D K

Uruguay

LAGUARDA TRIAS Rolando A

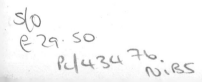